PLACE IN RETURN BOX to remove this checkout from your record.
TO AVOID FINES return on or before date due.

DATE DUE	DATE DUE	DATE DUE
————	————	————
————	————	————
————	————	————
————	————	————
————	————	————
————	————	————
————	————	————

MSU Is An Affirmative Action/Equal Opportunity Institution

The Ring-Necked Pheasant

Goshawk foiled by briars. (From a painting by Walter A. Weber.)

The Ring-Necked Pheasant

and
ITS MANAGEMENT
in NORTH AMERICA

Edited by W. L. McAtee

Published by
The American Wildlife Institute
Washington, D. C.

1945

Copyright 1945

THE AMERICAN WILDLIFE INSTITUTE

PRINTED IN THE UNITED STATES OF AMERICA
BY THE MONUMENTAL PRINTING CO.
BALTIMORE, MD.

Dedicated to

HOWARD MARSHALL WIGHT

1889-1942

Distinguished Service Cross and Croix
de Guerre for valor, World War I.

Pioneer teacher of wildlife managers.
Wise counsellor and good friend.

Foreword

THE FOUNDATION of this book is a report on the ecology, life equation, and management of the ring-necked pheasant in Ohio. Supplementary are chapters relating to several other important centers of pheasant distribution and one on artificial propagation of the bird. All of these have been prepared by employees of the federal Fish and Wildlife Service and are largely products of the Cooperative Wildlife Research Units, jointly sponsored by that Service, certain land-grant colleges, the respective state conservation departments, and the American Wildlife Institute. An introduction and a chapter on classification and distribution are by other authors.

Until the information was developed by Fish and Wildlife Service personnel that heavy populations of pheasants live in the sandhill region of Nebraska, it was thought that these birds could thrive only in the presence of agriculture, including grain farming. Even this new finding does not invalidate the general conclusion that pheasants depend largely upon crop residues for their subsistence. For the other great essential of their livelihood, protection, they require cover of which a reasonable amount must be available at the time of greatest need—usually winter.

As one reads the following chapters, he comes to realize that management principles for the maintenance of conditions favorable for pheasants are of broad application. The differences to be noted from region to region are mainly those necessitated by changes in food and cover resources. The manager must work with the crops and coverts available, suggesting an occasional modification in farm practice, seeking to establish a new covert here and there, but claiming outright for wildlife only tracts that have no direct value to agriculture. Management must conform to the prevailing system of agriculture.

Areas available for special use by the wildlife manager may include field borders in wooded country, open woodland not under forestry management, stream, ditch and pond banks, hedgerows, poorly drained bottomlands, outcrops, sinkholes, and other waste spots. These are of value mostly for cover production although their vegetation may also supply some foods as buds, nuts, and berries. They should adjoin croplands where grain wastes, weed seeds, and insects are liberally available and the more thoroughly they are distributed (if of good quality), the more generally will the countryside be productive of wildlife.

Pheasants powerfully respond to such a well-balanced place to live but so do all wild creatures, including pheasant enemies. Then arises the question as to how many of these can be tolerated. Here all of the manager's wisdom will be required for there is little doubt that as a rule the natural enemy problem has been as poorly handled as any in the whole domain of management.

What has been found most advisable in that respect as well as in other particulars of pheasant management in most of the principal pheasant ranges of the United States is set forth in the following pages. Also presented are the leading elements of pheasant biology, upon careful study of which, the management recommendations are based. It is hoped that the work will prove informative and useful to conservation administrators and to pheasant managers, breeders, and hunters in whose interests it has been prepared.

W. L. McAtee.

viii

THE AUTHORS

BAILEY, WOODROW W., B.S., formerly Biologist, Economic Wildlife Investigations, Division of Wildlife Research, Fish and Wildlife Service, Bowie, Maryland; now Captain, U. S. Army.

BENNETT, LOGAN J., Ph.D., formerly Leader, Pennsylvania Cooperative Wildlife Research Unit, State College, Pennsylvania; now Lieutenant, U. S. Naval Reserve.

DALKE, PAUL D., Ph.D., Leader, Missouri Cooperative Wildlife Research Unit, Columbia, Missouri.

DELACOUR, JEAN, President, International Committee for Bird Preservation; Technical Adviser, New York Zoological Society, New York, N. Y.

EINARSEN, ARTHUR S., B.S., Leader, Oregon Cooperative Wildlife Research Unit, Corvallis, Oregon.

ENGLISH, PENNOYER F., Ph.D., Professor, Department of Zoology and Entomology, Pennsylvania State College, State College, Pennsylvania.

ERRINGTON, PAUL L., Ph.D., Research Assistant, Iowa Agricultural Experiment Station, Iowa State College, Ames, Iowa.

HICKS, LAWRENCE E., Ph.D., Leader, Ohio Cooperative Wildlife Research Unit, Columbus, Ohio.

LEEDY, DANIEL L., Ph.D., formerly Instructor in Zoology, Ohio State University, Columbus, Ohio; now Lieutenant in the Army Air Corps.

McCLURE, H. ELLIOTT, Ph.D., formerly Graduate Assistant, Iowa Cooperative Wildlife Research Unit, Ames, Iowa; now Leader, Upland Game Bird Project, Pittman-Robertson Wildlife Restoration Program, Ord, Nebraska.

McKEAN, WILLIAM T., M.S., formerly Graduate Assistant, Utah Cooperative Wildlife Research Unit, Logan, Utah; now Leader, South Dakota Big Game Survey, Pierre, South Dakota.

NESTLER, RALPH B., B.S., Biologist, Economic Wildlife Investigations, Division of Wildlife Research, Bowie, Maryland.

PEARCE, JOHN, M.F., Assistant Regional Director, Fish and Wildlife Service, Boston, Massachusetts.

RASMUSSEN, D. IRVING, Ph.D., Leader, Utah Cooperative Wildlife Research Unit, Logan, Utah.

SHARP, WARD M., Ph. D., Refuge Manager, Red Rock Lakes National Wildlife Refuge, Monida, Montana.

WALCOTT, FREDERIC C., A.B., D.Sc. (Hon.), ex-United States Senator, President, American Wildlife Institute, Norfolk, Connecticut.

WIGHT, HOWARD M., M.S., Late Associate Professor of Forest Zoology, Department of Forestry and Conservation, University of Michigan, Ann Arbor, Michigan.

ERRINGTON, Paul, President, International Committee for Bird Preservation, Published Alfred, New York Zoological Society, New York.

SHARP, WARD M., Ph.D., Refuge Manager, Red Rock Lakes Migratory Waterfowl Refuge, Monida, Montana.

ix

CONTENTS

CONTENTS

Historical Introduction

By FREDERIC C. WALCOTT

MAN HAS BEEN acquainted with the common pheasant a long time, as he has with every natural product that is good to eat. Recorded history does not extend far enough back to tell us the antiquity of knowledge of these birds but remains from kitchen middens plainly show that primitive men ate them. Indeed the presence of pheasant bones in such ancient refuse heaps in Europe confuses the historical picture and, in the judgment of some, indicates that pheasants were native to that continent.

As history goes, however, about the tenth century B.C., they were brought to Europe by the Argonauts from the Caucasus in southwestern Asia. There in the watershed of the Phasis (now Rion) River the Greeks knew the birds to be abundant. Hence they named the species *Phasianos ornis* (phasian bird) and from this old geographical, and adopted zoological, term have come the names of the species in most of the European languages (faczan, Hungarian; fagiano, Italian; faisan, French and Spanish; faisant, Flemish; faisão, Portuguese; fasaani, Finnish; fasan, Danish, German, Norwegian, and Swedish; fazant, Dutch; pheasant, English) as well as the Latin term Phasianus adopted by science for the genus. From Colchis, name of the province through which the river Phasis flows, is derived the specific name of the common pheasant whose technical name is *Phasianus colchicus*. When a third term is added, as in the Check List in the following section by Jean Delacour, it indicates a geographic race or subspecies, that from the original home being *Phasianus colchicus colchicus*.

1

Old as the Greek records are, those of the Chinese are earlier; paintings of pheasants are known by artists of that nation which antedate Grecian references probably by a thousand years. Almost everything known of natural history was collated by Aristotle in his time (B.C. 384-322) and sure enough he mentions the pheasant. "Some birds dust themselves," he says, "and others bathe. Those that . . . live on the ground dust themselves as the domestic fowl, partridge, grouse, lark, and pheasant."

The early writers at least noticed things that were characteristic. Turning from a Greek to a Roman, in Pliny's Natural History of nearly 2000 years ago, we find the following: "In Colchis, Asia Minor, there is the pheasant, a bird with two tufts of feathers like ears which it drops and raises every now and then."

The spread of pheasants in western Europe is thought to have been due to introductions by the Romans when they were expanding their empire. Thus the bird may have reached England in the days of Julius Caesar who invaded that country about the middle of the first century B.C. Yet the first definite British references to pheasants are centuries later. In the excellent *Dictionary of Birds*, Alfred Newton (Newton and Gadow, 1896) cites a reference from the tenth century which reads, "There are three barking hunts: a bear, a squirrel, and a pheasant." The explanation is that when the pointers found a pheasant they chased and treed it, when their baying turned the event into a "barking hunt."

On the hunting of the pheasant, Professor Newton further remarks: "Formerly pheasants were taken in snares or nets and by hawking but the crossbow was also used and the better to obtain a 'sitting shot' for with that weapon man had not learned to 'shoot flying'; dogs appear to have been employed in the way indicated by the lines under an engraving by Hollar who died in 1677.

" 'The feasant cocke the woods doth most frequent,

Where spaniells spring and pearche [i.e. tree] him by the sent' "

In the time of Edward I of England (1272-1307 A.D.), oaths were sworn on the swan, the peacock, and the pheasant, all of which were looked upon as royal birds. When Neville the Chancellor was made Archbishop of York in 1465, two hundred "fessauntes" were among a wealth of game served at a banquet.

Neither in England where so many strains of domestic animals—cattle, sheep and horses—were perfected nor elsewhere during man's long acquaintance with the pheasant has this bird become truly domesticated. Prehistoric man tamed apparently all of the creatures most susceptible to the process and historic man has added nothing to the list. The pheasant succumbed to neither but preserved its innate wildness.

This very quality is what won for the species widespread and agelong transportation and propagation for the sake of sport. It is not shooting that makes the pheasant wild; rather the bird is hunted with more relish because it is wild. Though broadly adapted to a range that extends the whole breadth of Asia, the largest continent, and tempted always by the easy life of domestication, the pheasant has retained its independence, alertness, vigor, and strong flight and thus maintained a popularity for food and sport that has resulted in its spread to all suitable parts of the world.

Pheasants were introduced to the United States as early as 1790 by Governor Wentworth to his estate in New Hampshire and Richard Bache, son-in-law of Benjamin Franklin, to the shore of the Delaware River in New Jersey. Neither of these attempts to colonize the birds were successful. Doubtless these importations were of the so-called English black-necked pheasant, that is, the typical Colchican strain. In the course of time a number of other varieties have been liberated, including Japanese, Mongolian, and Chinese pheasants. They have become thoroughly mixed but have a preponderance of Chinese blood, especially toward the west, and are generally known as ring-necked pheasants.

The first real success in establishing pheasants was with the Chinese ring-neck in the Willamette Valley, Oregon, in 1881. From this stocking the pheasants multiplied until in 1892 a shooting season of two and a half months was opened and 50,000 birds were reported to have been killed the first day. Concurrent with this experience and especially later as a result of it, pheasants have been propagated and released by states, clubs, and individuals until they have been established practically everywhere that they can live in the United States and Canada (figure 1).

They are listed as game in a great majority of the states, possibly to some extent through confusion with the native pheasant or ruffed

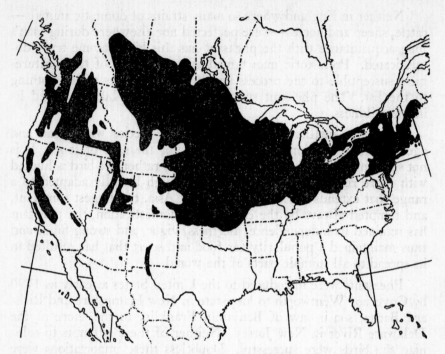

Figure 1.—Range of the ring-necked pheasant in North America in 1941. It included the North Atlantic Coastal plain, Northeastern Maritime District, Erie Canal Belt, Central Farming Region, St. Lawrence Valley and Lower Lakes Region, Northern Wheat Region, Great Plains south to latitude 36°, and the Willamette and Puget Sound valleys. To a limited extent pheasants are found also in the valleys of California and of the Gila and Salt Rivers in the southwestern plateaus. Within the range indicated, there are many areas where pheasants are not found, their presence is uncertain, or they are localized.

grouse. In recent years, however, there has been an open season on them in 18 states and in the most favored regions the kill has been tremendous, up to a million or more annually in single states.

This great assisted invasion by a foreign bird has not been without its critics. Pheasants have been reported as destructive to the eggs and young of other game birds, especially grouse and quail, and they have also been accused of killing young rabbits. If these depredations really occur, it seems to be on a scale too small to be of much consequence.

Pheasants do some damage to tomatoes and other truck crops,

but their greatest damage is to newly-planted or newly-sprouted corn. Even so, the birds may be blamed for some of the work of crows. (Methods of controlling such damage are discussed on pages 108-110.)

Pheasants are highly granivorous but most of the grain they consume is waste. They do some good through the destruction of weed seeds and insects, especially by the young, which in their earliest life in the wild are reared almost exclusively upon insects. With the permission of the state conservation department, individuals or coveys that cause damage may be trapped and removed or even killed. The value of the birds as a food supply alone would seem to entitle them to the degree of protection accorded them as game.

Classification and Distribution of the Game, or True, Pheasants

By JEAN DELACOUR

THE GAME, or true, pheasants are now so widespread in Europe and in America as sporting birds that it may be of interest to trace their origin.

In a wild state, pheasants of the genus *Phasianus* are found from the northern Caucasus through central Asia to China and Japan. They have a continuous range in eastern Asia, but elsewhere they inhabit numerous separate areas. These include valleys and mountain slopes, plains and oases, in other words, ground affording the different forms the sort of habitat which they require. It usually consists of open country with sufficient water, covered with long grass and dotted with bushes and trees. Unlike practically all other pheasant allies, the true pheasants do not live in forests. They are attracted by cereal cultivation, as in corn, wheat, and paddy fields. They are accustomed to cold and changeable climates and have, therefore, been easy to acclimatize in the middle latitudes of North America and Europe.

All true pheasants are so closely related that fertile hybrids between any two forms can be produced. They are almost alike in anatomy and habits. This has led various authors to consider all of them as subspecies of one species. One is tempted to admit that they are geographical races and in reality form one large natural genus or superspecies. But it seems advisable to divide them into three distinct taxonomic species on account of their widely different color patterns.

In the western half of their range (figure 2), one finds birds

Figure 2.—Distribution of the true pheasants.

with a more or less homogeneous general red color, the lower back being always reddish-brown; I consider them as belonging to the species *Phasianus colchicus*. The best known form of this group is the black-neck, five very closely related races of which live north and south of the Caucasus and west and south of the Caspian Sea. It has even been asserted that the birds from eastern Bulgaria, Thrace, and European Turkey along the Black Sea, represent a genuine wild form, *P. c. europaeus* (Hachisuka, 1937). It is difficult either to admit or reject this opinion in the present state of our knowledge.

The second most popular member of the black-neck group is the Mongolian pheasant (*P. c. mongolicus*), much larger and greener than the *P. colchicus colchicus*, it has white in the wing and a white collar.

The Prince of Wales's pheasant (*P. c. principalis*) from southeastern Turkestan, a very red bird without a white neck ring, was introduced into Europe in the early eighteen-nineties, but has since disappeared. Other related subspecies, with or without collars (the white neck ring is a variable, hence unimportant character) are mentioned in the accompanying list. Their distribution is not continuous, each variety being confined to a definite range surrounded by desert or high mountains where pheasants cannot live.

The third or eastern group of pheasants constitute the species *Phasianus torquatus* of which the Chinese ring-neck is the most familiar. They have a more varied plumage than the western birds, the rump and lower back being always grayish-green. Usually the upper back and flanks are yellow, spotted with black, the wings chestnut-red and gray, and the tail pale greenish or brownish, barred with black. Three forms, which link the two groups, are found isolated in oases of western China and Turkestan, while another one is native to Formosa. All the other forms have a more or less continuous distribution in China, reaching northern Burma, Tonkin, and Corea. The Chinese ring-neck (*P. t. torquatus*) has become acclimated in large numbers in North America and Europe, where the Corean ring-neck (*P. t. karpowi*), Manchurian (*P. t. pallasi*), and the Formosan (*P. t. formosanus*) also have been introduced.

Th green pheasant of Japan (*P. versicolor*) has a very different color pattern and represents a separate species, with the underparts entirely green. There is a slightly differentiated race in the southern island of Kiu-Siu. The green pheasant has been repeatedly imported into Europe and to a limited extent in the United States as a game bird but with little success.

Pheasants were introduced first by the Greeks and later on by the Romans into many parts of Europe. The form involved probably was the south Caucasus bird, *P. colchicus colchicus,* very closely related to the so-called Old English black-neck. The bird must have remained in a pure state for many centuries as it seems that the Chinese ring-neck, and other races, were not imported and released in any numbers until the nineteenth century. At present, European birds vary in different countries and districts, and even in the same covert, according to the degree of infusion of new blood with the old stock of black-necks. The Chinese and other ring-necks (Pallas's, Corean, Formosan), the Prince of Wales's, the Mongolian, and the versicolor, pheasants have been added in different degrees to the complex, the Mongolians, for instance, to increase the size and the versicolors to develop high flight and speed.

In North America, most of these birds of differing color and characteristics have been introduced within a shorter period so that the black-neck is less dominant. In certain regions of the northwestern United States, the Chinese ring-neck (*P. t. torquatus*) is found quite pure.

Several accidental color phases of pheasants have occurred and have been selected for breeding purposes, as the white, Isabelline, and lavender varieties. During the latter part of the nineteenth century (about 1888) a very interesting dark mutation suddenly appeared among the hybridized feral birds of England. It long remained scarce, but by 1926, it had become fairly common and was named *P. c. tenebrosus* by Hachisuka. It does not exist in a true wild state in any particular locality, hence does not deserve a subspecific name. This bird, now well known as the melanistic mutant, is admired for its novelty, its strong, high-flying capacity, and greater weight. It is now being reared and liberated all over the world. This type has become fixed but has a tendency to grow darker and darker. Today there is a strain of birds in which both cocks and hens are almost entirely dark purple, green, and blue.

Following is a check list of the varieties or subspecies of the three species of true pheasants: *P. colchicus*, *P. torquatus*, and *P. versicolor*. Their approximate geographical distributions are indicated on the map (figure 2).

CHECK LIST

Caucasian Pheasants

1. Rion Caucasian Pheasant (*Phasianus colchicus colchicus*)— Western Transcaucasia.
2. Northern Caucasian Pheasant (*P. c. septentrionalis*)—North side of the Caucasus.
3. Lorenz's Pheasant (*P. c. lorenzi*)—Eastern Transcaucasia.
4. Talisch Pheasant (*P. c. talischensis*)—Southwest of the Caspian Sea.
5. Persian Pheasant (*P. c. persicus*)—Southeast of the Caspian Sea.
6. Prince of Wales's Pheasant (*P. c. principalis*)—Oases of Merv and neighboring country in southern Russia.
7. Zarudny's Pheasant (*P. c. zarudnyi*)—Middle Amu-Darya, southern Russia.
8. Zerafshan Pheasant (*P. c. zerafschanicus*)—Bokhara, Russia.
9. Bianchi's Pheasant (*P. c. bianchii*)—Upper Amu-Darya, southern Russia.
10. Khivan Pheasant (*P. c. chrysomelas*)—Lower Amu-Darya, southern Russia.

11. Syr-Daria Pheasant (*P. c. turcestanicus*)—Southwestern Russian Turkestan.
12. Mongolian Pheasant (*P. c. mongolicus*)—Northeastern Russian Turkestan.
13. Yarkand Pheasant (*P. c. shawi*)—Western Chinese Turkestan.

Chinese Pheasants

14. Tarim Pheasant (*P. torquatus tarimensis*)—Eastern Chinese Turkestan.
15. Satchu Pheasant (*P. t. satchuensis*)—Northwestern Kansu, China.
16. Tsaidam Pheasant (*P. t. vlangali*)—Tsaidam and neighboring country, China.
17. Strauch's Pheasant (*P. t. strauchi*)—Kansu, southern Shensi, northern Szechuan, China.
18. Stone's Pheasant (*P. t. elegans*)—Southwestern Szechuan and northwestern Yunnan, China, and Shan States, Burma.
19. Kweichow Pheasant (*P. t. decollatus*)—Eastern Szechuan, western Hupeh, northeastern Yunnan, and Kweichow, China.
20. Rothschild's Pheasant (*P. t. rothschildi*)—Southeastern Yunnan, northern Tonkin.
21. Tonkin Pheasant (*P. t. takasukasae*)—Southeastern Tonkin.
22. Ring-necked Pheasant (*P. t. torquatus*)—Eastern China and northeastern Tonkin, Indo-China.
23. Shansi Pheasant (*P. t. kiangsuensis*)—Northern China.
24. Corean Pheasant (*P. t. karpowi*)—Korea and southern Manchuria.
25. Manchurian Pheasant (*P. t. pallasi*)—Eastern Manchuria and southeastern Siberia.
26. Kobdo Pheasant (*P. t. hagenbecki*)—Northwestern Mongolia.
27. Formosan Pheasant (*P. t. formosanus*)—Formosa.

Green Pheasants

28. Versicolor Pheasant (*P. versicolor versicolor*)—Hondo and Shikoku, Japan.
29. Kiusiu Pheasant (*P. v. kiusiuensis*)—Kiusiu, Japan.

The Pheasant in Pennsylvania and New Jersey

By LOGAN J. BENNETT

ONE OF THE earliest introductions of pheasants into the United States was that of a shipment of birds received by Richard Bache, the son-in-law of Benjamin Franklin, a few years after the Declaration of Independence. Bache obtained English pheasants about 1790 for his estate near Beverly, New Jersey (Phillips, 1928). About 1800 a second attempt at stocking pheasants was made by a landowner in the vicinity of Belleville, New Jersey. Apparently those early attempts at introduction met with failure. Pierre Lorillard released many pheasants in northern New Jersey about 1800, and in 1887 Rutherford Stuyvesant brought a number of birds from England for stocking the Tranquility Game Preserve at Allamuchy, New Jersey. Within a few years pheasants became well established in that region. The first birds stocked in Pennsylvania were probably liberated about 1892. The Pennsylvania Game Commission began releasing pheasants in 1915, and by 1938, 517,280 cocks were killed in that State. New Jersey has an annual kill of about 100,000 birds. The speed of acclimatization is well illustrated by the average bag for 5-year periods in Pennsylvania since 1915 (table 1).

TABLE 1.—Average annual kill of pheasants during 5-year periods in Pennsylvania

Years	Average annual kill
1915-19	4,417
1920-24	28,499
1925-29	141,159
1930-34	266,741
1935-39	381,847

11

EFFECT OF PHEASANTS ON PRESENT DAY SHOOTING

The pheasant became abundant in the East during the same period that man gained a high standard of living, and had considerable time for recreation. A large number of people with increased time for sport naturally took to hunting. The establishment and increase of pheasants provided an upland game bird for the larger number of hunters. It has often been pointed out that the pheasant has relieved the shooting pressure on other game birds. This is no doubt true for today the average pheasant hunter is one who does not hunt ruffed grouse or quail. The pheasant is a fairly large bird; its flesh is delicious; it thrives in areas with dense human populations; it is fairly easy to hunt; and its flight is not too fast or erratic for the shooting eye of the average sportsman. Thus, it has become the leading game bird in various states.

Pennsylvania has between 600,000 and 700,000 hunters, roughly a tenth of all in the United States. To those who have not seen the opening of a hunting season in an area with such a concentration of hunters it is difficult to give a convincing picture of the occasion. In the pheasant territory of Pennsylvania on the eve of the shooting season and the day that follows, there is a gala atmosphere. No national holiday compares with the opening of the pheasant season in respect to anticipation, celebration, crowding of restaurants and hotels, heavy automobile traffic, and general confusion. On the night before the opening day in many towns and cities in the good pheasant areas, it is bedlam. Hundreds of khaki-clad sportsmen, with dogs of all descriptions from mongrels to highly-trained bird dogs, crowd and mill in the drinking, eating, and boarding places. People are out because they have leisure time and because the cock pheasant becomes legal game the next day. Hundreds of thousands of dollars are spent on transportation, food and drink, outdoor clothing, lodging, guns, ammunition, dogs, and other accompaniments of the sport. On the first day of the season many schools close and allow all who want to hunt to take the day off. Numerous places of business are closed for the day for the benefit of owners and employees.

On the opening day of the small game season in Pennsylvania, hunting is not allowed until 9:00 a.m. Eastern Standard Time. This law is primarily to further the safety of the hunters. During the remaining days of the season the shooting day begins at 7:00 a.m.

From daylight until 9:00 a.m. the hunters spread over the selected hunting areas. At the given hour the rush begins and literally a barrage opens up. The first half-hour is a roar of gunfire from .410 single barrels to 10-gauge magnums. The fields are crossed time after time by groups of hunters. (In Pennsylvania small-game hunting parties are limited to not more than five people.) Often two groups may enter different sides of a field as one group departs. There is danger and too often accidents occur.

Such a concentration of hunters brings about many problems in game administration. As a result of the hunting pressure, many private lands are posted, resulting in increasing demands upon the Game Commission to find means to prevent the exclusion of hunters. Many landowners, becoming weary of hundreds of hunters crossing their property, lease the hunting rights to small groups of sportsmen. As much as $350 per year has been paid for the shooting rights on 475 acres. The Pennsylvania Game Commission is attempting to counteract this development through its Cooperative Farm-Game Program.

Fortunately, on the other hand, many landowners look forward with pleasure to the pheasant season. They may enjoy the hunting or meeting the hunters, or they may appreciate the income from hunters, or the change from everyday happenings. It is such landowners that have preserved public hunting. The great majority of hunters are law abiding and conscious of property values. Through their good behavior they have helped to retain the privilege of public hunting on much of our private land.

Where there are large concentrations of hunters, there is also a law-enforcement problem. Violations of the law may be caused by ignorance or by lack of respect for the law, or both. Although only a small proportion of the hunters are willful violators, many deplorable incidents occur that injure the true sportsman, the landowner, and the sport. A broken gate, a stolen pig, or game illegally taken may be the deed of one man in a thousand but such acts may result in the exclusion of a thousand real sportsmen from the hunting territory. True sportsmen should give complete cooperation to game protectors in detecting violators. It is the violator and the man who disregards property rights who cause the posting of most of the "no hunting" signs.

METHODS USED IN HUNTING PHEASANTS

The most common method used in hunting pheasants is the driving system. Several hunters line up 20 to 50 yards apart and systematically cruise through cornfields or other types of cover, attempting to flush the birds ahead of them. Dogs may or may not be used in such hunting. Dogs rout out many birds that otherwise would sneak away or hide from the hunters and are most useful as retrievers (plate 1). The value of dogs in keeping down crippling losses cannot be overemphasized.

After the first few days of the open season, the fields, woods, and swales are not nearly so crowded with hunters. It is then that the individual with a trained dog can get the most sport. He works the fencerows, small patches of ground cover, and other likely spots.

Many varieties of dogs can be trained to be good pheasant routers and retrievers. Some beagle hounds and even mongrels make excellent pheasant dogs. The most spectacular aids to good hunting, however, are the setters and pointers. It takes a smart bird dog to learn to out-maneuver the pheasant. The most successful are those that circle the bird, point, head toward the hunter, and thus prevent it from running. Springer and cocker spaniels and Labradors and other retrievers make excellent hunting dogs. Perhaps springers are the best all-round pheasant dogs. They usually work close to the gun and flush a high proportion of the birds within shooting distance. Their great ability to retrieve fallen birds is internationally known.

Some gunners still-hunt pheasants in much the same manner as the wild turkey is hunted. The place chosen is usually at the edge of a woods bordering fields or in a wood lot. The sportsman hides, remains quiet, and waits for a bird to come by. To those who like to hunt with the minimum effort, this is very satisfactory.

A rather unscrupulous method, but legal in Pennsylvania, is that of shooting roosting pheasants out of trees on foggy, rainy, or frosty mornings. However, there are but few hunters who can not hit a pheasant unless it is sitting or walking.

Unfortunately, illegal methods of hunting also are in evidence. One of the most frequent is that of shooting from an automobile or other vehicle. A few hunters make no attempt to distinguish females from male birds when only cocks are legal game, and some shoot the hens intentionally. The illegal hunters are a minority but make a problem for both the true sportsman and the game commission.

ANALYSIS OF PHEASANT RANGE

In general the pheasant is a bird primarily of agricultural communities. Although it is found in every county in Pennsylvania, it attains high populations only in rich farming areas. As the quality of soils influences farming practices, there is a close correlation between soils, crops, and pheasant range. High human population densities have few curtailing influences on the pheasant if the environment is good. About 85 per cent of the first-class pheasant range in Pennsylvania is in the southwestern part of the State. This area covers about 2,500,000 acres, including some of the richest farm land in the country; and more than 4,000,000 people live there. This territory is one of the most heavily human populated areas in North America and it is subjected to some of the heaviest gunning pressure. However, it has provided up to a 26-shooting-day season for a number of years despite the large number of hunters.

The good pheasant range in New Jersey is mostly confined to the northern, agricultural half of the State. The 1930-31 annual report of the New Jersey Board of Fish and Game Commissioners stated: "After a survey of the records of the pheasant situation in the southern zone of New Jersey over a period of ten years, taking into consideration the kill of birds by counties . . . it is generally known that pheasants are not furnishing the return to sportsmen consistent with the amount of money spent on their propagation in this section of the State . . . In the northern zone of the State the propagation and planting of pheasants has been in reverse ratio to the southern zone. Here the kill of pheasants has been phenomenal in view of the fact that every county in the State has had an equal distribution for the past ten years, the ratio of the kill to release being over ten to one, that is for every male bird released ten were bagged, indicating that 9/10 of the kill represents birds raised in the wild. In conclusion it is recommended that the planting of pheasants be confined to the northern zone for a period of five years except possibly in a few districts where it is known that pheasants are suited, and that money saved from this be expended in restocking the southern zone with quail, which we know is suitable for the birds."

In various states, the main limiting factors upon pheasant populations are land use and crop production. In Pennsylvania, areas with large pheasant concentrations have at least 60 per cent of the land in grain crops. Many food habit studies of the bird have brought out the fact that the choice of foods of the pheasant is grains or weed seeds found in cultivated land. The fall food habits of Pennsylvania pheasants well illustrate this fact (table 2). If land is of poor quality or economic factors prevent the production of grains, there is little food present for pheasants over winter.

TABLE 2.—Contents of pheasant crops taken during the fall (English and Bennett, 1940)

		Per cent by volume	
Contents		1938	1939
Crop seeds and attendant crop weed seeds		74	76
Noncrop seeds (grape, dogwood, etc.)		16	18
Animal matter		6	3
Gravel		4	3
Totals		100	100

The layman often brings up the point that pheasants eat grains and weed seeds in farming country because there is no other food present. However, the fact remains that in the East, high pheasant populations are not found outside of grain-producing areas. In Pennsylvania the most important nesting cover is alfalfa and this is a companion crop to corn in most good farming areas.

In the Keystone State, dearth of brushy fencerows and other woody cover is not a limiting factor of the pheasant range. Lancaster County, one of the richest and most intensively farmed areas in the State, with a minimum of woody cover, is one of the best pheasant ranges. In Lehigh County, Pennsylvania, where at least 60 per cent of the farmland is in crops and the overwinter pheasant population ranges from seven to twelve birds per 100 acres, there is comparatively little brushy fencerow and other woody cover. Brushy cover is needed for winter shelter but the amount can be of very low acreage. The second- and third-class pheasant areas have by far more woody cover than the first-class range. From what the writer has seen of pheasant ranges in other eastern states, this situation prevails generally.

Pierce E. Randall made intensive management studies of the pheasant in Pennsylvania in 1938-40 (1940a). Part of his studies was carried on in Lehigh County on an area of 1,675 acres that had fall populations of 55 birds to 100 acres in 1938 and a population of 50 birds to 100 acres in 1939. This district is in the best of the first-class range. Analysis (table 3) of the land use on this area illustrates the constituents of excellent pheasant environment.

TABLE 3.—Lehigh County, Pennsylvania, study area. Land use, summer 1938
(Randall, 1940A)

Crop	Acreage	Per cent of total area
Wheat	489	29.2
Corn	326	19.5
Potatoes	300	18.0
Alfalfa and clover	206	12.2
Barley	123	7.3
Oats	104	6.2
Wasteland	50	3.0
Pasture	19	1.1
Soybeans	12	0.7
Orchards	7	0.4
Sweet clover	5	0.3
Conifer plantations	3	0.2
Farmyards, etc.	31	1.9
Totals	1,675	100.0

Within a few miles of the area Randall studied, there is a private estate reported on by Gerstell (1937). He said: "That estate has a total area of 1,400 acres, all extensively farmed. The soil is of the Hagerstown type and immediately overlies a base of Trenton limestone. Cover conditions are exceptionally good and the agricultural practices are carried out with full respect for the pheasant crop thereon. Only limited shooting is allowed on the tract.

"Censuses on the area have been made by the writer at various seasons of the same and different years, but the great abundance of birds makes highly accurate work practically impossible. In January, 1934, a two-day field study showed approximately 3,500 birds on the estate. A similar investigation in February, 1935, revealed a population estimated to approach 5,300 birds. Also during four consecutive winters, the Game Commission trapped from 900 to 1,200 pheasants on the tract and shipped them to other points for restocking purposes, while from 50 to 200 additional male birds were shot on the estate during the same years. Thus, an area of over one thousand acres annually produced without artificial restocking and without any noticeable decrease in the population density, approximately one bird per acre over a four year period, during which time the winter concentrations reached an average high of at least 3.7 birds per acre." In conversation with the writer, Gerstell brought out the fact that heavy gunning pressure on surrounding areas during the shooting season doubtless drove many birds into the estate.

Randall (1940b) made an extensive study of the pheasant ranges throughout Pennsylvania, and his evaluations are as follows: "From the inception of the study, it was felt that there must be basic reasons for the failure of the pheasant to succeed in those areas designated as second-range. Listed among possible causative agencies were the minerals available in the soil, and the agricultural practices as they affected winter food, winter cover, and nesting cover. Each of these was carefully investigated.

"Some authorities have suggested that there might be a correlation between the available minerals and the habitable pheasant range. These minerals would be obtained by the pheasant from the grit which is taken almost daily. This assumption was given emphasis by the findings of McCann (1939). He reported that part of the calcium needed by pheasants to carry on their life functions properly was obtained from the grit.

"It has also been pointed out that in Pennsylvania the greatest pheasant concentrations occur on the limestone-derived soils of southeastern Pennsylvania. These limestone soils, comprising the Hagerstown soil series, were derived from the weathering of the underlying Trenton limestone formations (Shaw, 1914). These same Hagerstown soils extend across Cumberland and Franklin Counties, both of which are in the second-class range. The Nittany Valley of Centre County and the Kishacoquillas Valley of Mifflin County are also limestone-derived but as yet neither has proved to be good pheasant range.

"In better than half of the first-class pheasant range, the soils were formed from noncalcareous rocks and contain minute amounts of lime. Such soils include the Chester, Berks, Penn, Lansdale, and Manor groups, all of which were derived either from non-metamorphic rocks or from shales and sandstones.

"The second-class pheasant range of Butler, Armstrong, Allegheny, Indiana, Westmoreland, Washington, and Fayette Counties lies on the Westmoreland soils which were formed by the weathering of limestones, sandstones, and shales. Throughout this entire series, limestone entered into the make-up of the soil mass.

"At the present time there appears to be no correlation between soil types or their geologic origin and the success of pheasants insofar as the minerals in the grit are concerned. Soil types do affect pheasants indirectly inasmuch as the agricultural practices are to a large extent dependent upon the capabilities of a soil.

"For the purpose of securing quantitative information on the agricultural practices in the various sections of the State, the percentages of the total land area of each county occupied by each crop were determined.

"An examination of the data revealed a close correlation between the corn crop and the pheasant range. Those counties where a large amount of corn was raised were first-class pheasant counties. In those counties where at least half of the total land was first-class pheasant range . . . at least 9 per cent of the land was in corn.

"Only four of the second-class counties intruded into this select group. Adams, Cumberland, Franklin, and Montour Counties each had more than 10 per cent of their total land area in corn. Several other counties—including Snyder, Union, Lawrence, Northumberland, and Dauphin—were close enough to the first-class counties in the amount of corn grown to warrant investigation. The majority of the second-class range contained from 4 to 7 per cent of corn.

"None of the third-class counties approached the first-class counties in the amount of corn grown. The most corn occurring in any county in the third-class range was in Greene, where 4.56 per cent of the land area was occupied by corn.

"For the purpose of determining how much of this corn was available to pheasants for winter food and cover, a survey was instituted in March 1939 and during the winter 1939-40 was extended to nearly all of the first- and second-class pheasant range.

"Data on the prevailing winter land use practices in each county were secured by tallying the cover type in each field along the road from an automobile as it was driven through a representative portion of each county. In a large number of samples, the size of the fields balanced; and fairly accurate information on winter food and cover was obtained. Fourteen types were recognized in this survey. The corn land was broken up into three parts: standing corn, machine-picked corn, and stubble. Probably some cornfields that were classified as machine-picked had been picked by hand and the stalks broken over by a disc harrow or planker.

"The first areas visited in this survey were those four counties in which more than 10 per cent of the land was planted in corn but where pheasants were scarce. Not a single standing cornfield was encountered in driving 40 miles through the agricultural sections of Franklin County. Fourteen per cent of the fields contained corn stubble, but few ears had been left on the ground. In Cumberland County the situation was similar—a large acreage devoted to corn but none left standing throughout the winter.

"Adams County presented an interesting condition. In the western and central parts of the county standing corn occupied only about 2.4 per cent of the land. This was second-class pheasant range. The eastern part of Adams County lay within the first-class pheasant range, and here standing corn comprised 8.1 per cent of the crops. Similar situations were found to prevail within the first- and second-class ranges in Columbia and Dauphin Counties. Other second-class counties examined included Snyder, Union, Northumberland, Montour, Erie, Crawford, Mercer, Lawrence, Beaver, Westmoreland, Indiana, Blair, Huntingdon, Juniata, and Perry. Conditions were generally the same as in Franklin and Cumberland Counties. Often considerable corn was grown, but it was generally cut and the stalks placed in silos or hauled to the barn in the fall. The only area in the group where any amount of standing corn was found was in Northumberland County. That part of the county lying close to the west branch of the Susquehanna River was examined, and 4.9 per cent of the land area was found to be occupied by standing corn. However, this may be less than the minimum amount necessary to maintain pheasants in abundance.

"In order to determine how the corn crop was utilized in the first-class pheasant range, the survey was extended to several first-class pheasant counties. In the counties maintaining high pheasant populations, the amount of standing corn varied from 7.9 per cent of the land area in Lebanon County to 10.5 per cent in Lehigh County.

"Certain other areas usually classified as first-class range but which have not supported the large populations found in southeastern Pennsylvania were visited. The first-class range of Columbia and Bradford Counties fell into this category. The standing corn in

Plate 1.—Good dogs aid in cutting down crippling losses. (Photograph by Pennsylvania Game Commission)

Plate 2.—Upper. Food patch of standing corn. (Photograph by Pierce E. Randall)
Lower. The English flushing bar. Short lengths of chain suspended on wires from
the bamboo pole drag through the crop and flush the pheasants ahead of the cutter.
(Photograph by P. F. English)

Bradford County's first-class range occupied 4.3 per cent of the land; and in the Columbia County first-class range, 5.6 per cent.

"Apparently, in those regions where dense pheasant populations have been maintained naturally, from 7 to 10 per cent of the land area has standing corn during the winter months. Cover and nesting conditions being favorable, a fairly good pheasant population may be maintained as long as a minimum of 4 per cent of the winter cover is standing corn.

"Other agricultural crops, although essential to first-class pheasant range, failed to exhibit the close correlation to the pheasant-range classes that was shown by the corn crop.

"It was recognized that hay had a definite place in the ecology of the pheasant because of its value as nesting cover. Hay did not seem to be a limiting factor of pheasants in the second-class range, as most of the counties in this group contained a sufficient acreage of hay to furnish nesting cover for a far greater number of pheasants than they have ever possessed.

"Wheat, barley, and oat fields were found to be valuable as nesting sites and as sources of food and cover. But, once again, the second-class counties produced as much and in some cases more small grains than did the first-class counties. Thus small grain was not a limiting factor.

"In concluding this phase of the discussion, it must be pointed out that one of the factors exhibiting a correlation with the pheasant range on a statewide basis is the amount and method of utilization of the corn crop. In some counties a lack of sufficient winter food appears to be responsible for the scarcity of pheasants. Standing corn would supply the necessary food regardless of the severity of the weather."

Randall's studies in Pennsylvania have given many practical clues for management. However, there are no doubt factors as yet undiscovered that determine range. Years of research on pheasants, soils, climate, foods, farming practices, and other topics are needed before management can be perfected.

FACTORS THAT INFLUENCE PHEASANT POPULATIONS

It has been pointed out that land use and agricultural practices are important in limiting pheasant range. In addition to such staple range requirements, there are also a number of other factors that cause fluctuations of populations.

From a study of the causes of loss and gain in pheasant population on the experimental area in Lehigh County, Pennsylvania, it became apparent that various factors and events influenced pheasant numbers. For instance, 28 per cent of the fall crop of birds was utilized as legal game. Crippling losses during the hunting season were very high, representing 14 per cent of the fall population, and the illegal kill was 3.6 per cent. About 22 per cent of the birds were driven from the area by intensive hunting and about 8 per cent strayed off, probably in an effort to seek better winter cover. These losses would have been cut materially had there been a small refuge available. The net winter and early spring losses were about 10 per cent due to predation, accidents, straying, and other causes. All of these losses cut the population down to 15 per cent of its maximum before the breeding season. These birds suffered great losses in the reproductive effort as only 45.2 per cent of the hens finally had broods. By far the greatest factor at this season was nest destruction, and it was mostly (56.6 per cent) caused by acts of man, chiefly mowing.

Predation accounted for 76 (30.7 per cent) of 310 nests under observation, the leading offenders being the striped skunk and the crow.

Analysis of nest losses by dates, locations, and success shows that the time of mowing has a great deal to do with the failure or success of the nests. About half of the nests in the study area were in alfalfa. In Pennsylvania the first harvesting of this hay crop occurs from the last week of May throughout June, weather conditions causing variations in the date. Rainy weather delays haying operations and every week that the first cutting is delayed allows more pheasant nests to be successful.

During the winter the amount of standing corn determined to a large extent the bird-holding values of this area. There was a total loss of 78 birds attributed to wandering and most of these birds left that part of the tract which had only 1.5 per cent of its acreage in standing hand-picked corn. There was but a small amount of straying from the half of the plot that had 14.1 per cent of the acreage in standing hand-picked corn. The birds that left during the winter represented a great theoretical nesting loss the next spring. The value of standing corn was also of great importance during the hunting season. Of all the agricultural crops, the cover offered by standing corn was the best.

Refuges made up of posted farmland, private sanctuaries, natural havens, and state land also play a great part in giving protection to birds driven from a hunting area. Refuges preserve breeding stock which populates surrounding country that otherwise would be understocked. An excellent example of a very effective refuge is that of the Reading, Pennsylvania, watershed refuge within sight of the city. This tract of about 2,000 acres harbors several thousand pheasants during the hunting season and in winter. This watershed has been planted to conifers that provide excellent cover. (When conifers are 6 to 8 feet in height, they produce the maximum amount of ground cover.) The surrounding farmland is extensively cultivated with a high proportion of the acreage in grains. Although food patches are planted annually on the refuge, many birds go out from the refuge to the farms for food, especially for corn.

MANAGEMENT RECOMMENDATIONS

There are a number of management practices that improve pheasant ranges, resulting in higher populations. Their cost and practicability vary in each section. The following discussion treats some of the more important management possibilities.

Refuges.—The primary purposes of pheasant refuges are to provide a haven of safety for the birds during the gunning season and to afford protection during severe winter weather. The location of a refuge in relation to the pheasant production areas is very important. Refuges provide safety for the largest number of birds when they are near the center, or at least well inside the boundaries, of good pheasant territory. On private property where the acreage under one ownership is relatively small, a wood lot, preferably one planted to conifers, is a good refuge site. A swamp or swale grown up to tall marsh vegetation such as cattails also is excellent. One good way to determine whether an area has refuge possibilities is to note whether pheasants have a tendency to use it as it is.

On private property where the owner desires to assure an overwinter population and where there are no natural sanctuary sites such as wood lots or swales, a field of standing corn will give excellent results. The stalks afford cover, and ears a supply of food. Pheasants spend much of their time in such fields.

On refuges that have been established in wood lots, managed watersheds, marshes, and swales, it is of value to have an adequate food supply within or near the site. If the soil is sufficiently rich and can be cultivated, there is nothing better than corn (plate 2, upper). On poorer sites, food patches of sorghums, barnyard grass, millets, and other grains are of value. However, none of these will stand up as well as corn during heavy snowfall.

The number of food patches should vary according to the size of the refuge and the number of birds to be fed. On large private- or state-owned refuges, 5 to 10 acres of corn to each 100 acres of woody or marsh cover is ideal. On a small private refuge as one owned by a farmer on a 150-acre farm, one or two food patches of one-quarter to one-half acre in size on or near the refuge are adequate. Often farmers leave 10 or 15 rows of standing corn, including about 25 per cent of the grain adjacent to protected areas.

On game projects involving private land in Pennsylvania, the Game Commission establishes small retreat refuges designed specifically to provide escape from hunting. Wood lots, swales, marshes, and waste areas are used to great advantage in the program. There is a safety law in Pennsylvania that further aids pheasant and other game management. This makes it unlawful for any person while hunting or trapping to shoot or discharge a firearm within 150 yards of an occupied building without specific permission of the tenant or owner thereof. As there is often good cover within 150 yards of buildings, many refuge areas are created by this law.

Winter Feeding.—If an adequate food supply is provided by food patches or standing corn, there is little need for winter feeding. However, there are many areas where food patches and natural foods should be supplemented by winter feeding, particularly in prolonged periods of severe weather. The best places to feed pheasants are those where they seek protection. One of the best foods for winter feeding is corn; however, other grains are readily taken. There are many types of shelters that will protect the grain and at the same time keep it available for pheasants. The brush lean-to type of feeding shelter is very good. A wood bar 10 or 12 feet long held up off the ground about 30 inches by supports at each end forms the frame upon which the butts of limbs and saplings can be laid, forming a sloping shelter. The brushier this construction is, the more game will use it. The open side should face the direction having the least exposure to prevailing storms. Grain should be scattered under the shelter. The number of birds using the station will determine how often the food supply should be replenished.

Another good type of feeding station is that of several shocks of corn stacked loosely together on a protected site in heavy cover. Grain can be scattered under, on, and around the shocks periodically as the supply becomes exhausted.

A number of mechanical feeders have been used with success. Many of the poultry feeders can be used. However, most of these devices require close attention as they easily become clogged with snow and ice.

Bundles of grain can be hung from fences, trees, and shrubs with varying degrees of success. The main point in winter feeding is that the food should be placed where the birds can get it with the minimum of exposure; in other words it should be in close proximity to good cover.

Modifying Farm Practices.—The value of corn and other grains has been fully discussed. In Pennsylvania the amount of standing corn largely controls the size of the winter population. This fact must be borne in mind when a high population is desired. On land where pheasants are given a great deal of consideration, it would be wise to arrange the crop rotation in such a manner that a field of standing corn would be left standing over winter each year near a wood lot, brushy fencerow, or marsh. It should also be kept in mind that machine-picked corn offers but little food and cover during severe winter weather.

Controlling Crop Damage.—In Pennsylvania, in certain years, many complaints are registered by farmers concerning pheasants damaging tomatoes. Langenbach (1940) reported on a study of such depredations made in 1939 in Lancaster County, where tomatoes are grown primarily for canning. The study was made at the height of the harvesting season. Pheasants had done some damage, but there was only $0.22 damage per ton from all birds as compared with $3.16 damage per ton from rotting. It has been claimed by farmers that early tomatoes, grown for the market trade, also are often damaged by pheasants but the degree of this damage has not yet been ascertained.

At times pheasants, crows, other birds, and mammals pull fresh-ly-sprouted corn. The use of repellents and other devices has been helpful in preventing such damage (pp. 108-110). Pheasants have also been known to damage sweet corn by stripping the ears.

Pheasant Control Probably Not Needed in Relation to Other Animals.—It is a common belief that pheasants seek out and kill young cottontails. A pheasant is physically capable of killing a nest-ling cottontail, but if such acts occur, they are few. Some of the best cottontail areas are in heavily pheasant-populated districts. On game farms it is not uncommon for cottontails to rear young in pens where there are hundreds of pheasants.

It is often stated that pheasants crowd out or kill bobwhites. In areas where the environment is more suitable for pheasants than for quail and the pheasants thrive, it is possible that quail will not toler-ate the pheasants and give up their range. It is very doubtful, how-ever, that actual combat occurs.

Occasionally a cock pheasant will invade a barnyard and chal-lenge the roosters. Sometimes such a bird may be very belligerent and cause the farmer considerable trouble. Usually, however, the situation is more comical than serious.

Reducing Nesting Season Losses.—In Pennsylvania and in many other states, alfalfa is the most important nesting cover despite the great nest destruction resulting from its mowing. On land that is owned primarily for pheasant production, the first cutting should be delayed until June 30. Where partial consideration is given to the nesting pheasant, each week of delay in cutting operations up to June 30 will increase the yield of pheasants.

On the average farm where pheasant management is not given much attention, there is little that can be done to cut down nest destruction. The present day high-speed tractors make the flushing-bar ineffective, as the speed of the tractor is too fast for the bar to give sufficient warning to the nesting female, and often young birds, to escape the cutter. The compactness of the modern mowing ma-chine also prevents the installation of a practical flushing-bar. On farms where old type, slow-speed tractors or horse-drawn mowers remain, use of a flushing-bar, such as the English (English, 1934) type (plate 2, lower), will save many adult and young pheasants. Even though the operator raises the cutter bar to save the nests, not many of these will be successful after being cut over and glaringly exposed to predation.

In many areas, individuals, game commissions, and sportsmen's organizations have prevailed upon road commissions to withhold roadside mowing operations until July 1. This is good practice. In addition to many nests and pheasants being saved, innumerable cottontails, quail nests and quail, and other beneficial animals are allowed to reproduce and rear their young in safety until they are old enough to escape the mowers.

Regulating the Kill.—To maintain a constant population year after year in good pheasant ranges, it appears that no more than 70 per cent of the fall population should be shot, killed through other causes, or driven from an area. Crippling losses can be cut down materially by careful hunting aided by well-trained retrievers (plate 1). Refuges can be established that will hold birds on the area and prevent them from being driven off.

Restocking.—When the breeding population has been reduced below that necessary for sustaining the number of birds that an area can carry, stocking is needed to bring the population back in the shortest possible time. In some of the more heavily human-populated areas there may be a definite shortage of cock birds in the spring. In the wild, probably an ideal sex ratio during the mating season is 1 male to 3 to 5 females. When the ratio becomes greater than 1 male to 5 to 7 females, it is no doubt good policy to stock males in sufficient numbers to correct the shortage, but it is doubtful if enough stocking can be done to affect the population to a noticeable degree. In areas where both sexes are below the breeding capacity of the range, stocking should be done according to the need. Most releases of breeding stock are made in March.

The need for restocking in most cases is based on belief rather than on fact. In many instances the number of birds released for restocking purposes has an infinitesimal effect on the total population. If a county had 30,000 cocks in the fall and 15,000 were bagged and 5,000 lost through crippling, there would be 10,000 left. If there were 3 hens to each cock at the beginning of the season, there would have been 90,000 females, and winter losses affected both sexes about the same, in the spring there would be 1 cock to about 9 females. If a very heavy spring stocking of males were carried out at the rate of 1,000 birds to the county, the sex ratio would still be 1 male to about 8 females or only slightly better than before. In most states, the hunting public demands restocking, and after it is made the common thought is that much has been accomplished, while in reality the benefits are often so meager as to be beyond detection. Game commissions are forced to make such releases and in most cases they charge it up to public relations—oil for the machinery of good feeling between game administrators and the public.

Some people believe that it is too expensive and unproductive to stock pheasants in areas that are not good pheasant range. The writer of this section believes such stocking has merit, however, so the subject will be discussed. In regions where the hunting pressure is low the trend of thought referred to may be justified. However, in states where hunting pressure is very high, there may be a definite need for stocking poor ranges. There are thousands of acres of farming country in Pennsylvania, as well as in other eastern states, where farming practices are not conducive to holding year-round pheasant populations, and as a result only a few pheasants normally live there. There are many tracts where the crops, particularly corn, are cleared from the land before fall, leaving little or no winter food or cover. This is particularly true in dairying and livestock sections. However, during the summer these areas can and do produce pheasants if breeding stock is present. Thus the pheasants in such areas must be looked upon as a crop for total harvest. Is it wise to stock birds when the job will have to be repeated each year? In areas where thousands of people hunt, the writer believes that it is, even if the stocked birds are expensive. In such areas, thousands of hunters go out each season, and the animal making up their bag is the cottontail. If during the season they get one or two shots at a pheasant it enlivens their days in the field to a great extent. In other words, the pheasant is the relish, not the main meal, in those areas. Under such circumstances the cost of a bird or the suitability of range can not be the sole factors in determining stocking policy.

Live-trapping vs. Artificial Propagation.—The Ohio system of refuges (pp. 101-121) is a fine management plan, but there are many areas in Pennsylvania and other states where conditions prevent such a system from working as efficiently as it does in Ohio. In Pennsylvania, where most of the first-class pheasant range is located in some of the most heavily human-populated areas on the continent, there are many controlled shooting areas and much posted land. Furthermore, the land is very expensive, and in most areas refuge sites would cost $100 to $300 per acre. It would be impossible in many such areas to acquire or lease refuge land at reasonable prices, and opposition to cutting down the shootable area would be great.

Pennsylvania has many refuge areas similar to those in Ohio, and they are valuable in maintaining high populations of pheasants; but there are not enough such tracts to fulfill the demand for birds for restocking purposes in all the areas removed from the vicinity of such refuges. The Pennsylvania Game Commission began live-trapping pheasants from refuges and overstocked areas in the winter of 1929-30, but the live-trapping of 2,000-3,000 birds does not meet the all-State demand. Thus, the game farm still has its place.

The Pheasant in the Northeast

By JOHN PEARCE

In the present chapter the intent is to discuss only those phases of pheasant life history and ecology that are unusually significant in New York and New England, the region hereafter being referred to as the Northeast.

Taking the region as a whole, there are no outstanding pheasant-producing areas. Certain parts of New York State offer good natural conditions for the bird, but these are not typical of the State or of the region. The pheasant in the Northeast is often exposed to rather inhospitable surroundings which are made worse by extreme over-shooting. This latter condition arises from a population density of 197 people per square mile against 44 per square mile for the entire nation. However, the pheasant in terms of recreation afforded by the number of birds bagged probably means more to hunters in the Northeast than to those in some other sections. Pheasant hunting provides the only wing shooting large numbers of them get. The pheasant management problem in the Northeast is that of meeting a very great demand for pheasants to shoot while working with relatively unproductive habitat.

The success of pheasants in this region depends upon a few critical factors, particularly soil fertility, land use, and hunting pressure. The birds are strictly farm-game, reaching greatest abundance on the most fertile soils. In this area it can be said they usually succeed in direct ratio to the richness of the soil. The potentialities are not always realized, however, because unfavorable land use practices and widespread overshooting also have much to do with success or failure of pheasants. However, requirements for sustaining pheasants can generally be met in the region if the combination of soil values and farming practices permits maintenance of types of cover needed at the different seasons. Yet, no matter how ideally cover types may be blended through accident or management, the birds cannot hold their own without conservative regulation of the kill. There are far too many gunners to warrant any other type of management than that designed both to improve habitats and to safeguard the breeding stock.

Factually, this chapter rests on the work of investigators who have studied the pheasant in the Northeast. In recent years, research has largely been done by the state game departments under the Federal Aid in Wildlife Restoration program, made possible by the Pittman-Robertson Act of 1937. Started prior to that time, but continuing, are certain studies conducted by universities, individuals, and state game departments. The author's part is that of a compiler, and full acknowledgment is gratefully made of material gleaned from the works listed in the bibliography.[1] Despite personal familiarity with conditions throughout the region, this chapter, without the background these studies provide, would be based only on opinion.

INFLUENCES OF CLIMATE AND LAND

The value of understanding the rudiments of pheasant ecology[2] in the Northeast lies in the fact that if they are ignored, failure in management is practically certain. Incredible losses of released stock frequently occur in a short time.

Mortality, especially with pen-reared birds that have not been range-hardened, is often very high. If liberated in late winter or early spring, such birds lose weight rapidly because they cannot maintain themselves at that season in the bleak New England covers. Weakened, they die of exposure or are easily taken by predators. Instances are known where pen-reared males released at the start of the crowing season have been killed or badly injured by wild cocks in combats over crowing grounds. Released birds often drift away

---

[1]By Philip Barske, Ben Bradley, Gardiner Bump, Arthur Clark, Ernest W. Gould, Earl E. Hoover, Neil W. Hosley, H. J. Ord, Ronald W. Rood, Thomas Wright, George Wallace, and others whose work is referred to in this chapter.

[2]Relations to their surroundings.

and are dissipated. It is thought that in this drifting process undue loss from predation occurs. Studies have shown that losses of stocked adults may be from 25-75 per cent of the release in a few weeks' time, and in addition, more frequently than is generally realized, stocked birds do not breed. All of these failures arise from lack of adjustment to the environment. The relationships between the pheasant and its surroundings, therefore, deserve careful thought by those interested in sound methods for increasing the sport of pheasant shooting.

The bird is so hardy that it exists—though it does not thrive—in many submarginal habitats. This gives rise to costly false impressions in the mind of the casual sportsman. Because he sees pheasants at one time or another in poorly suited places, frequently as a result of unwise stocking, or because they have been driven there by hunting pressure, he is apt to think that any rough, overgrown land not yet in forest is suitable for the birds. In southern New England, for instance, a good many pheasants are shot in the dense, hardwood swamps that dot the landscape. These are locally considered good places for pheasants. If unmolested, the birds seldom seek the heart of these tangled growths, but prefer to feed in the fields and to use swales or weedy places for escape cover. However, under the extreme pressure to which they are subjected over a relatively long open season, they not only seek swamps for shelter but are able to feed in them due to the fortunate occurrence there of certain seeds and fruits, especially of skunk cabbage seeds in the fall.

Consideration of pheasant ecology may also refute some of the ill-advised clamor for pheasant releases in grossly unsuited areas that constantly hampers state game officials. Failure to perceive that land use inimical to the maintenance of pheasant food or cover as well as too much gunning often create obstacles which the most lavish stocking program cannot fully overcome has cost the shooting public millions of wasted dollars and much disappointment. Pheasant success in this region is not a matter of chance as is so often thought, rather it is dependent upon the inexorable workings of environmental factors, which we are pleased to call ecology. A brief survey of the more important of these factors bearing on pheasants in the Northeast should be interesting for the light it throws upon the widespread idea that all these birds need is plenty of room.

Climate.—As to climate, great variation is found from severe winters in upstate New York, Vermont, and Maine and in most of New Hampshire, western Massachusetts, and Connecticut to relatively mild conditions along the coast. Foote (1942), in his Vermont studies, has shown that towns having the least annual snowfall have the most pheasants. He also found that the 500-foot contour appears to be the dividing line between inhabitable and noninhabitable range in Vermont. Occasional 3- to 4-inch snows and sleet storms that may coat the cover for days, or subzero spells down to -30° F., alone do not ordinarily restrict pheasant increase. As a rule, if good food and cover are available, the birds can be counted upon to hold their own against the elements in the Northeast without unreasonable losses.

Lay of the Land.—Natural land formations to a great degree affect the potential pheasant range of the Northeast. Thousands of square miles in the mountainous and hilly country in Maine, New Hampshire, Vermont, New York, western Massachusetts, and Connecticut are topographically unsuited to agriculture. In addition, a majority of the interspersed valleys, which do permit farming, represent isolated pheasant ranges too small to be of permanent value, or, as is often the case, have too short a frost-free period for growing corn, the grain crop most useful to pheasants. Large bodies of water total an estimated 5,000,000 acres, or about 7 per cent of the gross area. This coupled with the forests, occupying nearly 40,000,000 out of a total of 70,000,000 land acres, besides a considerable area in urban developments still further decreases the possible pheasant range. These aspects of the problem of providing shooting for the millions in the region are very significant although unheeding them the average hunter ruefully compares his lot with that of sportsmen in the more favored pheasant-producing states where vastly greater acreages of superior range for pheasants are available. In the Northeast, the better pheasant sections (plate 3) are in the valleys of large rivers, as the Connecticut, Mohawk-Hudson, Merrimack, Housatonic, Allegheny, and St. Lawrence; on the larger lake plains as the Ontario-Erie area which supports the best pheasant population in the Northeast, and those of the Finger Lakes and Lake Champlain; also along the coast where some farming is feasible, especially on Long Island and to a lesser degree locally east to Casco Bay, Maine. Outside of these areas, potential pheasant range is scattered. Relatively well-populated spots may be found here and there, but they are of only local importance. However, these smaller ranges should not be dismissed as of little value, for in a region where all farm-game cover is at a premium, even small areas may be of use.

Soil Fertility.—It is important to remember that the pheasant is no exception to the axiom that in the long run wildlife is most abundant on the more fertile soils. Soil fertility, while essential to the production of the food and cover pheasants must have in quantity, is not in itself an independent regulating factor. It must be employed in the right sorts of land use. Thus there are many fairly fertile areas once in farms that are now suburban or urban areas. Others for economic reasons have reverted to forest, which if cleared and properly farmed could support pheasants. Soil fertility is of considerable importance where it is necessary to establish artificial food patches or to subsidize the growing of grain to be left for winter feed.

Viewed on a regional scale, fertility of the soil is undoubtedly a limiting factor in pheasant distribution. In nearly every instance, the sections of greatest abundance of the birds are agricultural districts with superior soils. A notable exception is the coast from southern Maine to Long Island where more temperate climate appears to offset in part the usually infertile land characterizing the coastal strip with its sands and frequent rocky outcrops.

Land Use.—It has been amply shown by every investigator making a comprehensive study of the wild pheasant in this region that for all practical purposes the bird is a farm species. Hardy and resourceful as it is, the pheasant cannot cope with forest conditions. This fact alone makes approximately 55 per cent of the land in the Northeast useless to the bird. The pheasant's inability to occupy forest is ample refutation of the claim that it drives out grouse.[3] It is not sufficient merely to indicate that the pheasant is a farm bird. The same investigations which made that conclusion so clear have shown that not only the productivity of the soil, but the nature of the crops, the intensity of farming practice, the size of the fields, methods of harvest, and numerous related factors influence pheasant abundance. In Aroostook County, Maine, a section of fertile land

---

[3]The minimum area of woodland tolerated by grouse is roughly equivalent to the maximum pheasants usually tolerate. Hence they seldom come in contact. See Moss (1939) for an interesting correlation of grouse and pheasants with forest and farm land use in Connecticut.

but severe winters, pheasants have not succeeded. The land use (predominantly potato growing) is such that pheasant food and cover is reduced to a minimum. Modern contour farming, embodying permanent terrace drainage and the development of hedges holds much promise. The opportunities for combining farm practices and game management in this way are well described by Edminster (1942).

Granted a supply of standing corn and access to winter cover, the small diversified fields of northeastern farms appear with surprising frequency to fulfill basic requirements. Large fields, such as characterize some dairying sections, may be limiting factors according to Foote's (1942) findings in Vermont. It is to be noted that over much of the region dairy farming is the chief land use. This is not conducive to high pheasant populations as it requires little or no small grain to be grown and the cornfields are cut clear for ensilage. It may also be said that while intensive "clean" farming will not create optimum conditions for pheasants, neither are these birds benefited so much as the bobwhite quail by the haphazard farming often described as "one gallus."

COVER AND FOOD

Pheasant food and pheasant cover are often inseparable in this region. The food supply should, of course, be in close association with protective cover to avoid undue exposure of foraging birds to weather enemies. Need for the correct kinds and quantities of food is operative throughout the life cycle of the pheasant. Aside from food, the principal requirements which must be met are for special seasonal cover for crowing grounds, nesting and brooding and roosting sites, and for daily loitering between feeding and roosting times. The chief function of loafing cover is to give protection from predators. Most needs of the pheasant are reasonably well supplied on the average northeastern farm, but winter food and cover are generally insufficient outside of the better ranges. Consequently, these two essentials are stressed in this chapter.

Wild plants of the region have all of the qualities necessary to provide roosting and loitering shelter during snow, sleet, and subfreezing weather, but they are not always present where needed. Swamp edges and depressions occupied by cattails and marsh grasses are preferred and quite adequate cover. Heavy growths of weeds also are frequently utilized. Hedgerows, vine tangles, young oak stands, and coniferous growth in its younger stages, or of prostrate species such as pasture juniper, are the only other important kinds of protective winter cover. All these types of cover also serve as havens in time of danger, providing escape cover.

As to food plants, no suitable wild species exist in sufficient abundance over large enough areas to meet fully the winter needs of a substantial pheasant population. In fact many otherwise excellent habitats do not provide feed enough to sustain even a few birds for an entire winter. There is, on the other hand, a variety of wild fruits, which at least will tide birds over critical periods. Those of thornapple (*Crataegus*), apple (*Malus*), Japanese rose (*Rosa multiflora*), skunk cabbage (*Symplocarpus*), ragweed (*Ambrosia*), burdock (*Arctium*), grapes (*Vitis*), staghorn sumac (*Rhus hirta*), and Japanese barberry (*Berberis thunbergii*), have been found especially useful.

However, these foods should be supplemented by grain. Local food studies, of which McLaughlin's (1942) is the most comprehensive, show that a wide variety of fruits and seeds, and some insects and leafy vegetation are utilized in winter, but that corn is by far the most important food. Other cultivated grains are readily eaten but in the Northeast these either are grown only in small amounts or they are not available during deep snow or sleet periods.

It is fortunate that corn—the best known staple food for pheasants—is the leading grain crop of the region. It is available to some extent at least in fall. However, there is much less corn grown in the Northeast now than formerly. Connecticut in 1935, for instance, had only 5,000 acres or about 9 per cent of the acreage that was planted to corn in 1880. Making this adverse condition worse are the production of ensilage rather than shelled corn and the effect of corn borer regulations which require cutting and disposal of stalks. The net result is to deprive pheasants of nearly all corn in winter. In their search for winter food, pheasants are often forced to make use of manure heaps and freshly-manured fields from which they glean undigested fragments of grain.

As to cover, as that necessary for crowing, nesting, and brooding areas, details are given under management practices. The numerous small fields interspersed with permanent hedges, orchards, brush patches, and woodland edges, which characterize the New England landscape, in most instances, provide ample crowing territories. They afford nesting and brooding coverts also, although these uses are largely transferred to hayfields. The general picture is one of abundant edges with their beneficial effects in relation to wildlife.

Open water has not been demonstrated as a direct need of the pheasant but in this region the birds show a strong tendency to drift toward stream bottoms, swales, and swamp edges. In some parts, as along the coast, the birds spend much time near the water, the upper tide flats often being fed over in winter. Of two otherwise similar areas, one well-watered and the other not, the first undoubtedly will attract and hold more pheasants.

Food-grinding requirements are seldom a matter of concern in this region, most of the area having an abundance of grit. Gravel roads and graveling of icy paved roads in winter augment the natural supplies that are available most of the time at least along streams. The hurricane of 1938 has left pits made by the uprooting of trees that supply grit over much of New England. The thornapple which is readily eaten during the fall and winter has hard seeds that appear to serve as food-grinding material. In periods of prolonged deep snow, providing grit at feeding stations may be advisable.

LIMITING FACTORS

Aside from the take of the hunting season, the principal losses among northeastern pheasants are those due to predation, winter kill, hazards of the nesting and brooding seasons, disease, accidents, and illegal shooting. These can hardly be ranked in order of importance for the whole region as their effects vary locally and from year to year. There is in addition a most important loss, as yet imperfectly understood, which is due to drift and panic flights occurring after release or during hunting disturbances. This is especially serious in the smaller, isolated coverts.

Predation.—In recent years predation in relation to its effect on game populations has been widely studied. If these studies prove any one point, it is that predation alone, even when severe, is rarely the basic cause of failure of a prey species to maintain its numbers. It is now known that on range with adequate food and cover and where other environmental factors are favorable, prey species can evade paying more than an endurable toll to the so-called "vermin."

This is a vital concept in pheasant management. Too much time and money have already been lost by the shooting public through stressing "vermin" control to the exclusion of practically all other measures, especially the crucial one of habitat improvement. These comments are not to be taken as indicating opposition to all predator control. New England studies have indicated that on managed areas some sort of control often is necessary. The plea is rather for a change of emphasis from "vermin" control to environmental improvement.

The larger winged predators attack the pheasant from the time it hatches, but only the great horned owl, Cooper's hawk, and goshawk (frontispiece) appear of consequence in this region. Losses are highest in late winter and early spring, apparently because at this time the pheasants are often forced into the open in search of food which is then very scarce. Thus the habit of great horned owls nesting in February and March is unfortunate for pheasants in that the necessity of feeding the young owls stimulates the predatory activities of the adults at the very time the pheasants must take greater risks in seeking food. It should be noted that a great deal of the better northeastern pheasant range does not provide much opportunity for these owls because they prefer to nest in rather dense woodlands of a greater size and less open nature than are provided by the typical farm wood lots in fertile country. However, excellent nesting sites for owls usually occur in close proximity to the more heavily wooded ranges which local groups of sportsmen often insist on having stocked with pheasants. In consequence of that policy, it is considered by some investigators that practically none of the New England pheasant range and very little of that in New York State is not in the hunting territory of a pair of great horned owls in their nesting season.

The principal ground predators that may be locally or seasonally injurious throughout the region include skunks (which are most destructive to the nests), foxes, cats, and dogs. Raccoons, weasels, and minks also may kill pheasants, but so seldom that they may be disregarded. Foxes take their greatest toll of male birds in the spring, while later as nesting gets under way, they catch more hens. The crowing behavior of the cocks seems to expose them unduly. Apparently the low pelt values of the past decade have allowed foxes to reach unheard-of abundance over much of the pheasant range. The

Vermont studies (Foote, 1942) disclosed that on a 2,300-acre tract, 5 out of 7 fox dens had pheasant remains about them. Eleven banded birds (30 per cent of an April release) were found at these dens 6 weeks later. Cats and dogs either completely feral or those simply prowling away from home, are a constant detriment to pheasant and other wildlife populations.

Winter Killing.—Outright mortality among pheasants from the effects of winter weather is rather rare in the Northeast. Given sufficient food and the proper type of cover for roosting and daytime loitering, the innate hardiness of the birds seems to pull them through very bitter weather. Strange as it may seem to some, the provision of good winter food and protective cover, as a general rule, is more important than predator control at this season.

However, it must be recognized that all adverse weather conditions cannot always be fully offset even by the best of improved habitat. Excessive snowfall, followed by heavy crusting may seal in some of the birds. Prolonged sleet storms, and protracted sub-zero weather will eventually take a toll. These conditions have a cumulative effect, gradually sapping the vitality of the birds, and making them more susceptible to disease and predation. Ice storms aside from depriving the birds of food, may cause ice to form under their wings or freeze their tail feathers to the ground. While extreme winter conditions conceivably can result in catastrophe for the pheasant populations, to date no authentic instances have been found in studies in this region.

Investigations in New York, New Hampshire, Connecticut, Vermont, and Massachusetts have shown that contrary to what might be expected, the winter season is not the period of greatest natural losses, even on range where conditions were far from ideal. Nonetheless, from the management standpoint, large portions of the potential pheasant range in the Northeast are not producing pheasants chiefly because of deficiencies in winter food and cover.

Nest and Brood Destruction.—Nesting losses are always high. Ground predators and hay cutting are the principal causes. Mowing (plate 5, upper) destroys many birds because pheasants use the hayfields for nesting and incubating well into the haying season. However, hay cutting may appear to be responsible for a greater share of the losses than it should actually be credited with for two reasons.

First, in haying nearly every loss is noticed, while this is not true of other types of nest destruction. Second, some of the losses due to haying would be sustained sooner or later, anyway, as a result of predation.

Foxes, skunks, and crows appear to be the leading natural causes for nests being broken up, although dogs and cats are frequently of first importance near heavily populated areas. Individually, the fox has been found to be most destructive because it is more likely than the others to kill the hen as well as eat the eggs. Generally speaking, the skunk and crow simply destroy the eggs.

Spring freshets, or other floods, cause nesting losses in some localities. In others, mowing of small grain (winter oats and wheat) and the burning of fallow land in spring also are detrimental factors. There is further the poorly understood factor of the hen pheasant's efficiency as a mother. To all appearances she does not have so strong a nest-building instinct, nor does she incubate so steadfastly as the native upland game birds. Seemingly she is also more likely to desert her nest. However that may be, nesting losses from all causes usually aggregate 40 to 60 per cent.

The gamut of lethal dangers the pheasant chick must survive includes the usual predators, a few diseases, getting lost, accidental death, and other causes. By the time the birds take up independent existence in late summer or early fall, losses to the broods also run from 40 to 60 per cent or more of the total hatch. The reasons for this heavy drain are not easily learned. Brood survival of pheasants is a difficult subject for field study, usually calling for an expenditure of time out of all proportion to the amount of useful management data obtained. Despite the appalling array of circumstances adverse to reproduction, the wild pheasant under proper conditions nevertheless breeds successfully and effectively.

Shooting.—Among established adult pheasant populations, shooting is ordinarily the greatest cause of loss in the Northeast. This is in keeping with good management, but it is brought up at this point to round out the picture of pheasant mortality. Aside from excessive local decreases in the cock population which can scarcely be avoided under present laws and existing conditions, there is illegal killing of hen pheasants to an important extent in each northeastern state where the species is commonly hunted. In a Massachusetts study by

Wandell,[4] it was found that the chief limiting factor was the illegal killing of hen pheasants in the open season on cocks. This was so high as to reduce the hen-pheasant population by 60 per cent. The findings took on additional significance when it was found that hen pheasants which wintered over on the area produced more young per hen than did the spring-liberated stock.

Accidents and Disease.—Accidental deaths from flying into fences, wires, and buildings occur regularly, as do collisions with moving trains or automobiles along the highways. In the main, these losses, tending to occur in proportion to the number of the birds, are negligible in effect upon the pheasant population.

Disease has not been demonstrated to be a limiting factor in this region among wild pheasants, except on densely-stocked preserves. Bacillary white diarrhea or pullorum disease, which has only recently become better understood, may well have been responsible for many epidemics in the past. It appears that insistence on pullorum-free stock should be made mandatory for state and private stockings alike. Theoretically, individual pheasants are subject to a long list of diseases and parasites including many of those affecting domestic fowl, but apparently adult birds in the wild are little troubled by them.

MANAGEMENT

Pheasant management practices in the Northeast vary according to objectives. Preserves, for example, are common in New York and Connecticut. Due to the highly specialized conditions upon which pheasant preserve shooting rests, the methods used are not ordinarily of direct concern to those charged with supplying public shooting. Accordingly, this form of management is not considered in detail here, but it should be noted that preserve practices will repay careful study. The main problem is in keeping a supersaturated population of birds long enough to put them before the guns and at the same time hold a good stock on the preserve. The methods by which this is done are an art in themselves. Natural environment cannot be depended upon to produce the required number of birds and cover manipulation centers on holding the birds and getting them over the guns so as to provide the best sport possible. Cost is often

---

[4]Unpublished project reports, Federal Aid in Wildlife Restoration, Mass. Project 3-R-1, Farm Game Research—Pheasant.

a secondary consideration. By way of contrast, state game departments and most other groups normally must operate economically and therefore depend chiefly on natural reproduction.

The state organizations seek to increase pheasant shooting for the average hunter who buys the regular state hunting license. This is illogical as he would not be content with the bag of pheasants his ridiculously low license fee really entitles him to take under a strictly equitable ratio between bag limits and cost per bird to the state. To illustrate, a license to shoot pheasants in the northeastern states in 1942 cost from $1.25 to $3.35. The cost of each released pheasant shot by conservative estimate exceeds $2.00, while the maximum daily legal kill ranged from 1 to 3. It is obvious that the sport is not upon a self-sustaining basis and that the bulk of the kill is from wild stock produced on mostly private lands. An attempt to keep the kill on a reasonable basis is represented by the setting of seasonal limits, but there is very little evidence to show that this is more than a gesture. It appears that the only enforceable restrictions are the daily bag and possession limits.

It is to be noted, however, that if not the average hunter, at least a surprising proportion of the license holders will pay additional fees for the privilege of shooting over lands on which better-than-average sport can be expected, that is on managed areas. This is the key to one of the most significant trends in pheasant management today. Intensively managed lands either in private ownership and under lease or cooperative agreement, or public shooting grounds appear to be the most promising developments of the past twenty years.

In either case the approach to success is through maintenance of seed-stock refuges scattered over the shooting territory—a management practice to which the ring-necked pheasant is peculiarly amenable. This refuge system is fitted into a more or less readjusted land-use and farm-practice program intended to produce favorable pheasant coverts, as natural limitations and local farm practices will permit. To be effective this type of management must be applied to what for the Northeast are rather large areas of continuous pheasant range. It has been estimated by Wilder (1941) that 2,000 acres is probably the minimum that can be managed as a self-sustaining unit.

The ultimate in economy would be to produce enough birds to

supply a reasonable amount of sport exclusively from wild stock. Unfortunately, the shooting public is not satisfied with the bag that can be had in that way. Even if it were, there is always strong pressure from certain groups to stock their hunting grounds with additional birds just prior to the season and at suitable (the more the better) intervals during it. This is in effect imitating the ways of luxury game preserves and is not economically defensible as a public activity. It is not generally understood that unless care is taken, saturation stocking tends to build up the number of un-accounted-for birds faster than it increases the bag. Nor is it generally known that this loss is very high even on shooting preserves, which rarely account for more than 50 per cent of the birds liberated on their properties. Under extreme immediate hunting, the kill of birds on public lands during the season may be much higher than half the release. Connecticut hunters in recent years have shot as high as 80 per cent of the birds liberated on some areas just prior to, and during, the open season.

However, no state game department is yet justified in devoting its entire attention to managing selected areas. It is questionable whether any state can handle enough of these to satisfy the shooting public. So long as that is true stocking birds on private lands that are open to shooting but not under intensive management will be continued.

It will have been gathered, from what has been said, that the opportunity for pheasants to thrive on their own, or even with planned assistance in the Northeast is restricted to reasonably fertile farming areas that can be improved by game management practices to meet fully the specialized needs of the birds. It is not necessary, nor desirable to discuss improving every habitat requirement of the pheasant in these remarks on management. Instead, comments are limited to those concerning living facilities that are usually deficient or are of critical importance.

The following recommendations are intended to present fundamental principles applying over the Northeast at large. Where possible these are supported by the findings of investigators in the separate states. The body of specific knowledge bearing upon pheasant management is much greater than it was a decade ago, but there is still much to be learned. It should constantly be remembered that intimate knowledge of the territory under management is equally necessary to success as is appreciation of general principles. Technicians are not yet in a position to supply universally applicable formulas. Hence sportsmen interested in the improvement of conditions for pheasants will be well repaid for the thought and study they give to the relation of the birds to local environments.

Cover Requirements for Reproduction

These needs are for crowing sites for the males in late winter and early spring, nesting cover for the hens, and brood cover in which the young birds can be reared.

Crowing Territories.—In the Northeast, crowing starts from February to April, depending on the latitude. In general, territories are well established by mid-May. The small fields and diversified use of farms in the region usually provide adequate crowing grounds. Studies in New York, New Hampshire, and Massachusetts showed that most of the time crowing cocks utilize hayfields, fallow or recently abandoned land, orchards, and brushy edges of fields. Since the birds appear to be polygamous, if not promiscuous, and crowing territories seldom exceed 75 acres, it is rarely that scarcity of crowing territories limits reproduction. The number of crowing birds may be used as an index to the population; limited studies in our area indicated that 1.01 to 1.25 broods per crowing area are all that were successful. There is fighting between cocks, at times, because they defend their territories vigorously. It is not thought that this necessarily means that all of the hens in the vicinity are mated to a single male, but the present belief is that a ratio of 1 male to 4 or 5 females is advisable at the start of the breeding season.

Nesting Cover.—The propensity of the hen birds for making nests in hayfields is a matter of serious concern. It frequently means that the nests are disturbed by mowing, usually with disastrous results. Studies in Massachusetts with apparently typical findings showed that more than 50 per cent of all nests are in hay- (or alfalfa) fields and that a third of them are destroyed by mowing. Reed canary grass has been advocated as permanent nesting cover (Wilder, 1941). It would also provide good escape and roosting cover. Hedges, brushland, and ditches also are utilized. In fact, lack of nesting places rarely limits pheasants in the Northeast.

Considerable tolerance is shown by the hens in the selection of nest sites but certain requirements should be borne in mind when providing nesting cover. It should be within half a mile (preferably much less) of a crowing ground. During the incubation period, there should be protective cover lanes between the nest and food and water. Likewise, the nesting site should be adjacent to brood cover to obviate undue initial exposure of the brood. These matters are not difficult to arrange on most farms in New York and New England.

Brood Cover.—In common with other gallinaceous birds, newly-hatched pheasants subsist mainly upon insects. The requirements for brood rearing are: cover dense enough to protect the birds from enemies but not so dense as to be a handicap in keeping the chicks together and which also produces an abundance of insects. Hay meadows and various cultivated crops frequently meet these demands. Brood cover should be adjacent to, or at least near, the nesting sites. Hazardous stretches of open land, broad ditches, and streams between the two, especially should be avoided. Brood cover should also border on that used by the maturing birds as they begin to adopt the feeding and living habits of adults.

Cover Requirements of Adult Birds

The shift to adult habits brings the need of different cover for feeding, loitering, and roosting. In late summer and fall the normal countryside usually provides these. Requirements are for the necessary amounts of cover types in the proper relation to each other and in their being of high quality. During the winter, cover deficiencies are common.

Feeding Cover.—Cultivated croplands, fallow fields, hardwood swamps, fencerows, and grown-up edges constitute the bulk of the feeding grounds. Studies have shown that the seasonal food habits of the birds in the Northeast are much like those reported for other agricultural regions. Seeds (or grain) and fruits are staples most of the year, supplemented in season by greens and insects (figure 3 from McLaughlin, 1942). Areas largely devoted to cultivated crops provide the best summer and fall feeding grounds. A substantial part of the diet at these seasons is weed seeds, especially those of ragweeds (*Ambrosia*), smartweeds (*Polygonum*), and foxtail grasses (*Setaria*). In general, it may be said that the game manager's chief concern is to provide adequate watering, feeding, dusting, loitering, and roosting areas connected by well-protected travelways, hedges, and weedy or brushy gullies and ditches. Temporarily, strips of fallow land, overgrown areas, and unmown hay or alfalfa will serve. Alfalfa also provides roosting cover and is an important food.

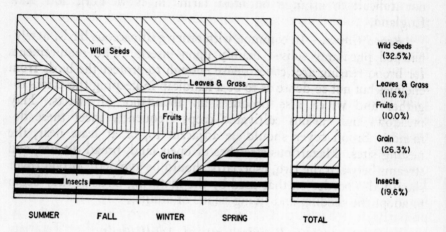

Figure 3.—Pheasant food in the Connecticut River Valley, Massachusetts.

Following crop removal and frosts, food supplies gradually become depleted until by midwinter they may be quite inadequate. This means that barring some fortunate benefit of land use, as failure to harvest grain, the birds must either be fed in emergencies or have prepared for them in advance adequate sources of food. The provision of standing food (to be available in deep snow) is made by: (1) Leaving uncut grain or unpicked corn adjacent to cover; (2) leaving shocked grain in the fields; or (3) planting special food patches (plate 5, lower). Each of these expedients has drawbacks that can be overcome only by definitely directed planning and expenditure of funds. The corn must be cleared away from the fields in the fall in some states to combat the corn borer, leaving neither shocks nor strips of standing corn available for winter pheasant food. Even where corn may be left standing, it usually is in outside rows with small runted ears owing to the competition or shade of nearby trees or hedges. This defect can be overcome by leaving a wider strip.

Shocked corn in otherwise bare fields offers very little protection to the feeding birds although it is far better than no food at all.

Food patches require the expenditure of time and money. If grains are to be produced in quantity, the plots must be properly tilled. This entails plowing, liming, fertilizing, and in some instances cultivating. If the site happens to be on a sterile old field overgrown with sod or brush, these practices become expensive. Experimental patches have cost from $25.00 to $40.00 an acre.[5] This could be reduced by the interested individuals doing the necessary labor. Two or three, quarter- to half-acre patches well distributed, are much better than a single larger one of equal total area. A half-acre patch will usually provide for 6 to 10 pheasants for the winter. Difficulties arise in developing a series of food patches as it is not easy to persuade farmers to take time at their busiest season to put them in.

Much experimenting and discussion have been devoted to the composition of food patches. The weight of experience in New England indicates as preferable a straight planting of corn, where borer regulations permit. A standard variety such as Canada Flint, properly drilled and cultivated, is the most certain to produce. A broadcast intersowing of buckwheat such as Silver Hull or Tatarian after the last cultivation will provide additional food if enough frost-free time (65 days) remains to mature it. In mixtures, the different species appear to compete too much with each other. Various grain plants that are suitable in other regions get so battered down here that their kernels are not available in deep snow. In parts of southern New England, there are areas of light snowfall, however, where some of the small grains, as buckwheat and soybeans, can be utilized. Nearly all of the state game departments are now in position to give definite recommendations as to pheasant food patches if they are informed as to the location of the planting area and are furnished with the results of soil tests.

It has been repeatedly demonstrated that some provision for supplementing winter food must be made where ample supplies of corn (or other grains in sections of light transitory snows) are not assured. Conservative management should seek to provide at least

---

[5]Unpublished report Conn. Pitman-Robertson Project 4-R, James S. Bishop, Leader, Philip Barske, Technician.

the minimum requirement of food in the form of an assured crop. In the average instance, this means that a sound plan for winter management can be built around a staple such as corn. Yellow varieties of corn appear to be preferred over those with white kernels.

Throughout the winter range, special effort should be made to provide in abundance at least several of the natural emergency foods listed in the discussion of ecology (page 38). The purpose of developing variety is to avoid food shortage if some of the species should fail, and to strengthen the diet as no one of them alone can be depended upon to maintain the birds for long periods. The most economical way to get the desired results is to encourage the better plants already present, but at times planting seedlings or cuttings may be required.

Winter feeding, in most regions, is held to be an emergency practice, but here it does not pay to wait for a crisis to start feeding pheasants. In order to be sure of getting the feed to the birds at critical times, it is often necessary to do enough feeding in late fall to get the birds coming to the stations. This is especially needful when dealing with a handful of birds on poor range. Feeding stations should be located with an eye to convenience in keeping them supplied as well as in allowing birds to feed without exposing themselves to danger.

A feeding station or food patch should not be placed in a line of flight taken by crows traveling to winter roosting areas as these birds can exhaust the food in short order.

Roosting Cover.—Pheasants in this region follow the preference shown elsewhere for swales, dense weed patches, and similar cover for roosting. Tree roosting is relatively uncommon and is usually caused by heavy winter storms. The denser young coniferous trees are then used. Swales of sedge (*Cyperus*) or cattail (*Typha*) appear to head the list of preferred roosting places and both are excellent.

There are necessities in planning roosting sites as there are in the location of all cover types. Some swales, for example, are avoided or only partly utilized by the birds because air drainage from slopes above makes them frost pockets, several degrees colder than surrounding areas. Prevailing winter winds may drift in much of the swale with deep snow for more or less extensive periods. Other part-time roosts are flooded in winter thaws. Such factors should be fully considered and offset by the provision of alternative coverts.

Here again only experience in handling areas will determine the practices best adapted to them. The general rule that special cover types should be accessible by means of protected lanes holds good also for roosting sites. About sundown pheasants may fly to their roost from a distance of 200 yards or more, yet the value of adequate travel lanes by which they can reach the roost without exposure is self-evident.

Seed-stock Refuges

The primary purpose of seed-stock refuges is to give some of the birds a chance to survive the shooting season. They also serve to spread the kill over a longer period. If respected by the hunters, correctly-organized and well placed refuges are highly effective. Essentials for the Northeast are met by blocks of 25 to 40 acres, containing escape cover, fall food plants (or at least one food patch), and roosting sites. Frequently the escape cover will be the same as the roosting cover but, in general, a separation of these coverts should be sought. Small patches of hardwood swamp, oak thicket, young conifers, particularly in dense plantations, with water nearby will increase the chances of success.

A thorough working knowledge of local pheasant habits, both under normal conditions and when hunted, is needed before final adjustments on a series of these refuges can be reached. The number which should be established should likewise be decided on the basis of local experience. Tests in New England, as yet incomplete, indicate at least 10 per cent of a managed area should be set aside. Very often quality counts more than acreage and small, attractive refuges can be more useful than large areas comprising barren fields. However, a strip of that type around good cover may tend to discourage trespass by hunter and dog and reduce the area of better habitat to be reserved. In western New York where extensive cattail marshes are common, these serve as places of refuge when hunting pressure is heavy (unpublished report, New York Pittman-Robertson Project 1-R, Lee Kutz, Leader. Pheasant Supplement).

It should be noted that under a long shooting season and heavy hunting, even the refuge system will not always guarantee survival of an adequate breeding stock as it is not ordinarily practical to close enough land to contain the fall range of several bands of pheasants.

Stocking

Stocking of pheasants in the Northeast is something of a necessary evil that is justified in view of the enormous recreational demand for pheasant shooting in areas where it can be provided only by stocking. Over the years, most states in this region have tried every conceivable method from the distribution of eggs and chicks to the release of adult birds during the open season. In recent years, returns in the form of birds in the hunters' bags from the various methods of stocking, as well as the investment these represent, have been carefully studied and in most instances the results have not been encouraging.

All forms of stocking under which it is intended to release hardened, reasonably wild birds for the shooting season are accompanied by severe losses in the stocked birds either before they can be shot or before they breed. A possible exception is achieved by the stocking on heavily hunted areas just prior (2 to 3 days) to the opening, or during the shooting, season. It is quite true that the birds used sometimes have never been on the wing before they are flushed for the first time by the hunter and there is a great outcry that this gives the sportsman a sorry target. This may be the case but the fact remains that experience in several states shows that in the last analysis the average gunner mostly wants a pheasant regardless of how long it has been running wild.

The practical objection to stocking for direct gunning is, of course, the cost. It has not been the experience of game officials that providing every hunter with a single day's bag limit by any means puts an end to the demand for more stocked pheasants, although providing even this small kill usually costs more than the license fee.

The best compromise on cost to date for stocking good sites where predation is not severe appears to be through releasing moderate numbers of 10 -to 12-week-old birds one or two months before the season. This will undoubtedly give more sporty shooting, if that is of importance. In the distinctly marginal covers, liberation immediately before the season, or during it, appears to result in the most birds bagged per dollar spent.

Releases of adult birds in the late fall to insure a good cock to hen ratio (1:4 or 1:5) and thoroughly hardened birds at the breeding season appears to be the best method for increasing natural production. The releases must be in good cover and careful watch must be kept on the birds to avoid undue predation or failure of food supplies if improvement in results over those from spring stocking is to be obtained.

The methods of actual release, now under intensive study in Massachusetts, also are important. Panicky, distraught birds may scatter wildly. In many New England covers this means they end up in unsuitable habitat and are speedily lost to sight. It may even mean they go across the border to another state. There is some evidence that the phenomenal flights of 25 to 50 miles within a few days after release, which occasionally come to light, are the results of head injuries inflicted in handling the birds. The pheasants should be allowed to enter good cover quietly, leaving the crates of their own will. A great deal of valuable information on the fate of stocked game birds has been lost in the past through failure to band them before release. Banding, with the cooperation of the public, will throw much light on how many are utilized as game, how far they travel, how long they live, and the like. Not all sportsmen bother about returning bands. Possibly, if it were more commonly realized that each band is the potential clue to what happens to several hundred dollars of sportsmen's funds, more care might be taken.

Shooting in Relation to Stocking

Aside from suitability of the habitat of the birds, the greatest factor in success with pheasants is the amount of shooting permitted. This is controlled by the policies of the state game departments. Widely varying seasons, ranging from a few up to 60 days, are demanded by the sportsmen in this region. In the longer seasons, the bulk of the birds taken after the first 3 weeks appears to be derived from in-season releases. There are many indications that better shooting would often be had if the prolonged pressure could be cut down.[6] In all areas the bulk of the pheasants bagged are shot in the first few days. For instance, on the Canton area in Connecticut, a

[6]Long Island consistently maintains a high annual kill despite a special 30-day season. There the mild winter, constant escape of pheasants from many private preserves, and the regular stocking program make this a far from typical case.

small detached range,[7] a reduction of more than 80 per cent in the known cocks present was made in the first two weeks of shooting. Theoretically, if only cocks were killed, only cocks should be released to maintain populations and this could be done in the early spring. Two facts complicate this seemingly simple matter. First, there is heavy loss among spring-stocked males, and second, in addition to other hen losses, important numbers of females are illegally shot.

It all comes down to a question of ethical sportsmanship. Are the hunters willing to forego taking an extra bird or two more than the law or their license fee entitles them to take, or is the breeding stock to be killed?

Similarly, with newly liberated stock, if more birds and longer seasons are wanted, without regard to condition of the birds at time of shooting, they can be had, but the price will be higher hunting fees and open acceptance of an inferior type of shooting. This kind of sport is entirely unwarranted because the ring-necked pheasant has long since won its laurels as magnificent game once it has become hardened in the wild.

---

[7]Unpublished quarterly reports, Pittman-Robertson Project 3-R, James S. Bishop, Leader, George P. Spinner, Technician.

Plate 3.—Upper. Typical Connecticut Valley upland pheasant habitat, South Amherst, Mass. This is some of the best range in the State. (Massachusetts Department of Conservation, Pittman-Robertson Project 3-R-1)

Lower. Typical orchard type of pheasant habitat found in Connecticut Valley uplands. Areas such as these are important pheasant cover over most of the Northeast. (Massachusetts Department of Conservation, Pittman-Robertson Project 3-R-1)

Howard Marshall Wight
1889-1942
To Whom This Book Is Dedicated

The Pheasants in Ohio[1]

By DANIEL L. LEEDY and LAWRENCE E. HICKS

PHEASANTS BELONG to the great group of gallinaceous or fowl-like birds, known to the early naturalists as Rasores, or scratchers, from their habit of digging among leaves or into the ground with their claws and uncovering seeds, grubs, and other bits of food (Beebe, 1936). The introduced species has this ability well developed, being able to obtain food even when buried by heavy snow. In Ohio, pheasants have been observed using both claws and beak in digging through 4 to 10 inches of·snow and feeding on corn or soybeans that would have been unavailable to less vigorous and adaptable birds.

LIFE HISTORY

Food Habits.—General observations indicate that much of the pheasant's food consists of waste grain and weed seeds and in a spe-

[1]Acknowledgments.—The authors desire first to credit the pioneering in pheasant management of Edward L. Wickliff, for many years Chief of the Bureau of Scientific Research of the Ohio Division of Conservation, and of Game Manager A. D. Meagley of Wood County. Acknowledgment for assistance of varied kinds is made to Milton B. Trautman and Charles F. Walker while research assistants of Wickliff; Edward S. Thomas of the Ohio State Museum; Robert B. Gordon, E. N. Transeau, and H. C. Sampson of the Department of Botany, Ohio State University; Game Protectors O. E. Neimyer, Ted Reigle, Lloyd Ohl, Jean Copeland, Jim Stitt, and Howard Langstaff; officers of farm cooperatives, especially Dewey Hendricks of Plain Township and A. O. Barker of Liberty Township, Wood County; and to Aldo Leopold, Wallace Grange, and Ralph Yeatter for discussion in correspondence and in the field. The Ohio Division of Conservation has aided in many ways; particularly helpful have been the contributions of Management Agents J. R. Benjamin and Hayden Olds.

cial, though limited, study in Ohio, plant materials were found to make up more than 90 per cent of the subsistence. Of this, corn alone, averaged nearly 55 per cent. Wheat and the seeds of lesser (or common) ragweed, foxtail grasses, and smartweeds each contributed significantly to the diet. During the growing season and even in fall, pheasants eat much greens and insects. The latter are mostly grasshoppers, cutworms, and beetles.

The principal complaint against the pheasant on the score of food habits is that it pulls sprouting corn. So it does, but it receives blame for part of the work of that well-known corn-puller, the crow. Moreover corn pulling by both crows and pheasants can be lessened by various control methods. (These are discussed under refuge management, pp. 108-114.)

At all times of the year, pheasants eat considerable quantities of waste corn, wheat, oats, rye, barley, and buckwheat and this prevents the development of much volunteer grain which might carry over crop diseases from year to year, defeating one of the benefits of crop rotation. It is thought that this service more than repays for any damage done to sprouting corn, except in areas where the birds are especially abundant. Where these unusual pheasant numbers occur, the financial return possible through game management and sale of hunting permits, promises a reward many times greater than the loss to the corn crop.

In the Wood County, Ohio, investigations, some interesting results were obtained as to the amount of crop wastes available to, and consumed by, pheasants. Near one of the refuges a 13-acre field of soybeans was harvested by combine in the fall. By means of sample counts, the amount of waste beans per acre was calculated at 112 pounds. Hence in this field there were about 1,450 pounds of soybeans available as food. By February 9, the beans remaining amounted to only 2.23 pounds per acre, or 29 pounds in the entire field. Making an allowance for those eaten by other birds or mammals and for decomposition, it is probable that pheasants consumed 750 to 1,000 pounds of beans in this single small field during the winter.

An indication of the amount of corn eaten by large concentrations of pheasants on refuges is given by another survey. In 1937 there was an average of about 600 pheasants on the Plain Church Refuge, Wood County, during a 16-week period following the opening of the hunting season in November. Observations were made on the feeding habits of these birds during the winter, and records were kept of where they fed and how far they traveled from the refuge. Feeding was confined chiefly to five cornfields on, or immediately adjacent to, the refuge. After considerable surveying, including the counting of corncobs from which the corn had been eaten by pheasants in sample plots in the five fields, it was calculated that approximately 186 bushels (13,020 pounds) of corn were consumed by the pheasants in the 16-week period. Of that amount, 15 bushels (8.1 per cent) were taken from unhusked corn in shocks, and its consumption was therefore detrimental. The remainder or 171 bushels (91.9 per cent of the total) was waste left in the fields by harvesters. Assuming that 600 pheasants consumed the 186 bushels in 16 weeks, an average of 1.4 pounds of corn was taken per pheasant per week. Corn probably constituted more than half of the total diet of the pheasants during the period. No winter feeding was necessary on the refuge.

This survey indicated the potentialities pheasants have for crop damage when they are concentrated in large numbers. However, very little damage was done in this case because most of the corn had been harvested before the pheasants flocked to the refuge. Corn grown near refuges and not intended for pheasants should be harvested before the hunting season concentrates the birds.

In this food-habit section may well be discussed the effect of pheasants upon other game. To whatever extent it exists, it depends upon food habits either through direct predation or through competition. The relations between different kinds of game birds are of considerable public interest, it usually being assumed that introduced species are likely to bring about a decrease in native stocks. Some indication of the relative abundance of pheasants, bobwhites, and Hungarian partridges in the major pheasant belt of northwestern Ohio was obtained in a survey made in 1939. More than six thousand farmers, representing about 200 selected farms per county or 15 per township, furnished information regarding the relative abundance of these three birds. It was indicated that average relative abundance in the 31 counties was: bobwhites 100, pheasants 77, and Hungarian partridges 19.

In general, counties with the largest concentrations of pheasants had relatively fewer bobwhites. It is possible that large numbers of pheasants in an area have some detrimental effect on the numbers of quail. Bobwhites are noticeably scarce on some of the better refuges. However, these birds sometimes share the same feeding station with pheasants, and partridges are often found in the same fields with their larger relatives.

With respect to the Hungarian partridge, there is probably some intolerance. Bent (1932) states also that the ring-neck pheasant may have to be reckoned with as an enemy of the partridge and cites as an example the finding of three partridges killed by pheasants. So far as known, however, the marked increase in numbers of pheasants in northwestern Ohio cannot be considered a major factor in the gradual decrease in partridges.

Rabbits are much more numerous on the refuges than away from them, but there is apparently very little conflict between these animals and the pheasants. It is sometimes thought that pheasants kill young rabbits, but, if this occurs at all, it must be rare.

Weights.—Leffingwell (1928) stated that the average weight of five 2-day-old chicks was 18.2 grams and that of one 4-day-old chick 19 grams. Bent (1932) noted that the gain in weight of young pheasants is at first rather slow, but that the weight is increased nearly sevenfold at three weeks, and at five weeks of age the chicks weigh about fifteen times as much as when first hatched.

Incidental to pheasant disease investigations for the Ohio Wildlife Research Station, Dr. Clarence Woodhouse and Dr. Paul Bennett obtained the weights of 302 male birds killed in Wood County during November 1936, 1937, and 1938. The averages agreed very well for the different years and were: lowest, 2 pounds, 2 ounces; median, 2 pounds, 9 ounces; and highest, 3 pounds, 6 ounces.

Another series of weights of Wood County pheasants included those of 407 adults taken in every month although mostly in the hunting season. The birds were lightest in late summer and heaviest in winter. The maximum for a male in this lot was 4 pounds, 7 ounces; minimum, 1 pound, 14 ounces; and average for 348 individuals, 2 pounds, 12 ounces. For 59 females, corresponding figures are: 3 pounds, 1 ounce; 1 pound, 10 ounces; and 2 pounds, 3 ounces.

Locomotion.—The wings of a pheasant are short and rounded, and move rapidly in flight. Once under way, much of the flight is accomplished by soaring glides. Leffingwell (1928) describes pheasants as swift but not strong fliers and states that they can attain a speed of no more than 30 to 38 miles per hour.

The flight of a pheasant varies a great deal, depending upon where the bird is flushed, the distance to cover, and the cause of flight. The height ordinarily reached varies from 2 to 60 feet. Measurements were made of the height of flight of 278 pheasants (140 males, 138 females) and the average was found to be 11.5 feet. The distances ordinarily flown range from only a few yards to more than 300 and average 115 yards (farther during the hunting season). Pheasants flushed within a mile of a refuge, especially after being shot at, reach heights well over 50 feet and attain great speed in flying to a refuge, a trait which accounts for many birds being saved. The writers have several times observed cock birds climb to elevations of 150 to 250 feet to escape gunfire and have known them to make flights of from 1½ to 2½ miles.

Pheasants can run rapidly, and winged birds often give dogs a good chase before being caught. They occasionally swim, a chick less than a week old being observed to swim across a drainage ditch 10 feet wide.

Flushing Distances.—The distance at which pheasants flush depends on the kind of cover, the speed of approach of the observers, the season of the year, the sex of the birds, and even the time of day. When pheasants are approached quietly in dense cover, they often run rather than fly. This is especially true of adult males. During the hunting season, it is common to find pheasants running ahead of hunters, sometimes at a distance of several hundred yards. After crossing a field in this way, pheasants frequently flush near the margin. Good hunters keep on the alert and ready to fire to the very edge of the field. Most of the pheasants that are bagged flush within 25 yards of a hunter.

In the morning before feeding time, when pheasants are flushed in the vicinity of their roosts, they tend to fly from the roosts toward the feeding grounds. In the evening they are prone to go in the direction of their roosts. At midday pheasants can often be approached more closely than when they are feeding. Pheasants flushed near a refuge fly to the refuge.

In observations on some 1,300 birds, it was found that in September, a large percentage of birds flush at distances of less than 25 yards. The flushing distance increases during October and November, and during the winter, as the cover becomes less dense, and approaches a maximum in the spring. The average distance is shortest in summer (July-August). On the whole, females stay in cover somewhat more closely than males.

Dusting.—Pheasants are fond of dusting, a habit that probably aids in controlling lice and mites. Loose soil in cornfields or in dirt roads is frequently used for dust baths. The wallowed depressions averaged 2 inches in depth and a foot in diameter.

Hearing.—The sense of hearing is very acute. According to an article in *Science* (Anonymous, 1923), during World War I pheasants showed evidence of being greatly disturbed by air waves resulting from explosions that were inaudible to human beings. At a distance of 216 miles from the battle of Dogger Bank, pheasants squawked themselves hoarse. The greatest distance at which the birds were observed to be affected was 320 miles. It was suggested that the birds did not hear the explosions but were sensitive to the quivering of the branches upon which they were sitting. In northwest Ohio, dynamiting in limestone quarries, even though several miles away, causes the birds to squawk.

Gregariousness.—With the approach of autumn, when the young birds are about 3 months of age, it is common for several broods of pheasants to flock together. They are highly gregarious birds, a fact that facilitates trapping them, and makes them adaptable to refuge management. The accompanying graph (figure 4) indicates the amount of flocking prevalent each month of the year and is based upon observations of 21,305 pheasants in Wood County, Ohio. Adults in groups of two or more were listed as flocks. Note that pheasant gregariousness (percentage of all adults seen in flocks) ranged from a high in February (97 per cent) to a low in August (14 per cent).

The largest flocks were observed during the fall and winter when more than 400 pheasants were sometimes found together. The flocks scatter during the spring and summer. The cock birds are relatively better represented in the smaller, than in the larger, flocks. Hens are more gregarious than cock birds at nearly all periods of the year.

Sex Ratio.—The sex ratio of pheasants observed in the field varies considerably: (1) According to the season of the year, (2) following differential mortality of the sexes in the hunting and mowing seasons, (3) with age classes, (4) with distance from a refuge,

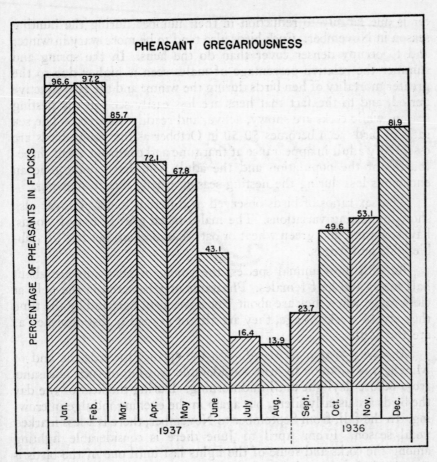

Figure 4.—Pheasant gregariousness. The graph shows the percentage of all adult pheasants observed which were in flocks of two or more. (Based on 21,305 pheasants seen in Wood County, Ohio, September 1936 to August 1937.)

and (5) with the kind of cover in which observed. In a study of this subject, records were kept of the number of males and females seen each day for a total of 64,337 pheasants observed in Wood County, September 1936 to March 1940.

The average percentage of males seen, by seasons, was: Fall 38, winter 19, spring 27, and summer (also for the entire year) 28. The sharp drop in the proportion of males observed during the winter is due largely to reduction in their number during the hunting season in November. Cock birds also tend to be more wary in winter and to occupy denser cover than do the hens. In the spring and summer the relative percentage of males seen is higher due to the greater mortality of hen birds during the winter and the reproductive period, and to the fact that hens are less easily seen in the nesting season, while cocks are showy, active, and readily observed. The sex ratio of birds seen becomes 50-50 in October as the young birds are essentially adult in appearance at that time and comprise about three-fourths of the population and the adult hens have undergone an enormous loss during the nesting season, chiefly due to mowing.

The sex ratios of birds observed in different kinds of cover also show interesting variations. The males make greater use of woods, hay, soybeans, and green wheat or oats than do hens but less of stub-blefields and weeds.

As with most animal species, the young of pheasants are about half males and half females. Pheasants may be sexed in the field at close range when they are about 7 or 8 weeks of age, and by the time they are 14 weeks of age, they are almost as readily distinguished as are the adults.

Breeding Season Behavior.—In the spring, towards the end of March, it is common to hear considerable crowing of cock pheasants from before daylight until midmorning. During the heat of the day the birds are usually silent, but again in the evening indulge in crowing. In the fall, from September to November, there is a less marked vocal season. From April to June there is considerable fighting among the cocks and some of the fights last until one of the birds is completely beaten and exhausted.

Wight (1933) states that a cock pheasant defends an area for himself and family against the intrusion of other cocks. He calls these territories crowing areas, because each cock monopolizes an area throughout the spring and summer, and announces his right to do so by loud crowing.

Observations in Ohio indicate that such territories are not always clearly defined, although the male bird often stays close to one or more nesting females, and the range of individual males and females may not be more than a few acres. It is interesting to note in a 25-acre field of sweet clover in Wood County containing 130 nests, that the nests were in groups of 2 to 8. Each of these groups may have represented the crowing area of one cock.

In Wood County in 1937, the season of display began about April 7 and the first attempt at copulation observed was on April 15. The laying season usually begins in April. The eggs are ovate, rounded at the smaller end, and olive-green in color. Their average size is 1.67 by 1.31 inches (Leffingwell, 1928). The incubation period is about 23 days, and the females usually incubate the eggs with no assistance from the males, although rare exceptions have been reported. In most cases the nests are in a natural depression, or in one scratched out by the female from one-fourth to one and one-half inches deep. They are lined with whatever materials are at hand, as bits of grass, leaves, and twigs.

Hens tend to desert their nests if disturbed soon after beginning to incubate the eggs. Many desertions are caused unwittingly by mushroom hunters and hikers who flush birds from their nests early in the season. Dogs and cats also cause desertion and destruction of nests. Training bird dogs in fields where pheasants are nesting results in nest mortality.

After a hen has incubated her eggs for two weeks, she stays more closely on the nest. This results in a very heavy mortality during the mowing season when about 32 of every 100 hens nesting in hay are killed or crippled by mowing machines. Hens are reported to have returned to their nests and incubated until death resulted from bleeding, after both legs had been clipped off.

Laying eggs in the nests of other birds is not uncommon with pheasants. Leffingwell (1928) reported that pheasants were known to have laid eggs in the nests of mallard duck, Hungarian partridge, woodcock, domestic chicken and turkey, and the quail, ruffed grouse, and sooty grouse. Bennett (1938) found that 4.7 per cent of blue-winged teal nests in Iowa contained eggs of pheasants. In northwestern Ohio, pheasants occasionally deposit eggs in the nests of the domestic fowl, quail, wild duck, and Hungarian partridge, but this is so infrequent as to be unimportant.

Young pheasants are usually cared for by the females alone until they are from 6 to 7 weeks of age, after which time male birds also are often seen with the brood. A hen with partially albinistic, and therefore recognizable, young was observed to remain within 500 yards of the nest site until fall.

Clutch and Brood Sizes.—Of 563 pheasant nests observed in Wood County in 1939, the average number of eggs was 8.8. Clutch size decreased as the season progressed from 10.1 for those found in June, to 8.2 in July, 7.5 in August, and 6.6 in September.

Brood size similarly declined and in a total of 2,229 broods classified as to age, those less than 10 days of age had an average of 8.8 chicks; those from 2 to 3 weeks old, 7.0; from 4 to 5 weeks, 6.6; 6 to 8 weeks, 5.8; 9 to 12 weeks, 6.1; and 13 weeks or more, 6.0. The average number for all broods in a total of 2,348 (1937-1940) was 6.96.

Percentage of Females Rearing Young.—The percentage of female pheasants rearing young is also an excellent index of the reproductive efficiency. It should be remembered, however, that owing to season-connected mortality the hens observed near the end of the nesting season constitute only a part (about 58 per cent) of those present at the beginning of the period. In observations on 1,760 females with young in northwestern Ohio 1937 to 1939, including only undisturbed birds under favorable conditions, the average percentage of hens with young rose rapidly from June to August. During September it was: 1937, 77.3 per cent; 1938, 71.6 per cent; and 1939, 71.6 per cent—an average for the three years of 73.5 per cent.

This index varies from year to year and with the locality. In Wood County, in 1937 and again in 1938, an average of 77 per cent of the females observed in September had young; in 1939 the proportion was only 71.3 per cent. In poor pheasant range, the ratio is considerably less and the average brood size also is smaller. In extensive surveys made in western Ohio in June and July, the percentage of females observed with young was 53.9 in 1938 and only 14.5 in 1939. The average date of the 1938 survey was July 7, or 5 days later than that of 1939. This reconnaissance and others indicated that the 1939 nesting season was later and also less productive than that of 1938.

Nesting Success.—In the 1939 Wood County study, 58 per cent of the 563 nests observed were successful. About 92 per cent of the eggs were fertile. The most successful nests were those begun during the last 10 days of May and the first 10 days of June. The 319 nests, in cover types other than sweet clover, contained 2,933 eggs, of which 1,051 or 36 per cent hatched. As the sweet clover fields were cut late for seed, the 238 nests in them were highly successful, 208 or 87.4 per cent producing chicks.

Adult-juvenile Ratio.—The adult-juvenile ratio of pheasants, immediately following the nesting season, is an excellent indicator of reproductive efficiency. It is difficult to distinguish adults from young in the field after October 1, but some information may be obtained at that time through the closer inspection made possible through examining hunters' bags in November, and the birds live-trapped from refuges in the winter. Gower (1939) and others have described the use of the bursa of Fabricius as an indicator of imma-turity in game birds, including pheasants. Determining the condi-tions of that organ may be satisfactorily done until January 1 or later, but by the time sexual maturity is reached the bursa has dis-appeared. Fairly accurate identification of juvenile birds can be made also by plumage characters, and by the length, shape, and hard-ness of spurs of the males.

The adult-juvenile ratio was recorded for 24,663 pheasants ob-served in northwestern Ohio from June to October 1, 1937 to 1940; by the end of the nesting season, about three-fourths of the popula-tion was made up of young birds.

Longevity.—The pheasant population, as a whole, is relatively youthful, birds a year or more of age, making up only 17 per cent of the male, and 32 per cent of the female, contingents, or 28.6 per cent of the total. The average life span, according to the information at our disposal, is 9.85 months for males and 20.83 months for fe-males. The absolute maximum age reached in the wild is about 8 years.

In these statements we are considering only pheasants that attain at least 3 months of age, i.e., survive until October 1. The average pheasant life span is remarkably short, even when the tremendous juvenile mortality (occurring from the time the eggs are laid until October 1) is not considered. Actually, only about 21 to 25 per cent of all eggs laid result in living young pheasants on October 1 (about 36 per cent of the eggs laid hatch) and only about 60 per cent of the young hatched survive until October 1. Thus, average pheas-ant longevity, if based on total eggs laid, is only about one-fourth that indicated above, or, if based on total young hatched, the average pheasant longevity is only about 60 per cent of that indicated above. As a considerable part of all pheasant mortality occurs in juveniles before October 1, the average life expectancy of individuals reaching that age is considerably higher than it is for the total number of pheasants which begin life in the form of fertilized eggs, or for the total number of pheasant chicks which hatch.

CHECKS ON THE PHEASANT POPULATION
Hunting

Hunting Pressure.—There is an average annual hunting pressure of 16.4 hunters on each of Ohio's 40,740 square miles. Since for various reasons one-fifth of Ohio is nonproductive of game crops, the net hunting pressure is 20.5 hunters to the square mile on hunting lands or one hunter to 31 acres. It varies during the open season and from year to year. Weather conditions, game population densities, weekends, holidays, the staggered season, and other factors affect the number of hunters. In analyses of the pheasant hunting done by 774 gunners in Wood County in 1937 and by 775 in 1938, it was found that the total number of hunters, the average number of hours spent in hunting, the average number of pheasants bagged per hunter and per day, the percentage of the season's hunting done per day, and the proportion of the season's bag taken each day, all were highest for the opening day and decreased as the season continued; conversely the average number of hours required to bag each pheasant, increased.

A high percentage of all pheasants taken by hunters is killed during the first few days of the open season. Thus during three hunting seasons (1937 to 1939), 10,686 hunters took an average of 29.6 per cent of all the pheasants they bagged, on the first day; 17.9 per cent on the second day, and 8.0 per cent on the third. The first three days of hunting thus accounts for more than one-half (55.5 per cent) of the season's pheasant bag. Only 6 to 8 per cent of the pheasant bag is taken during the last three days of the season. There is a characteristic rhythm of hunting pressure, highest on the first day, dropping rapidly the next two, again rising on holidays or weekends (figure 5).

A so-called staggered season was tried in Ohio in 1939. Under its provisions, hunting was limited to Wednesday to Saturday, inclusive, of each week. Careful field study of the results showed that:

The total season's bag was somewhat larger than under the usual regulations. Little change was noted in the early season bag, but the late season kill was a fourth larger. The rest periods seemed to favor the assembling of unusually large flocks of cock birds.

The staggered dates influenced the hunters more than the game. The rest periods each week enabled both hunters and dogs to recuperate. This tended to increase the length of the hunting day and the

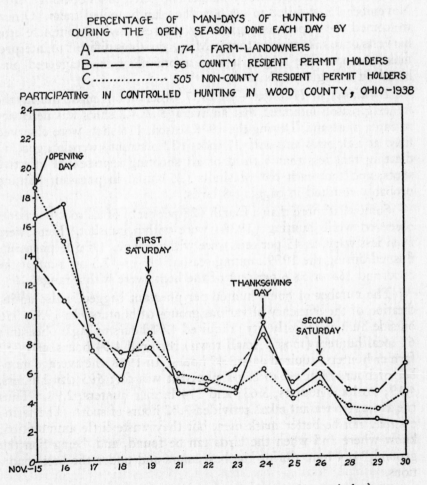

Figure 5.—What part of the season's hunting is done each day?

number of days hunted. However, the share of game per hunter was less, so hunting pressures late in the season were below normal.

The staggered plan did not spread the hunting pressure more evenly throughout the season—on the contrary, it concentrated it more than usual on the opening day, on Saturdays, and, to a lesser extent, on Wednesdays.

Most of the hunters with jobs appreciated the extra weekends available for hunting. Many farmers objected to an opening before November 15 or failed to see how the plan benefited them. Others welcomed the opportunity given by the rest days to complete crop harvests or to take trips to town. Many variables difficult to interpret make it impossible to give a final appraisal of the staggered plan based on a single year's trial.

Efficiency of Hunters.—In 1937, observations made during the hunting season indicated that an average of 4.2 shots was necessary to bag a pheasant. During the 1938 season, 116 shots were observed fired at cock birds and only 37 cocks (32 per cent) were bagged, indicating that less than a third of all shooting represented effective shots, and that each box of shells (25) used in pheasant hunting probably resulted in bagging 8 birds.

Somewhat more than a fourth (28 per cent) of all cock pheasants observed while hunting (1938) were within gunshot. Hens were even less wary, as 45 per cent were within range. Of 506 pheasants flushed during the 1939 hunting season, 115 or 47.3 per cent of the cocks and 154 or 58.6 per cent of the hens, were within range.

The number of hours hunted per pheasant bagged is also an indication of the efficiency of various groups of hunters. In 1937, 356 outside hunters (mostly city) required 4.01 hours to bag a pheasant; 61 local hunters (mostly small town) required 4.04 hours, and 357 farmer hunters required only 3.49 hours. In 1938, the average number of hours required to bag a pheasant was for: 505 city hunters, 4.19; 96 local hunters, 3.63; and 174 farmer hunters, 2.98. Thus the average pheasant taken provided 3.72 hours of sport. The farmers may not be better marksmen, but they waste little ammunition, know where and when the birds can be found, and, being "on the ground," can hunt during the best hours and under the best conditions.

Pheasant Take.—Intensive studies have been conducted yearly in Wood and other northwestern Ohio counties since 1936 to determine the annual pheasant take during the November hunting season. In 1937 the average kill of cock pheasants in Wood County was calculated at 89 per square mile, and the total for the county (612 square miles) at 54,000. Outside hunters shooting on game protective association grounds, bagged an average of 5.49 pheasants each during the 12-day open season, compared with 6.48 taken by the local hunters, and 4.78 by the farmer hunters. In the same area, farmer hunters bagged 6.35 pheasants each during the 1938 open season of 14 days, outside hunters 5.92, and local hunters 7.22. The average pheasant bag for all hunters was 5.58 in 1937 and 6.50 in 1938. Following the 1937 hunting season, 2,801 farms in 15 western Ohio counties were surveyed. These farms had 1,716 resident farmer hunters who reported killing 6,662 pheasants during the 1937 open season. The average bag per square mile in these 15 counties for farm residents only was 24.9 pheasants.

Following the 1938 open season, 6,258 farms in 31 western Ohio counties were studied. These farms had 3,968 farmer hunters who reported bagging 13,823 pheasants, indicating an average bag per square mile for farm residents only, of 24.5 pheasants. The calculated kill by the operators of farms in 15 western counties was 93,004 pheasants in 1937; in 1938, the kill in 31 counties was estimated at 182,084 pheasants. The total bag for the entire State has averaged about half a million annually in recent years.

Crippling Losses.—Interviews with hunters in Wood County (1937-1938) and in eight central counties (1937) revealed that 1,425 hunters who bagged an average of 5.24 pheasants per season, crippled 1,323 cocks (average 0.93 per hunter) and found 857 cocks dead in the field (average of 0.60 per hunter). Thus they reported crippling 17.8 per cent as many cocks and finding 11.5 per cent as many dead as they bagged. However, the actual amount of crippling is undoubtedly considerably more than reported.

The ratio of cock birds crippled to cocks found dead is interesting as an indication of the number of crippled birds that die as a result of shot wounds. For every 17.8 birds crippled, 11.5 were found dead—a 3 to 2 ratio. This is definite evidence that at least two-thirds of the crippled birds die before the end of the open season. Since it is likely that nearly a third of the crippled birds that die are never seen by hunters, it is obvious that nearly 100 per cent of the cripples fail to survive. That this is the case is further established by the observation that of the thousands of pheasants seen at close range on refuges during the hunting season, or handled during later trapping operations, no more than 2 to 3 per cent were cripples.

The crippling losses of cock pheasants could be reduced considerably if more care were exercised by hunters in their shooting. Modern heavy loads carry considerable distances and many hunters are encouraged by occasional lucky shots to continue to try for pheasants far beyond the normal killing range. If all shooting were done only at reasonable distances, more clean kills would be made and fewer injuries would result.

The use of well-trained retrieving dogs also would materially reduce crippling losses. Weather conditions and hunting pressures greatly influence the use of dogs. Only 9.5 per cent of the hunters observed in Wood County were employing dogs in 1937, and 8.4 per cent in 1938. However, of 174 farmer hunters reporting in 1938, 30.5 per cent used dogs at least one day during the season. Of the 3,186 hunters noted in Hancock, Hardin, and Wyandot Counties during the 1939 season, 13.9 per cent had dogs. The percentage of hunters with dogs increased toward the end of the season, the ratio of hunters to dogs being 100 to 11 on the opening day and 100 to 28 on the last day of the season.

Large groups of hunters tend to cripple more pheasants than lone gunners, and spend less time in searching for crippled birds as the individual hunters wish to keep up with the group.

Illegal Kill of Hens.—Interviews with 159 farmer hunters in Wood County following the 1937 hunting season revealed that they had found 171 hens dead as a result of shooting. This was an average of 1.08 per hunter, or a number equal to 19.4 per cent as many cocks as were killed by the hunters. In 1938, 174 farmer hunters found an average of 2.45 dead hens, or 37.0 per cent of the number of cock birds bagged.

Farmer hunters in the eight central Ohio counties reported an average of 0.13 hens dead in the field, or 22.8 per cent of the number of cocks bagged.

In 1937, 61 local hunters in Wood County saw 167 hens shot at, 38 hens killed in their presence, and 220 dead hens. City hunters, numbering 295, reported seeing 512 hens shot at, 87 killed in their presence, and 682 found dead. The ratio of cocks bagged to hens found dead was 100 to 55.7 for the local hunters and 100 to 42.1 for the outside hunters.

In 1938, 96 local hunters saw 164 hens shot at, 76 hens killed in their presence, and found 323 dead hens. City hunters (505) reported 711 hens shot at, 222 hens killed in their presence, and 1,219 hens dead in the field. The ratio of cocks bagged to the hens found dead was 100 to 46.5 for the local hunters and 100 to 40.7 for the city hunters.

Considering all of the information at hand, it appears that, on the average, for every 100 cock birds bagged there is an illegal kill of 38 hens. Dogs or other predators remove at least 5 per cent of the dead birds before they can be observed. Thus 38 plus 2 gives a total of 40 hen birds killed per 100 cocks bagged.

All evidence indicates that this loss of hens is a typical and regular occurrence. It is surprising how few appreciate the size of this population drain and how little sportsmen endeavor to eliminate it. The crop of the ensuing year is entirely dependent upon the number of hens carried over as brood stock. Legal kill of cock birds, except in most unusual circumstances, does not diminish the crop of the following year—in fact the removal of excess cocks relieves population pressure, including food competition, so that the survival of more hens is favored. The hen losses by illegal shooting noted above occurred in a county which for many years has ranked near the top in law enforcement. A limited amount of this illegal shooting is unintentional, but much of it is due to carelessness and a failure to realize that so far as success of the sport is concerned, the hen pheasant is "the goose that lays the golden egg."

It is obvious that an open season on hen pheasants would be disastrous—pheasant populations would dwindle and disappear in all save a few of the most favored counties. In addition to illegal kill during the hunting season, and a high basic mortality throughout the year, hens undergo mortality losses during the mowing season comparable to those suffered by cock birds during the hunting period. Further losses to hen pheasants determine the degree of success or failure in pheasant management.

Other Causes of Mortality

Mowing.—Of all the accidents to pheasants in Ohio, those caused by mowing are most disastrous. This universal farming operation principally affects incubating hens, inflicts some damage on broods of young, but causes little mortality of male birds, except when done at night. In addition to the killing or crippling of adults, the destruction of nests and eggs, and thus of potential birds, is astounding.

During the 1937 mowing season in Wood County, a survey was made to determine pheasant nesting density in hayfields. A total of 197 meadows (alfalfa and clover) comprising 2,566 acres, was investigated. In these, 914 pheasant nests were reported found by the farmers while mowing. For each 100 nests mowed over, 9.9 hen pheasants were reported killed and 20.8 hens crippled. Thus for each 100 nests, 30.7 hens were either killed or crippled. It is evident that most of the crippled pheasants are eventually caught by predators, or die as a result of their injuries, as only 3 of 1,610 hens trapped on Wood County refuges during the winter of 1936-1937 showed injuries possibly inflicted by mowing machines.

During the summers of 1937-1940, a large amount of information pertaining to pheasant mortality in hay- and grain-fields was obtained by extensive surveys in western Ohio; more than 200,000 acres were covered. Hen casualties averaged 32.4 per 100 nests mowed over in hay, 7.9 in wheat, and 4.5 in oats.

Weather or other factors that influence the date of cutting and also those of egg laying and incubation are extremely important in determining pheasant nesting success on farmlands. In general the later in the season that crops are cut, the smaller the percentage of nests destroyed. Two important exceptions to this rule pertain to the cutting of oats and the second crop of alfalfa. These cover crops, though mowed late in the season, contain many nests, as nesting in them begins later than in most others. Thus, winter wheat becomes attractive to pheasants as nesting cover several weeks before spring-planted oats are usable.

The dates of cutting hay and grain averaged several days earlier in 1939 than in 1938, while the pheasant nesting season was later. This resulted in a considerably higher percentage of nest destruction. In 1938 an average of 38.8 per cent of the nests found in hayfields had hatched at the date of mowing, but in 1939 only 21.6 per cent had hatched. Wheat and oats are usually cut later in the season than hay crops, hence a much higher percentage of the nests in fields of these grains are hatched before harvest time: 75.8 per cent in 1938 and 61.5 in 1939. Nest destruction in alfalfa, red clover, mixed hay, and sweet clover was proportionately greater than in other cover crops, largely due to the high percentage of unhatched nests in these crops on the date they were mowed.

Based on equal numbers of nests, every 100 casualties in alfalfa (first cutting) in 1939 were matched by 75 in red clover, 74 in the second cutting of alfalfa, 64 in mixed hay, 60 in sweet clover, 39 in timothy, 14 in wheat when cut by binder (12 when cut by combine), and 10 in oats. Pheasant casualties are fewer in combine-harvested wheat because the cutting date is later and the cutting bar travels higher above the ground.

The manner in which alfalfa and other hay crops are cut, is also important in relation to the number of pheasants killed and crippled. Most of the counties in Ohio with high pheasant populations are in the major alfalfa belt. Here hen casualties, 49 per 100 nests, are high due to the use of the rapidly moving power mowers. Whether a meadow is cut for hay or for seed also is of considerable significance in pheasant production. Average nesting success for all types of hay meadows was only 56.3 per cent as great as that in red clover or alsike clover fields which were cut for seed later in the season. Hence a trend towards more clover seed production would be of considerable importance in raising pheasant reproductive efficiency.

A comparison of pheasant mortality in 24 alfalfa fields (1939) during both the first and second cuttings indicated that the mortality per 100 nests was greater at the time of the second mowing when more young birds were killed, but on an acreage basis fewer nests were destroyed.

The destruction of cover during the mowing and harvesting seasons displaces pheasant populations and tends to increase highway mortality, losses through predation, and deaths due to miscellaneous causes.

In all, hen pheasants suffer losses during the nesting season almost as great as those of the cock birds during the hunting season. Ohio experience indicates that on the average farm the use of flushing bars is not a satisfactory solution of this problem.

Plowing.—Pheasant nests and incubating hens are often destroyed by spring plowing, more frequently when tractors operated at high speed are used. In plowing 287 acres of wheat, corn, and soybean stubble in Liberty Township, Wood County, in the spring and summer of 1937, farmers reported 5 nests destroyed and 2 pheasants killed.

Cleaning Fencerows and Roadsides.—The cutting and burning of fencerows and roadsides during the nesting season frequently results in the destruction or desertion of nests. Incubating females often are killed when machine mowers are used. Seven deserted nests were found in 9 miles of roadside that had been mowed in Wood County in 1937 and 16 in 2.6 miles of roadside in Union County in 1939. If the fencerow and roadside cleaning is delayed until after July 10, most of the destruction of pheasants can be avoided.

Highway Traffic.—Of the other accidental causes of pheasant mortality, highway traffic is probably the most noticeable. In surveys of highway mortality in Wood County (1936-1937), 20.9 pheasants were found dead per 1,000 miles in an area with a pheasant population averaging 210 per square mile. On this basis the annual mortality is about 5 per square mile (2.38 per cent). Approximately two-fifths of the pheasants killed by highway traffic are young.

Of the adult pheasants killed by automobiles, 12.8 per cent were males and 87.2 per cent females. Thus highway mortality is selective, destroying a disproportionate number of the valuable hen birds upon which the year's crop of game depends.

Observations indicate that on the average, pheasants killed on a highway remain visible for three or four days, which indicates that an observed kill of 20.9 pheasants per 1,000 miles is repeated twice weekly. On that basis, the pheasant highway mortality in Wood County (with 612 square miles and 1,450 miles of roads) would total about 3,030 birds per year.

The greatest pheasant losses along highways occur where high-speed roads traverse choice pheasant territory. Mortality is usually proportional to: (1) Density of pheasant populations, (2) average auto speed, (3) amount of auto traffic, and (4) attractiveness of roadside cover and highway materials to pheasants. Accidents are more frequent in the early morning and the late evening. In the morning, pheasants are vulnerable to highway losses due to their habit of frequenting the roads or roadsides until the dew evaporates from the grass and other cover into which they then go and feed. In the late evening they often cross roads enroute to roosting sites.

Traveling pheasants tend to accumulate along highway embankments, as the road constitutes a partial barrier to progress. Birds frequently proceed parallel to the pavement for some distance before crossing it. Pheasants are attracted to bordering ditches which provide depressions sought for safety or shelter from the elements. Nonpaved roads are highly attractive as sources of grit or as dusting places. All of these factors tend to increase the pheasant toll along highways.

Pheasant highway mortality is very apparent and causes considerable concern among sportsmen and the general public. Moving about more, pheasants suffer relatively greater losses than sedentary species as the bobwhite. However, observations to date indicate that pheasant highway losses are usually not a major factor in limiting the population.

What can be done to minimize the losses of pheasants caused by automobiles? Known pheasant crossings on the highways, especially near refuges, might well be posted with signs similar to those used in several states to warn motorists of deer crossings. Conservation departments should urge motorists to drive with care and save wildlife. Refuge and cover management areas should be set back from highways. Several feet of the roadside immediately adjacent to the pavement can be kept mowed to reduce cover near the stream of traffic.

Railway Traffic.—The mortality caused by trains in some of the better pheasant range in Ohio is surprisingly high. During August and September 1939, 34.5 miles of railroad tracks were surveyed on foot in Wood County to determine the number of pheasants that had been recently killed by trains. The dead pheasants observed included 7 young birds, 6 adult females, and 2 adult males, or a total of 15, equivalent to 435 per 1,000 miles of railroad. In the area where these observations were made, there was a pheasant population of about 300 birds per square mile. In September 1939, an average of 250 birds killed per 1,000 miles of railroad was found in 11 northwestern Ohio counties. In September 1940, 26 dead pheasants were seen on 72.2 miles of railroad in 8 northwestern Ohio counties (360 dead pheasants per 1,000 miles).

Observations in the field and interviews with railway men indicated that most of the mortality occurred in the early morning. At that time, pheasants can often be seen perched on the rails or standing in open areas along the railroad, where they can avoid dew and wet grass. It is apparent that the gravel and cinders of the roadbeds also are attractive to pheasants. Dead pheasants may be observed and enumerated many days or even weeks after being struck by trains. Hence it is difficult to evaluate the yearly toll.

Miscellaneous Accidents.—Other causes of accidental death, including flying into telephone and telegraph wires and fences, account for a large but unknown loss of pheasants. Some nests are destroyed by livestock. In the pheasant-nesting study made in Wood County in 1939, it was found that such animals were responsible for the loss of 10.2 per cent of all nests destroyed on noncultivated lands.

Predation.—Among Ohio animals likely to prey upon pheasants are: dogs, cats, a few wild mammals, crows, several species of hawks, and great horned owls. The crow is destructive to pheasants only during the nesting season, when many eggs and a few young birds are taken. A great many pheasant eggshells are found scattered in the wooded portions of the refuges in the spring, probably by crows. As the nesting cover becomes more dense, fewer shells are found. During the mowing season, crows consume practically all of the eggs left unbroken by the mowing machines, but, in so doing, cause little harm, as very few hens continue incubation after their nests have been uncovered by mowers. Kalmbach (1937) in a report on crow-waterfowl relationships recorded the opinion that eggs have a maximum attraction for crows during their own reproductive period, and that crow damage to duck eggs is governed fully as much, if not more, by the nutritional demands of the crow itself, as by early season availability of eggs. This generalization probably applies also to crow predation upon pheasant nests.

Hawks are occasionally destructive during the winter, especially of pheasants that are underfed or weakened by adverse weather. Observations in northwestern Ohio indicate some correlation between the number of pheasants found dead, due to predation, and the number of hawks seen per day. The fall and spring periods of hawk migration correspond roughly with those in which most pheasants are found dead due to predation. This is partly coincidence, as most mammalian predators also are more active in spring and fall than in midwinter.

In most parts of Ohio, however, species of hawks which might prey upon young pheasants are uncommon to rare, or even absent, during the breeding season. In general, predation by hawks is not serious. These birds probably render valuable service in consuming crippled and sick birds, especially during and following the hunting season. They also tend to keep the pheasants wary and gamy. The Cooper's and sharp-shinned hawks, which are considered the species most destructive to birds in Ohio, constituted 21.9 per cent of 346 hawks seen in Wood County, September 1936 to August 1937.

Great horned owls are usually too few to be of much consequence as predators upon pheasants, although they undoubtedly kill some birds on the roosts.

Red foxes, if present in large numbers, do considerable damage. However, Kenneth Mitchell found that game birds (mostly pheasants) made up less than 2 per cent (1.96) of the yearly food of the red fox in a Madison County, Ohio, area which had an average of 1.5 foxes and 13.0 pheasants per square mile. Raccoons, opossums, skunks, red squirrels, and perhaps other mammals, are responsible for occasional but unimportant mortality.

Natural predation is not a serious factor in maintaining pheasant populations in Ohio, except when such populations are low, when new areas are being brought under management, or when pheasants are concentrated on refuges or wintering grounds.

Of far greater consequence, however, is predation by domestic dogs and cats. Sixty farmers interviewed in Wood County in July 1938 reported having 80 dogs and 203 cats, an average of 1.35 dogs and 3.38 cats per farm. Hicks found that 4,603 farms in 31 western Ohio counties in 1939, averaged 1.17 dogs and 3.41 cats per farm. These averages would indicate that the domestic predator population of Ohio's 216,296 farms totals 256,575 dogs and 747,800 cats— more than a million flesh-eating mammals, nearly all of which take some toll of Ohio's wildlife. All evidence indicates that these domestic predators are responsible for losses far more important than those due to natural predators.

In the chief pheasant territory of Ohio, one can frequently see cats or dogs carrying dead pheasants or pheasant eggs. Young pheasants and incubating hens appear to be especially vulnerable. Cats and dogs are also responsible for much of the loss in connection with the live-trapping of pheasants, dogs alone accounting for more than 50 per cent of that mortality.

Disease.—Relatively little is known about maladies of pheasants in the wild, and still less about proper methods of controlling these diseases. Game managers usually seek to obtain high population levels and these in themselves may create conditions favorable to disease transmission. However, despite high concentration of pheasants in parts of northwestern Ohio, there have been no serious outbreaks of disease. The pheasants trapped and handled on the refuges in winter are, with very few exceptions, healthy.

During three hunting seasons (1936-1938), the Ohio Wildlife Research Station employed Dr. P. C. Bennett and Dr. C. A. Woodhouse of the State Animal Disease Laboratories and the Ohio State University College of Veterinary Medicine, respectively, to inspect large numbers of cock pheasants taken during the hunting season in concentration areas of Wood County, Ohio, where if anywhere in the wild, conditions might appear favorable for diseases.

The viscera of 80 male pheasants collected in Plain Township, Wood County, November 17 and 18, 1936, were examined by these specialists who found 1,039 caecal worms of the genus *Heterakis* (probably *gallinae*) and 8 tapeworms belonging to the genus *Raillietina* (probably *R. cesticillus*).

A similar examination was made by Woodhouse of 106 pheasants collected in Plain Township, Wood County, Ohio, November 15 and 16, 1937, to determine whether there had been any increase in parasitic infestation. A rise of 13 per cent over the 1936 rate in the number of pheasants infested with caecal worms was found, although the average number of worms per infested bird was lower. The percentage of pheasants infested by tapeworms was greater by 7 per cent in 1937. An intestinal nematode (*Capillaria*) not found in 1936 was present in four birds taken during the 1937 study. In addition a small intestinal fluke of the family Echinostomatidae was found.

Experiments by Dr. Bennett indicated that the ingestion of varying amounts of lead shot, as high as two grams, had no pathological effect on pheasants and that the lead administered had little, if any, effect on ovulation.

Dr. Bennett also experimented with the reaction of pheasants to infection with known cultures of *Salmonella pullorum*. The birds, 2 males and 2 females, continued in apparently good health, although a female with the disease failed to produce any eggs while a control bird laid 37 eggs.

At another time, 12 males and 14 females from game farms, were given the agglutination test for pullorum disease and 5 males and 4 females reacted positively.

Tests made on 3 pheasants indicated that pheasants were not susceptible to acute infection with *Salmonella suipestifer*, the causative agent of swine paratyphoid. No definite conclusions are warranted, however, due to the small number of birds tested.

It is probable that certain poultry diseases may be acquired by pheasants visiting chicken yards and there is further danger of such maladies being transmitted to pheasants through the rather common practice of throwing dead chickens on manure piles which are later hauled to the fields. This procedure should be abandoned.

Field Study of Pheasant Mortality.—In Wood County, 1936-1940, 726 pheasants were found dead. Of these, 497 (68.5 per cent) were adults and 229 (31.5 per cent) young. The causes of death were: Automobiles, 489 (67.35 per cent); natural causes including predation, 196 (26.99 per cent); farm machinery not including mowing losses, 18 (2.47 per cent); and miscellaneous and unknown, 23 (3.16 per cent). The seasonal rate of mortality expressed as the number of pheasants found dead per 100 days of field work was: Spring, 83.4; summer, 160.1; fall, 83.2; and winter, 64.2.

Combined Effect of All Checks

Primarily because of great mortality during the mowing and hunting seasons, pheasant numbers undergo marked fluctuation. The first of these causes of destruction is highly selective of females and the second of males. At hatching the numbers of the sexes are about equal but the hazards of life as a farm game bird affect them very unequally with the result that during the year, as a whole, females are considerably in the majority. Present evidence fails to indicate any long-term fluctuations (or cycles) in the pheasant population.

The following calendar of losses is based on the results of all the Ohio studies; it reflects average conditions in the whole pheasant range.

January—Mortality: 2 per cent of cock birds, 6 per cent of hens, leaving the sex ratio 24:76.

February—Mortality: 2 per cent of cocks, 6 per cent of hens.

March—Mortality: 2 per cent of cocks, 4 per cent of hens, leaving the sex ratio at beginning of the reproductive season, April 1, as 25:75.

April and May—Normal mortality: 2 per cent of both cocks and hens each month. The losses may exceed 2 per cent locally where aggressive measures are taken to control corn pulling.

June-August—Normal mortality: 3 per cent of cocks, 6 per cent of hens, the increase being incidental to the reproductive season.

Extremely heavy loss of incubating hens due to mowing and predation.

	Net per cent of loss
56 per cent of all hens nest in hayfields; 32 per cent of these are killed or crippled	17.92
20 per cent of all hens nest in wheat or oats; 5.4 per cent of these killed or crippled	1.08
24 per cent of all hens nest in other cover, 5.0 per cent of these are destroyed	1.2
Of all incubating hens, the percentage killed on the nests is	20.2

September—Mortality: 4 per cent of cocks, 3 per cent of hens.

October 1—The percentage of cock pheasants surviving from April 1 to October 1 is 93, and of hens 58.

The percentage of surviving females with young is 73 and the average brood with each surviving female is 6.

The sex ratio of young birds is 52:48; of adults, 32:68; and of the combined population, 47:53.

The adult-juvenile ratio is 25:75.

October 1-November 15—1.5 per cent mortality of both sexes (1 per cent per month).

November open season—Crippling loss 15 per cent, i.e. for every 100 cocks bagged, 15 are crippled and lost.

Illegal hen kill 22.3 per cent, i.e. for every 100 cocks bagged, 40 hens are killed.

Of all birds killed by shooting, 74.7 per cent are cocks, 25.3 per cent are hens. Of the cock birds killed (assuming that hunters kill proportionate numbers of the age classes), 17 per cent are adults, 83 per cent are young.

Per cent of the total population removed during the hunting season 46.6 (74.0 per cent of the cocks and 22.3 per cent of the hens).

December—Mortality: 2 per cent of cocks, 4 per cent of hens.

Applying these loss rates to a population of 10,000 pheasants, we arrive at the figures in the following table (4) showing the decrease in numbers of the sex and age classes during the year.

TABLE 4.—Decrease in one year of a population of 10,000 pheasants.

Season	Adults	Young	Adult males	Adult females	Young males	Young females	Total males	Total females
October 1, after the breeding but before the hunting season	2,500	7,500	800	1,700	3,900	3,600	4,700	5,300
November 15, start of hunting season	2,463	7,387	788	1,675	3,841	3,546	4,630	5,220
December 1, end of breeding season	1,506	3,753	205	1,301	999	2,754	1,204	4,055
April 1, start of breeding season	1,247	3,165	189	1,058	921	2,244	1,110	3,302
September 30, end of breeding season	790	2,120	161	629	783	1,337	944	1,966

The increase in "new" young is not shown but it amounts to 4,477 males and 4,134 females. These added to the surviving yearlings and older birds, 944 cocks and 1,966 hens (lower right in the table), make up a population of 11,520 indicating an increase of 15 per cent. Of course there is an increase only where there are living facilities that are not fully utilized. In a stabilized and completely occupied pheasant range, the annual increase, on the average and in the long run, would merely offset losses and the total population would remain about the same.

THE RANGE AND ITS MANAGEMENT

The ring-necked pheasant was liberated by sportsmen in several Ohio localities before the beginning of the present century. By 1903, it was well established in Allen, Ashtabula, Crawford, Erie, Hamilton, Hardin, Madison, Morgan, Scioto, and Summit Counties. Other parts of the State were populated by natural spread from these areas.

Many thousands of pheasant eggs and of artificially-propagated birds have been distributed throughout the State by the Division of Conservation. On the whole, the birds succeeded best along the Lake Erie shore between Toledo and Sandusky and in portions of Marion, Union, Madison, and Hardin Counties. Despite repeated heavy plantings, the hills of southern and eastern sections of the State are almost without pheasants.

Elements of the Range

The combined effect of a great many factors determines what is good or poor pheasant range. The present account summarizes what we have learned about them in Ohio.

Weather.—The greatest of all natural influences is climate, that is, the summation of all that we call weather. Weather influences the availability of food and cover. It may also cause mortality. Deep snows and sleet sometimes make grain, weed seeds, and other foods relatively unavailable to pheasants (plate 6). Such conditions, prolonged may result in starvation, but in the pheasant belt of Ohio, they are relatively rare. Rain sometimes floods and destroys pheasant nests in low places. However, a rainy period may delay the average date of hay mowing for a week or more at the height of the pheasant nesting season, and, in so doing, permit thousands of eggs to hatch that would otherwise be destroyed.

The effects of accumulated hours of daylight and degrees of temperature in spring probably determine the beginning of the nesting season. Light and heat of course continue to affect the pheasant as they do other creatures and wild crop plants throughout the season. During years with warm dry autumns and winters, corn is harvested and taken out of the fields earlier than when the weather is unfavorable and more corn is salvaged by hand after being machine-picked. This results in less waste grain being available for pheasant food.

Soil.—As the pheasant is largely a farm bird in Ohio, soils have much to do with its distribution and abundance. The best farming lands of Ohio are the limestone soils in the north and west, and they are most productive also of pheasants. Sandy and shaly areas of the eastern part of the State are definitely unsuited for pheasant production. Poor sandy soil in Ohio may be of value in pheasant

Plate 6.—Snow and sleet make life difficult for pheasants. (Painting by T. Heaton Cooper)

production if it is adjacent to more fertile land capable of producing corn, soybeans, and other crops used as food by pheasants. The sandy areas frequently make good refuge sites, but, of themselves, do not produce sufficient food.

Soils are of most importance to pheasants indirectly, through their influence on the kinds of crops and weeds that are produced. In general, dark-colored, fertile soils are utilized to a greater extent for corn and small grain production, hence produce more pheasant food than others.

There are also direct soil relationships, one of them through grit. This is not decisive, however, for in the best pheasant range most of the grit supply is foreign in origin, that is from road metals. Some clay soils are so sticky when wet that pheasant chicks traversing them may accumulate mud balls on their feet. These balls have been known to result in the death of Hungarian partridge chicks and may also detrimentally affect pheasant chicks to some extent.

The type of soil determines when it should be plowed to get best results. The heavy soil of the Killdeer Plains (northern Marion and southwestern Wyandot Counties) is likely to be plowed in fall, thus covering much pheasant food in the form of waste soybeans and weed seeds. Where fall plowing is general, the capacity of the district for wintering pheasants is greatly limited.

Lay of the Land.—The lay of the land affects pheasants as where it results in the washing away of topsoil and loss of fertility; thus the hills are unproductive. The rugged areas also are more continuously forested, a condition that is unfavorable for pheasants. In level country, the small amount of woodland remaining (often 10 per cent or less of the total area) is usually in well-spaced blocks. These tracts with surrounding croplands are ideal management units. Extensive flat, open areas, are not so good, however, as the fields tend to be larger, there is less interspersion of food and cover, and farming is more intensive. While the larger crops in these areas provide more pheasant food, cover is generally limited.

In the level Lake Plains region, any break in the topography is of value to wildlife. Except for some slight relief caused by the old lake beaches, much of the area is a flat expanse of farmlands broken only by roads and drainage ditches. The latter vary from 3 to 12 feet in depth. As their banks are usually well vegetated, they serve as sheltered travelways where pheasants may avoid severe winter wind-sweep.

Natural Vegetation.—Plants occupy the land so densely that they largely control the distribution of animals, including pheasants. These birds, like other creatures, can survive only where conditions are suitable.

The plant communities most indicative of superior pheasant range in Ohio are those of the swamp forest and wet prairie. Oak-hickory forests surrounding prairie openings generally indicate favorable conditions for pheasants. Beech-maple forests usually characterize lighter soils that are not so well adapted for producing corn and other food plant extensively utilized by pheasants. Forests of oak-hickory, oak-chestnut, and oak-pine, as found in southeastern Ohio, also indicate soils unsuited for pheasant production.

Trees characteristic of the better pheasant range in the northwestern part of the State include:

1. In wetter places: American elm (*Ulmus americana*), white ash (*Fraxinus americana*), black ash (*Fraxinus nigra*), soft maple (*Acer rubrum, A. saccharinum*), American linden (*Tilia americana*), pin oak (*Quercus palustris*), swamp white oak (*Quercus bicolor*), sycamore (*Platanus occidentalis*), and shagbark hickory (*Hicoria ovata*).

2. On dry, sandy beach ridges: Black oak (*Quercus velutina*), scarlet oak (*Quercus coccinea*), and white oak (*Quercus alba*).

Herbs abundant in the moister woods include: Clearweed (*Pilea pumila*), white avens (*Geum canadense*), wild geranium (*Geranium maculatum*), Virginia knotweed (*Tovara virginiana*), pellitory (*Parietaria pennsylvanica*), enchanter's nightshade (*Circaea lutetiana*), long-styled sweet cicely (*Washingtonia longistylus*), wood nettle (*Urticastrum divaricatum*), and spring avens (*Geum vernum*).

Those plants characteristic of the dry ridges are: Large blazing-star (*Lacinaria scariosa*), sandbur (*Cenchrus pauciflorus*), plantain-leaf everlasting (*Antennaria plantaginifolia*), hairy bushclover (*Lespedeza hirta*), hairy puccoon (*Lithospermum carolinense*), flowering spurge (*Tithymalopsis corollata*), woodland sunflower (*Helianthus divaricata*), frostweed (*Crocanthemum canadense*), and sleepy catchfly (*Silene antirrihina*).

Prairie indicators include: Bluejoint (*Andropogon furcatus*), Indian grass (*Sorghastrum nutans*), switchgrass (*Panicum virgatum*), dock rosinweed (*Silphium terebinthinaceum*), sawtooth sunflower (*Helianthus grosse-serratus*), smooth milkweed (*Asclepias sullivantii*), stiff goldenrod (*Solidago rigida*), and large blazingstar (*Lacinaria scariosa*).

Plants commonly occurring along the ditches are: (1) On the ditch bottoms: sedges (*Carex* spp.) and cattail (*Typha angustifolia* or *T. latifolia*); (2) on the sides of the ditches: sweet clover (*Melilotus alba*), timothy (*Phleum pratense*), greater ragweed (*Ambrosia trifida*), sunflowers (*Helianthus* spp.), asters (*Aster* spp.), teasel (*Dipsacus sylvestris*), dogbane (*Apocynum cannabinum*), smartweeds (*Persicaria* spp.), and burdock (*Arctium minus*).

The slopes of ditches that are frequently mowed are usually covered with bluegrass. Ditches that are unmolested for several years grow up with perennials, shrubs, and small trees, including grapes (*Vitis* spp.), greenbriers (*Smilax* spp.), bittersweet (*Celastrus scandens*), dogwoods (*Cornus stolonifera, C. amomum,* and *C. femina*), elms (*Ulmus fulva* and *U. americana*), and oaks (*Quercus* spp.).

General Farmlands.—In Ohio the pheasant is almost entirely a farm bird, the most important reason apparently being the amount of food in the forms of waste grain and weed seeds available on farms. Such grain may be present in fields in tons per square mile and weed seeds as those of smartweeds, foxtail grasses, lesser ragweed and others valuable as pheasant food in amounts up to hundreds of pounds per acre.

The weeds commonly found in cornfields in the better pheasant range include: Smartweeds (*Persicaria hydropiper; P. lapathifolium*), rough pigweed (*Amaranthus retroflexus*), foxtail grasses (*Chaetochloa viridis, C. glauca*), lambsquarters (*Chenopodium album*), jimsonweed (*Datura stramonium*), tumbleweed (*Amaranthus graecizans*), common ragweed (*Ambrosia elatior*), dogbane (*Apocynum cannabinum*), common milkweed (*Asclepias syriaca*), bladder ketmia (*Hibiscus trionum*), and Pennsylvania cocklebur (*Xanthium pennsylvanicum*).

Weeds common in wheat stubble are: Common ragweed (*Ambrosia elatior*), smartweeds (*Persicaria* spp.), foxtail grasses (*Chaetochloa* spp.), dogbane (*Apocynum cannabinum*), common milkweed (*Asclepias syriaca*), wild lettuce (*Lactuca virosa*), and horse-nettle (*Solanum carolinense*).

The importance of cropland and noncropland to pheasants varies with the season. Each element of the range has a different value for nesting, roosting, feeding, or other activity of the bird. Four-fifths or even more of the total annual food of pheasants may be obtained from the waste grain and weed seeds available on croplands (plate 7). But food is gleaned also from patches of shrubs and vines from the woodland floor, and about the margins of ponds, marshes, and ditches. The equally necessary shelter or cover is found seasonally or temporarily among crops and marsh plants and more permanently in the woody growths of fencerows, ditch banks, thickets, and wood lots. More than half of the pheasant nests are located in hayfields and another fourth on noncroplands on farms.

Wood Lots.—Although wood lots constitute only a small proportion of the total land area in the best pheasant range in Ohio, they are of considerable importance in pheasant production. Their value depends largely upon their distribution and composition, which in turn, often hinges upon post land-use practices, as timber cutting and the pasturing of livestock. Wood lots provide food and cover and serve as excellent refuge sites.

Wood lots of most value to pheasants contain an abundance of shrubby growth from 6 to 30 feet in height, with an understory or ground cover of briers and weeds, often in patches so dense that walking through the clumps is difficult. Seedlings and saplings are abundant in such wood lots, but are of different heights rather than of an even stand (plate 8).

The utilization of wood lots differs greatly according to the time of year. Based on observations of 64,337 adult pheasants in Wood County, Ohio, September 1936 to March 1940, an average of 13.5 per cent of all the birds were in woods in the fall; 29.9 per cent in the winter; 17.6 per cent in the spring, and 3.9 per cent in the summer. Thus an average of 16.2 per cent of all pheasants seen during the year were in woods. Male pheasants make greater use of woods than do females, particularly in summer.

From a special study in Wood County, it was found that more than three-fourths (79 per cent) of all pheasants seen in wood lots were within 25 yards of an edge. The cocks tend to go farther into the woods than hens, the sex ratio (cocks:hens) being 19:81 in the

Plate 5.—Upper. Hayfield nest mortality due to mowing. South Amherst, Mass. (Massachusetts Department of Conservation, Pittman-Robertson Project 3-R-1) Lower. Well located food patch of standing corn. Note proximity to permanent hedge. Valley in the middle distance offers winter roosting cover and hedge forms travel lane. (Massachusetts Department of Conservation, Pittman-Robertson Project 3-R-1)

Plate 7.—An excellent winter feeding place. This standing cornfield produced about 50 pounds of smartweed seed to the acre in addition to much waste corn.

outer 25-yard strip, 30:70 in the next zone, and 27:73 in the inner portion of the woods. The male birds also frequent heavier and denser cover than the hens.

During the hunting season, pheasants may travel up to 2 miles or more to a woodland refuge. In so doing they may pass by, or be driven from, wood lots that provide adequate cover but which are open to hunting. Due to their skulking habits, however, some pheasants survive in brushy wood lots despite intensive hunting.

As to management, it is well to bear in mind that severely pastured wood lots are of very little value in pheasant production. Most foresters and agronomists agree that wooded areas are generally more valuable when managed for timber, fuel, and forest products, than when they are pastured by livestock. Several have reported the injurious effects of pasturing wood lots, including the destroying of seedlings; packing the soil and disturbing the leaf mold, thus reducing the water-holding capacity of the soil and increasing erosion; injuring trees and tree roots by trampling, rubbing, and rooting; and creating unfavorable seed-bed and plant-growth conditions. In parts of western Ohio, up to 90 per cent of the wood lots are pastured. According to our experience, however, some pasturing can be permitted without seriously decreasing pheasant cover, especially if low dense thickets of brambles, wild roses, and hawthorns survive.

Although heavy pasturing over periods of years usually creates conditions very unsuitable for pheasant cover, unpastured yet uncut woods are also of relatively little value. In such woods, the canopy of the tree tops is usually so dense that its shade prevents the development of the undergrowth that is so necessary for pheasant cover. However, taking into account the effect of letting in light, cutting may be used to stimulate the growth of ground cover.

From information at hand, the following management suggestions are made:

1. Fence off all or most of heavily-grazed wood lots, and allow them to reproduce and develop to the desired stage. This usually requires about 10 years.

2. Small clearings can be made as needed to provide a rotation of those stages which contribute most to pheasant winter cover.

3. In grazed wood lots, allow species to remain that are resistant to pasturing, as hawthorn, prickly-ash, aspen, wild cherry, wild roses, and blackberries.

4. In severely pastured wood lots or in waste areas, improve conditions for the establishment and survival of natural tree reproduction. Procedures include: planting coniferous windbreaks, which in themselves are very valuable pheasant cover; plowing tightly sod-covered areas allowing them to grow up to briers and brush; and planting spots in which no natural tree reproduction is likely, with aspen, roses, or cuttings of shrubby willows.

5. When wood lots with attractive cover are closely spaced, the carrying capacity of the range is increased. Ideally there should be one for about every 2 square miles, thus requiring pheasants to travel less than two-thirds of a mile to reach excellent winter cover. There should be an average of more than 6 acres of superior woodland cover per square mile.

Field Borders.—Under Ohio conditions, a brushy woodland border immediately adjoined by a strip of sweet clover (25 to 50 feet wide), which in turn is bordered by several rows (or a whole field) of standing corn, provides ideal winter habitat for pheasants. The woodland border is especially valuable as a roosting site during severe winter weather. In the absence of a wood lot, however, a dense stand of sweet clover serves admirably as a nesting site during the summer and as a roosting place throughout the year. The corn bordering the sweet clover strip is utilized to the greatest extent as food during the fall and winter.

In their intensive nesting study in Wood County, Ohio, Strode and Leedy found 563 pheasant nests on 4 sections of land. Sweet clover constituted only 3 per cent of the area but yielded 63.2 per cent of all the successful nests on the 4 sections. In two sweet clover seed fields (23.3 acres) about 1,300 pheasant chicks hatched.

Fields along woods or streams are especially adapted to pheasant management. Field crops often cannot be profitably produced within 25 to 50 feet of a woodland because of shading and competition. Davison (1939) stated "it seems best to plan the entire strip for wildlife, water disposal and use as a turnover." The border strip between open fields and dense woods furnishes valuable food and cover for pheasants and other wildlife.

That part of the strip next to the woods might well be developed into a growth of fruit-bearing shrubs and bushes not large enough for the roots to extend out into the cultivated field. Such thicket growth, in addition to providing food and cover for wildlife, would also serve as a windbreak and decrease the drying effect of winds which sweep through open and unprotected wood lots. In this way, conditions would be made more favorable for the growth of seedlings in the wood lots.

Adjacent to this strip, and lying next to the field (as suggested by Davison), an herbaceous strip of legumes or grasses can be established which will tend to prevent the encroachment of the woodland into the field. Sweet clover is an excellent plant for the herbaceous part of the field border. It is, furthermore, of considerable value as a soil builder. Land taken out of cultivated crop production and put into soil-building crops contributes immensely to increased pheasant production, if used in cover strips.

Some maintenance would be required on each part of a field border to prevent the plant succession from reaching undesired stages. Trees and larger saplings should be cut down when necessary to keep the shrubby portion a dense thicket. The herbaceous strip could be maintained by mowing to prevent the growth of woody plants. The mowing should be done in late summer after the nesting season is over. When necessary, the strip could be plowed and reseeded.

Along creeks and river banks there is usually a strip of waste land which could be managed in a similar manner. This would benefit both game and fish and also prevent serious soil erosion losses. Sportsmen and beekeepers can profitably unite their efforts to persuade landowners to plant and leave field border and other uncut strips of sweet clover. Appropriate payments made by sportsmen to farmers for this service will usually bring game harvest dividends five to ten times as large as those from spending the same amount of money in buying artificially propagated birds for stocking.

Fencerows.—In the intensively cultivated areas of the Ohio pheasant belt, brushy fencerows (plate 9) constitute a large proportion of the available permanent cover. In addition they are also a source of food throughout the year. The most important pheasant foods found in fencerows are weed seeds and fruits. Food-producing species commonly include lesser ragweed, foxtail grasses, smartweeds, bindweed, wild grapes, panicled dogwood, red-osier or silky dogwood, nightshade, blackberry, and raspberry. Various fruits are relatively more abundant in brushy, than in the cleaner, fencerows. Insect populations appear to be more stable, that is with fewer destructive pulses or peaks along mature fencerows than in many types of cover.

Among the beneficial functions of between-field coverts listed by Grange and McAtee (1934) are: prevention of erosion; conservation of moisture by snow storage; protection of buildings from blizzards; protection of roads by living windbreak snow fences; reduction of windblown losses of soil; increase of those beneficial species that prey upon insects destructive to crops; encouragement of birds that eat harmful insects and destructive rodents; production of farm timber and posts, of berry crops, and of sumac for tannin extract. The production of nuts for human consumption may also be mentioned. Bates (1934) concluded that with ordinary field crops the benefit from windbreak protection more than offsets the loss of area sapped by the roots of trees and shrubs.

Fencerows may be used as indicators of pheasant range. On the basis of surveys in Ohio to date, 4 per cent or more of the fencerows should be of superior quality and 20 per cent or more should have fair to good cover value. In the better pheasant territory, there is a ratio of fenced field borders to nonfenced field borders of 2 to 1. This is indicative of the amount of pasturing in a region. In a county with 10 fenced fields to every unfenced field, the number of animal units per acre would far exceed the optimum, and indicate a type of farming not conducive to maximum pheasant production.

In Wood County, Ohio, with a fall population of about 287 pheasants per square mile, there are only 61 fenced, for every 100 unfenced, field borders; in Madison County with 20 pheasants per square mile, there are 100 field borders with, for every 7 without, fences. Thus only 38 per cent of the field borders of Wood County are fenced, while Madison County has 93 per cent. The effect of pasturing is readily apparent in such counties as Fayette and Madison, where most of the fields are fenced and pastured in rotation, and there are very few brushy fencerows.

The kind of fence, that is, whether wire, rail, electric, or other, is of some importance in regard to the amount of food and cover. Electric fences and, in some localities, barbed-wire fences are usually temporary, and are accompanied by relatively little food and cover. Electric fences are most common in northwestern Ohio where they are often used to enclose fields of picked corn. In 1938, 42 per cent of the pastured cornfields of Wood County were partially or entirely enclosed by electric fences. The pasturing of cornfields that have been harvested with mechanical pickers greatly reduces the amount of corn available as pheasant food. Hence, electric fences, which make possible the pasturing of more cornfields, may become detrimental to pheasant production.

As to pheasant utilization of fencerows, surveys made on tracking snows in Wood County (January 1940) indicated that brushy fencerows were used more than 30 times as much as clean fencerows. About three-fifths of the fencerows were very "clean" and devoid of cover, while about 12 per cent were brushy. Fencerows are sometimes occupied by roosting pheasants, the degree of utilization varying somewhat with the season of the year and the density of the cover.

More than 6 per cent of the nests found by Leedy in Wood County in 1937 were in fencerows. In 1939 Strode and Leedy reported that 41 (7.3 per cent) of 563 nests were in fencerows, during an intensive nesting study of four sections of farming land in Wood County; 43.9 per cent of these nests were successful. In 1940, Strode found in the same area that 45 (8.3 per cent) of 539 nests were in fencerows, 26.7 per cent of which were successful. Fencerows constituted only about 2 per cent of the total area on the four sections of farm land. The fencerows that are utilized most for pheasant nesting sites are not necessarily the densest, but rather those having a considerable amount of grass in them.

Fencerows are utilized as travel lanes during all seasons of the year. In the spring they serve as routes of dispersal from refuges and other wintering quarters. They are utilized most frequently if they form continuous cover from one wood lot or one food source to another. Territory adjacent to a refuge, if well supplied with brushy fencerows, is usually better stocked with breeding birds in the spring than that with clean fencerows. Thus the local distribution of pheasants is sometimes correlated with the distribution and quality of fencerows.

Pasturing, cutting, and burning are the three practices that are responsible for keeping more than half of Ohio's fencerows so clean that they are of little value to pheasants. Many farmers cut or burn their unpastured fencerows each year. These activities should be postponed (if done at all) until after the nesting season in order to prevent nest destruction. In Ohio this destruction is greatly reduced if the fencerow cleaning is deferred until July 10 to 20. Control of one or all of these factors would tremendously increase the value of fencerows for wildlife. Management must be of such a nature, however, as not to interfere with agriculture. In some localities where cover is inadequate, fencerow planting can be practiced. The following suggestions concerning fencerow planting are made:

1. In selecting food and cover plants, choose those species which are naturally of low growth and are tolerant of grazing, light, and crowding.
2. Include species which furnish food and cover through the year.
3. Include also some species that furnish fruits, nuts, and wood for human consumption, if desired.
4. Favor native species which will reproduce themselves, that are adapted to existing conditions.
5. Aim for a mixture of evergreens, vines, and thicket-forming shrubs.

For further suggestions, readers are referred to Edminster, "The Farm Fence in Wildlife" (1938).

Ditches.—Many people still recall when much of the land in the Lake Plains region of northwestern Ohio was swamp. Old residents of the area who helped clear off the forest often speak of the smudge fires they built as a protection against the hordes of mosquitoes so prevalent in the swamps. Today the Lake Plains region is one of the richest agricultural areas in the State; the change was brought about by the construction of thousands of miles of open drainage ditches. These waterways converted the swamps into tillable lands where corn is now the chief crop. Thus conditions became favorable for pheasants and when the birds were introduced, they were immediately successful. In addition to having this indirect, though controlling, effect upon pheasant production, the drainage ditches (as well as canals and natural streams) support on their banks a great diversity of plants of value to pheasants as food and cover (plate 10). The area of potential pheasant cover afforded by the 2,256 miles of drainage ditches in Wood County was calculated at about 3,600 acres, an average of 6 acres per section. Other counties, including Fulton, Putnam, Van Wert, Paulding, Henry, and Hancock, also have many miles of drainage ditch cover available.

In winter pheasants commonly frequent drainage ditches where

Plate 11.—Cattail swales benefit pheasants in winter. (Painting by T. Heaton Cooper)

they find shelter from the wind. In the thick growths of cattails and sedges found in the bottoms of many of the ditches, there are often hollows and channels through the snow. These are utilized by pheasants in severe winter weather. Although only a slight difference in temperature between the tops and the bottoms of ditches was found, the protection from the wind that sweeps across the level country is very noticeable in the bottoms. The south-facing slopes of drainage ditches are the first areas to become free of snow during prolonged periods when snow makes it difficult for the birds to obtain food and grit in adequate amounts. In digging the drainage ditches, the glacial till containing many pebbles is exposed and makes a good source of grit.

On ditch banks, cover, consisting largely of sweet clover, timothy, or bluegrass, makes excellent pheasant nesting sites. About 20 per cent of the nests found in wasteland in a nesting study in 1937 in Wood County were along ditches. The dense growths of dogwood, greenbrier, grapes, etc., furnish good escape cover and a considerable amount of food.

Swales that retain their cattail and other cover (plate 11) are of special value to pheasants in winter—a point observed not only in Ohio but in various other states.

About three-fourths of the drainage ditches in Wood County are cut or burned over each year. Ditches along state and federal highways are kept cleanest, while those along little-used dirt roads are often allowed to grow up to dense cover. The cleaning activities should be postponed wherever possible until after July 10 to reduce the destruction of nests and incubating hens.

Observations made in 1939 indicate that the larger ditches that have been unpastured, uncut, and untended for about 8 to 10 years are of most value to pheasants. The plant growth of the season following the cleaning of a ditch, depends upon several conditions, including the kind and amount of material dredged from the ditch, and how it is piled along the banks. If the dredgings are composed mostly of glacial till and piled as a deep mass of raw material, very little growth occurs upon it during the first year. When the till is mixed with loam or spread out thinly (to a depth of 2 inches or less), nearly three-fourths of the ground surface may be covered with vegetation in a year's time. Greater and lesser ragweeds, smartweeds, velvet-leaf (*Abutilon abutilon*), goldenrods, wild carrots, and other common weeds, are among the first plants to encroach upon the area. Trees such as ash, elm, and cottonwood, which have grown along the ditches and been cut off, may have sprouts 5 to 6 feet high a year following their cutting. The relatively steep slopes of the ditch next to the water are the last to be covered by plant growth.

Animal Associates.—Creatures that the pheasant may injure directly or through competition are discussed in the chapter on life history (pp. 59-60) and those that may damage the pheasant (predators) in the section on causes of mortality (pp. 78-80). Others are here briefly annotated.

Fox squirrels take considerable corn used as bait in pheasant traps. They also eat some of the corn scattered around fields in the spring to prevent corn-pulling by pheasants. They are competitors in the fall and winter, in that corn is one of their principal foods at those seasons. However, there may be concentrations of squirrels and pheasants on the same refuge without serious conflict (e.g., 120 squirrels and 1,200 pheasants on 80 acres of the Stitt Refuge in Wood County during several seasons). From a management standpoint, both species are desirable, and both can be live-trapped from a refuge for stocking purposes, thus providing multiple use for the area.

Pheasants often scratch and dust in the earth thrown up by woodchucks in digging their burrows. They also crouch in the entrance of the dens during severe storms, or even penetrate the burrow itself when frightened or wounded during the hunting season. A woodchuck den dug out by a hunter in Wood County contained a crippled, and two other, male pheasants. Another hunter crippled a cock bird in Knox County, and, not wanting it to die in a woodchuck hole, dug it out, finding not only the crippled bird, but three other pheasants.

Mourning doves, grackles, crows, and starlings may eat some of the shelled corn scattered around cornfields in the spring to prevent corn-pulling by pheasants. Most of these birds also eat some corn when it is still in the milk stage, pheasants commonly being given the blame for the damage.

Human Factors

In relation to a popular game bird, human factors are of surpassing importance. Leading among them are: Hunting pressure, farmer attitudes, land tenure, and land use.

Hunting.—A later chapter will be devoted to this great factor in the pheasant's life equation. Here it may be briefly stated that one of the severest drains on the pheasant population is through hunting during the open season. In Ohio this occurs during the latter part of November; when the hunting pressure is heavy there are about 17 guns per square mile. Several surveys have been made by the writers to determine the pheasant kill in Ohio and the participation of farmers and others in the harvest. An average of about two-thirds of the farmers in 31 counties of the pheasant belt hunted in 1938. The average bag per square mile (by farm operators only) in 31 western Ohio counties was 13.6 pheasants, 39.8 rabbits, and 1.0 Hungarian partridge. In some counties the kill was much higher and rural hunters averaged 6 or more cock pheasants each during the open season. Many cock birds crippled during the hunting season die later. Large numbers of hen pheasants also are killed during the season, some intentionally, others unintentionally. Mortality of hens from these causes is about 40 per cent as great as that brought about by the legal bagging of cocks.

Farmer Attitudes.—In order to have large concentrations of pheasants, it is desirable, in fact essential, to have the cooperation of the farmers. Unsympathetic farmers, by tramping and destroying nests, shooting pheasants out of season, and persecuting them in other ways, can do much to decrease the population. On the other hand, if farmers have a favorable attitude, they can be of invaluable service to conservation officials by practicing game management on their farms, helping in law enforcement, and doing winter feeding. All of our surveys indicate that, other factors being equal, pheasant population levels are proportional to the favorableness of the average attitude of farm residents toward the birds.

The kind of farming land determines to some extent the type of farmer living on the land. Farmers who are able to operate and maintain valuable farms in the northwestern Ohio pheasant belt are usually rational and intelligent people. As a class they are willing to cooperate with conservationists when a sound program is outlined.

They are usually law abiding and problem of poaching on their farms is not so serious as it is in most of the unfertile or eroded portions of the State.

Land tenure thus is important in any long-time conservation program. Refuges owned by the State are more stable than those leased. Farm operators who own their farms are generally better able to enter into long-time agreements than are tenants who move frequently.

There are many types of farm tenants and it is difficult to make any generalizations concerning them. It seems apparent, however, that tenants as a class do less to conserve soil than do owners. Thus, in that respect their influence operates against pheasant production. On the other hand, tenants are often less careful about keeping their fencerows "clean" and they raise less livestock and more grain. On their farms, food and cover conditions for pheasants are often better than on those operated by landowners. More than half of the farmland in the Ohio pheasant belt was rented in 1935.

Land Use.—The kind of crops grown and the manner in which they are harvested are of primary importance in determining the range of the pheasant in Ohio. In three counties from which good land-use information is available, it was found that pheasant populations corresponded more or less to the proportion of the total farmland used for rotated crops.

In general, fertile farming land devoted to raising a considerable amount of cash grain crops (including corn and soybeans) and relatively little livestock, that has numerous brushy thickets and fencerows, and a minimum of permanent pasture, is most desirable. Such range is most extensive in western and northwestern Ohio, particularly where large acreages of corn are husked from the standing stalks.

All of the ideal land-use practices for encouraging maximum pheasant populations are not likely to be found in any one area. Favorable land-use conditions for pheasant production in Ohio are listed below; these may be considered indicators of superior pheasant range.

1. Proportion of the total area in crops, etc.:
    (1) 25 to 35 per cent in corn.
    (2) 25 to 30 per cent in other grains (wheat, oats, soybeans).
    (3) 15 to 20 per cent in hay and rotation pasture.

(4) 60 to 75 per cent in soil-depleting crops.
(5) 5 to 10 per cent in brush and woods.
(6) 3 per cent or more in other wasteland, including brushy fencerows, ditch banks, etc.
(7) 75 to 95 per cent of the total farm area in rotated cropland.
2. Livestock production:
    (1) Animal units per 100 rotated acres—10 to 20 per cent.
    (2) Gross cash receipts from livestock—40 to 70 per cent.
3. Harvesting methods:
    (1) 45 to 75 per cent of the corn picked from the standing stalks.
    (2) 30 to 50 per cent of the picked corn harvested by machine.
    (3) 10 per cent or less of the corn put into silos.
    (4) 30 per cent or more of the wheat harvested by the combine method.
    (5) 75 to 95 per cent of all soybeans harvested for the beans by combine.
    (6) A relatively high percentage of the clover and alfalfa cut for seed and harvested late in the season.
4. Miscellaneous practices:
    (1) Allowing one-third of the cut cornfields to retain unhusked corn until April 1 or later.
    (2) Plowing of a low percentage (20 per cent or less) of the picked cornfields in the fall.
    (3) Pasturing of a low percentage (20 per cent or less) of the picked cornfields during the fall and winter.
    (4) Little or no (25 per cent or less) clipping of grain stubblefields in the late summer.

REFUGES AND THEIR MANAGEMENT

Purpose

The chief purpose of a pheasant refuge is to afford protection to the birds, especially during the hunting season and to serve as a winter holding area from which pheasants may later disperse to restock adjacent areas or be trapped and distributed to more distant coverts.

Size

The size of the refuge is governed by such factors as the number of pheasants to be accommodated, ownership of the land, character of bordering areas, proximity of other sanctuaries, hunting pressure, and type of cover. In pheasant territory such as that of northwestern Ohio, a refuge of 200 acres, including perhaps 40 to 60 acres of timber or brushy thickets and surrounded by cultivated cropland, is large enough to winter 2,000 pheasants. Even with such large concentrations of birds, winter feeding may not be necessary in superior pheasant range. Brushy thickets and wood lots no larger than 15 acres, if surrounded by 100 to 200 acres of grain crops (mostly corn and soybeans) and some wasteland, can winter from 500 to 600 pheasants each.

Location

State refuges of from 100 to 400 acres should be located near the center of each county and should serve as breeding areas for birds to be used in restocking. If more intensive management is desired, a state refuge might well be centrally located in each township. Auxiliary refuges managed by township game associations or private individuals also are of considerable value. They may be relatively small (100 acres or less) and should be interspersed as evenly as possible between the larger ones. A small refuge can adequately serve an area about 3 miles in diameter.

The refuges, when possible, should be located near the center of a section and away from main-traveled highways. This makes the problem of law enforcement easier, protects the pheasants from roadside shooters, and decreases the number of pheasants killed by automobiles.

The type of country adjoining a refuge is important, especially in the case of small refuges, because much of the food of the pheasants must be obtained from surrounding grainfields. It is desirable to have both productive agricultural lands and some waste areas near the refuge. Brushy fencerows and drainage ditches and unmowed roadsides through the cover of which pheasants can disperse from the refuge, also are important and should be considered in selecting the refuge site.

It is essential to success that the sentiment of the local farmers be for and not against the refuge. Otherwise trapping operations

and other management measures cannot be carried on without interference from dissatisfied landowners and farm operators. A reliable,
interested man living on or adjacent to the refuge can be of invaluable service in law enforcement, in winter feeding, and as a paid or
volunteer assistant in many phases of management work.

Ownership

State game refuges should preferably be state-owned. On state
lands, game managers can make plantings and control conditions to
a degree that would be impossible on leased lands. State-owned
refuges also are more permanent, as leases often depend on the whim
of the landowner and may be terminated without notice or good
cause, resulting in the loss of time, money, and management effort.
Usually it is expedient to lease lands for 3 to 5 years, with option to
buy at the end of the trial period.

Cost of Land

Although the value of land in some of the best pheasant-producing territory may be regarded as too high for state purchase, most
localities have unproductive waste areas, quite suitable for refuges
(when surrounded by more fertile land), that can be bought at low
prices. Lands to be purchased should be exhaustively investigated
and evaluated to insure that they will serve satisfactorily for a long
time. However, land value should be considered in relation to the
head of game likely to be produced per unit of area. Since pheasants
on good land frequently give yields per square mile from 2 to 20
times as large as those on low-priced lands, the expenditure for value
received is not out of proportion. Granted favorable local sentiment,
the purchase of 100 acres in the midst of high-value lands as a
pheasant refuge puts a much larger area in production, making possible a good pheasant harvest from about 25 square miles of land surrounding the refuge. Fertility counts in the production of pheasants
as in that of other crops and good land will more than repay its cost.

Food

The ring-necked pheasant is a hardy game bird and can adapt
itself to a great variety of conditions, but it requires adequate food,

cover that will provide shelter from storms and predators, and safe nesting sites.

The food of pheasants is chiefly of vegetable matter, largely waste grain, greens, and weed seeds gleaned from cultivated fields. Hence, considerable acreages of grain and hay crops near refuges are important in pheasant production. Small fields bordered by brushy fencerows, are especially valuable in providing food within easy access from cover.

Refuges sometimes harbor considerable numbers of pheasants and these, needless to say, require food in quantity. To illustrate the importance of the proper location of refuges with respect to food resources, two refuge areas were given exhaustive inventories.

The Liberty Township Refuge and the Auwerter Refuge, both in Wood County, are only about 4 miles apart. In the winter of 1936-37, more than 1,800 pheasants were trapped from the Liberty Township Refuge, but there was no surplus on the Auwerter Refuge. The Liberty Refuge has 2,000 to 2,500 (or more) birds each year, but the Auwerter Refuge usually has no more than 50. The most striking differences between the two areas are in the types of land and the kinds of farming nearby. The Liberty Township Refuge lies in an area in which a cash-grain type of farming is extensively practiced. Due to much limestone rocks outcropping, or lying very near the surface, and to tracts of poorly drained brushland, a smaller percentage of the area surrounding the Auwerter Refuge is devoted to the raising of grain; consequently there is less pheasant food.

A survey was made in January 1938 of six sections of land, including two on which the Liberty Township Refuge is located and four adjacent sections. It revealed that 100 acres of soybeans and 1,054 acres of corn were grown on the six sections. There was an average of 175 acres of corn per section and cornfields made up 27.3 per cent of the total area. It was calculated that the waste corn and soybeans on the six sections surveyed would total about 730,000 ounces (45,600 pounds or 22.8 tons). Assuming that a pheasant consumes about 2 ounces of corn or soybeans per day, the waste of these grains on these six sections would furnish enough food for 365,-000 pheasant-days.

During the four winter months (December 1 to April 1), 1,500 pheasants would require, at the above rate, 360,000 ounces of corn and soybeans. The survey indicated that this amount could be obtained within a radius of less than a mile of the refuge and yet leave more than a 100 per cent safety margin of food. Additional feed not included in the above calculations consisted of corn in the shock, some wheat and oats, and weed seeds.

It is entirely possible that a safety margin of this size is necessary, or at least desirable. The computation of food available was based on bare ground conditions but any snow deep enough to render 50 per cent of the food nonavailable would remove the entire margin of safety. Thus snows of long duration, leaving less than half of the food supply available, would reduce it below the minimum requirements of the birds.

A similar survey showed that six sections of land, including that on which the Auwerter Refuge was located, had only 51 acres of soybeans and 811 acres of corn (21.1 per cent of the total area). Thus the Auwerter Refuge area had only 38.1 per cent as much corn as did the Liberty Township Refuge area, only 51 per cent as many soybeans, and a total of only 40 per cent as much potential pheasant food in the form of waste grain. This difference in the amount of food available was at least partly responsible for the difference in the numbers of pheasants on the two refuges.

Observations made on, and adjacent to, Wood County refuges indicate that pheasants feed largely upon corn and soybeans during the winter. They usually do not travel more than about half a mile from their roosting site to a feeding ground. This is another indication that suitable food and cover should be made readily available and at close range, if pheasants are to utilize a refuge throughout the winter.

Cover

Cover is a very important element of a refuge but it may vary greatly with locality. In northeastern Ohio, pheasants may winter in tamarack bogs; along Lake Erie in the marshes; and in most of northwestern Ohio in wood lots. Probably the best wintering place in the last-named area is an oak-hickory wood lot. Such woods are often on sand ridges or other slightly elevated sites. Second-growth, scrubby timber is preferable to dense stands of large trees. Oaks have the advantage that the leaves of several species remain on the trees far into the winter. The oaks also furnish good cover and provide food in the form of acorns. Irregular boundaries add to the length of edge and furnish suitable habitats for many shrubs and vines not generally found in the interior of wood lots. Openings with clumps of briers are also valuable for loafing, dusting, and sunning places.

The wood lot should preferably be near the center of the refuge and adjacent to weedy fallow ground providing good nesting sites. It may be grazed so long as the ground cover is not too much reduced. Grazing probably tends to make a wood lot less attractive to predators. Nearby drainage ditches furnish a source of water and grit and their brushy banks serve as routes of dispersal from the refuge.

Although pheasants obtain much of their food on adjacent lands, most of them continue to roost on the refuges during the entire winter. A survey taken on a moonlight night (November 27, 1936) revealed that more than 600 pheasants were roosting in the Stitt Woods (a part of the Liberty Township Refuge) as 627 pheasants were actually counted. Of these, only 91 (14.5 per cent) were on the ground, the remainder being in trees. Favored locations were swamp white oak or pin oak trees having numerous scraggly branches. The birds roosting on the ground were in brush heaps and brier patches. A similar survey made in the other wood lot on the refuge showed that more than 500 pheasants were roosting in that wood lot with only 6 per cent on the ground. In these wood lots and in others observed, the northeast corners seemed to be preferred roosting spots, possibly because of greater protection from the prevailing southwesterly winds. During December, it was estimated that about 42 per cent of the pheasants roosted in woods, the remainder in stubblefields, weedy fencerows, and waste areas.

On the night of December 22, 1936, in walking back and forth through a wheat stubblefield adjoining a refuge, in such a manner as to flush all or nearly all of the birds in it, only one pheasant was started. Adjacent to this field and not even separated by a fence, was another of mixed red clover, sweet clover, and timothy that had not been mowed during the summer. The vegetation here was not dense but was from 2½ to 4 feet high. In this field, 116 pheasants were flushed in less than 15 minutes. This and other observations indicate that ground roosting cover for winter use should be higher than bindercut wheat stubble to be attractive to pheasants.

Nearby tracts in which pheasants can nest undisturbed are very valuable. A great many nests are destroyed by farming operations, but sweet clover, alsike, red clover, alfalfa, and other clovers, if left for seed and not cut until late, make excellent nesting sites. New ground, and other idle strips of land adjacent to the wood lot, if not subject to flooding, also are good.

Food and Cover Control

Food and cover control involves: Leaving patches of standing corn and soybeans, establishing strips of sweet clover for nesting or refuge cover, and in addition the managing of the shrubs and trees of wood lots and fencerows in such a way as to keep them productive of food and cover. On some refuges it may be desirable to plant trees, shrubs, and vines of species valuable to wildlife, but, in general, cover management consists mainly of fencing off parts of severely pastured wood lots or of encouraging the growth of shrubby fencerows. Among the shrubs valuable for producing food and cover for pheasants are: Low willows, blackberries, shrubby dogwoods, thornapples, blackhaws and other viburnums, prickly-ash, and wild plums. Trees suitable for food or cover include the oaks, aspens, mulberries, hawthorns, and wild cherries. The development of a dense woods-border of conifers, or of strips of shrubby and herbaceous cover, would be of great value on most refuges.

Winter Feeding

The chief functions of winter feeding are to: (1) Keep pheasants from starving, (2) build up reserve body weight and vigor conducive to increased survival and reproduction, and (3) prevent the birds from wandering from the refuges to other areas where they will receive less protection or where they cannot be trapped when wanted. Winter feeding: (1) Attracts additional pheasants to the safety of the refuges, (2) results in increased resistance to winter hazards and disease, (3) reduces the number of birds vulnerable to predation due to superior cover and protection on refuges, (4) enables the manager to learn the size and condition of the stock, and (5) produces heavier, healthier birds that nest earlier and with greater reproductive efficiency.

In many parts of northwestern Ohio where much corn is raised and a considerable part of it is picked from the standing stalks, no winter feeding is necessary during mild winters. Even during the severe winters of 1935-36 and 1939-40, very little feeding was required. Pheasants are usually able to get enough food from the corn, wheat, and other grains remaining in the fields, especially where these are supplemented by an abundant supply of weed seeds, fruits, and nuts. Leaving standing corn is most efficient in attracting and feeding pheasants. This is a natural method, and, at the same time, a most practical one, requiring no additional effort or attention. The food is always present when needed and remains in good condition. Some is always available, even when deep snows have completely covered all other sources of food. The cornstalks gradually weather and break over, regularly making available a new supply of grain. During prolonged periods of either deep snow or sub-zero temperature, artificial feeding becomes desirable and often necessary (plate 12).

Crop Protection

Some protection of crops is usually necessary on or near refuges where there are large concentrations of pheasants. The most common complaint against the birds is of their pulling corn in the spring. However, several methods have been used successfully in controlling this destructive habit. Although in some cases of damage it has been found that an abundant food supply near a cultivated crop probably conduced to the beginning of depredations, we have found by field tests, that feeding shelled corn relieves corn-pulling troubles in Ohio. Most of the damage is done just as the sprouts come through the ground. If, at this time, some shelled corn is scattered around the edge of the field, it will be taken by the pheasants and deter them from digging or scratching out the planted corn. Generally it is necessary to scatter the grain only where the cornfield adjoins brushy fencerows, thickets, or wheat fields that provide attractive cover at corn-planting time. This method has proved very satisfactory, even in fields on refuges where the pheasant concentration is very high. Usually one application is enough, as after the corn shoots reach a height of about 4 inches, they are seldom bothered. This method has the added advantage of feeding the birds at a time when natural food is scarce. Timing is very important; the grain should be scattered just before the sprouting corn becomes vulnerable, and not after much damage has already taken place. A bushel of shelled corn is more than enough to protect the average 40-acre field, the yield from which may be as much as 1,200 bushels.

In drouthy periods, sprouted or soaked corn may be more attractive than the dry grain. If satisfactory results are not obtained with dry corn, soaking the bait overnight before broadcasting is recommended.

A little experience, coupled with careful observations, usually enables one to distinguish pheasant damage from that done by other species. As a rule it is concentrated around the borders of a field—that of crows and most other birds is scattered throughout the field. Most rodents, including fox and ground squirrels, in obtaining the grain usually leave little mounds of soil alongside the holes they dig. They also remove only the germ or "heart," rejecting the remainder in the form of scattered bits.

Another method of protecting corn is the use of Crotox, coal tar, or other repellent. Treating the seed with such repellent prevents much of the damage by both pheasants and crows, and, if done correctly, does not clog the planter or reduce the percentage of corn that germinates. One quart of repellent (cost about $1) is enough to treat four bushels of seed. Coal tar, according to Kalmbach (1920, p. 16) "should be used in the proportion of about a tablespoonful to half a bushel of seed grain, the grain having been previously heated by the application of warm water, and then drained. A continued stirring of the grain will eventually result in an even coating of tar. The seed may then be spread out on a dry surface or may be dried by the application of an absorbent medium, as ashes, land plaster, or powdered earth." The same method may be applied to seed other than corn. Deep planting also tends to lessen the amount of corn pulled, but does not eliminate all of the damage, especially in sandy or other loose soils.

The drilling of an extra row or two of corn when there is space along field boundaries reduces the injury farther within a field. Generally there is enough corn in the planter boxes when the field is finished so that another 'round' can be drilled (not planted in hills) without much inconvenience. This results in a buffer row encircling the field which will absorb much of the damage.

Early harvesting, especially of the rows adjoining field margins with good cover, decreases the amount of damage done to standing corn. Pheasant damage to ripe corn is usually much less than it appears to be, since much of the grain taken is waste (from stalks broken down by wind or weakened by corn-borer infestation).

Pheasants frequently damage tomatoes and melons, especially in fields far removed from buildings and adjacent to dense cover. Feeding and watering prove helpful in such cases. The use of paper or cloth streamers hung from numerous stakes around the fields was found usually to be an effective control measure. Since damage is greatest on the edges of fields adjacent to cover, planting square, rather than rectangular, fields, tends to reduce it.

Pheasants occasionally eat soybeans soon after they come through the ground. In such cases the scattering of shelled corn or soybeans around the edges of the fields has been found to be an efficient method of control.

Control of Competitors and Predators

The pheasant refuge may serve also as a haven for bobwhites, fox squirrels, rabbits, and other birds and mammals. Fox squirrels and rabbits apparently are not of concern in pheasant refuge management except as they compete with the pheasants for food, as corn, or interfere with trapping operations. Large populations of raccoons, skunks, opossums, weasels, hawks, and crows, however, can adversely affect pheasant production. Where found to be definitely harmful, these species should be kept under control. However, with few exceptions, predator control need be directed only against men, cats, and dogs.

Dispersal of Pheasants from Refuges

Temporary refuges, or safety zones, established for the duration of the open season, can be used to attract part of the brood stock away from a congested central refuge. Later in the winter, differential feeding on the centrally located refuge and on the auxiliary refuges will bring about a distribution more nearly approaching that desired at the beginning of the breeding season.

Dispersion can also be achieved by eliminating artificial feeding, food patches, and standing corn or unharvested soybeans near or on an overstocked refuge. It may also be accomplished by men carrying lights traversing the refuge for several nights just before the breeding season begins. This results in a marked scattering but may also cause mortality.

These procedures just described reduce congestion in a refuge area, but merely result in driving birds from a belt in which the population pressure is excessive to one where it is somewhat less so. Trapping and distributing pheasants, however, enable the game manager to remove surplus pheasants to the more poorly populated sections of his county and make such areas more productive. These topics are more fully treated in the chapter on trapping and transplanting (pp. 111-121).

Law Enforcement

Adequate law enforcement is one of the fundamental phases of refuge management. Merely posting an area against hunting is not sufficient. A certain amount of patrol work is required to keep hunters from taking pheasants from refuges during the open season. It is usually necessary also to have a law enforcement agent cruise the roads adjacent to refuges in order to prevent roadside shooting of birds. There must be provision also for control of poaching during the close season.

One of the primary objectives of game protectors and managers should be to develop an understanding and appreciation among hunters of the value and purpose of refuges. When hunters realize that the brood stock preserved on refuges is a guarantee of pheasants being available to hunt the next year, they usually respect the boundaries of the refuges without question or resentment. The importance of law enforcement and the control of hunting can scarcely be overemphasized. These require the cooperation of everyone concerned, especially the farmer, the hunter, and the game protector or game manager.

TRAPPING AND TRANSPLANTING

The first trapping of wild pheasants on the Liberty Township Refuge in Wood County was done during the winter of 1931-32. Surpluses had developed there, necessitating considerable winter feeding and some payments for crop damage. Trapping was resorted to as a means of reducing the number of birds and the catch was used to stock other areas.

Preparations

It was learned that careful attention should be given to choosing sites for the traps. They should be placed along the margins of woody cover, across well used travelways, or in the midst of large more or less star-shaped patches of cover. Frequent observations on the refuge will reveal the places most used by large groups of birds. Nearby patches of standing corn or attractive supplies of natural food will reduce the efficiency of the grain bait used in the traps. Hence, traps should be set near or in attractive cover, but distant from food. Traps near favorite roosting sites are likely to make large morning catches. It is usually best to set up one trap for each 200-300 birds to be captured.

Traps should be constructed, if possible, before the hunting season as the birds may avoid for several weeks spots used by workmen. Traps weathered 2 months or longer also are more likely to be accepted as part of the environment.

After the site has been selected, a space large enough for the trap should be cleared of heavy vegetation and debris. If necessary, the ground should be leveled so that the lower rim of the walls can be staked and held in close contact with the surface. Except as required by these operations, the surrounding vegetation should be disturbed no more than necessary.

Materials Required for A Pheasant Trap

1.   About 67 feet of wire lawn fencing, 30 inches high, made of No. 11 electric-welded wire with horizontal spacings of 1½, and vertical spacings of 6, inches. This kind of fencing can be purchased from many jobbers and from the larger dealers in lawn fence. A 100-foot roll costing about $13.50 will make the walls of one and one-half traps of the recommended size. Cost per trap for outside walls, $9.

2.   Two strips of 2-inch mesh chicken-wire netting, each 20 feet long by 4 feet wide, to form the top. Cost, $2.

3.   Ball of heavy twine, or cord. Cost, $0.35.

4.   Eight to twelve notched stakes, each 14 inches long, to anchor the basal rim wire of the walls to the ground.

Approximate total (prewar) cost of materials per trap, $11.35.

Construction

The trap that has been found most effective and economical in trapping more than 11,000 pheasants in Wood County, and is now being used in a number of other counties, is a double "waterlily" type of trap, 20 feet long, 8 feet wide, and 2½ feet high. Each throat, or end, of the trap is so shaped that it forms a "V" which narrows down to a 4-inch opening through which the pheasants enter. Figure 6 indicates the appearance of the completed trap without top.

Cut the wire to be used for the walls the desired length (33 feet for each of two sides). Roll out the wire, shaping one piece like a long capital "C" and the other like a reversed "C" (see diagram). Stake the lower wire of the walls firmly to the ground with the notched stakes along the lines indicated by the illustration (figure 6).

The throats of funnels should be carefully shaped with the entrances about 4 inches wide. The upper half of the entrance gap may be closed, leaving an opening below, that is 4 inches wide by 12 to 18 inches high. A few long, curved wires woven into the walls of the throat and protruding a few inches into the trap will guard the opening, and discourage passage through the throat from the inside out. The projecting ends should be stiff so that they will not be bent out of position by captive birds and they should be blunt, not sharp.

The chicken-wire netting should be cut to fit the top of the trap (from two strips, each 4 feet by about 20 feet). Lace the two fitted strips together by their inner edges, and then lace the whole to the top of the trap walls, with strong cord. If the trap is to be permanent, size 14, soft wire, rather than cord, should be used for lacing.

Cut a man-door 1½ by 2 feet as indicated in the diagram. The horizontal wires extending from one of the vertical walls of the doorway can be bent for hinges. The pieces removed can be used as the door, and wire fasteners may be made to hold the door shut when the trap is set. An alternative is to make a manhole through the top. One end of the mid-line of the top of the trap can be threaded with a heavy stiff wire and this wire taken out to make a slit large enough to permit entrance of a man, and replaced when the trap is reset.

From two to four "escape doors," each 4 by 8 inches, should be cut at the bottom of the corners of the trap.

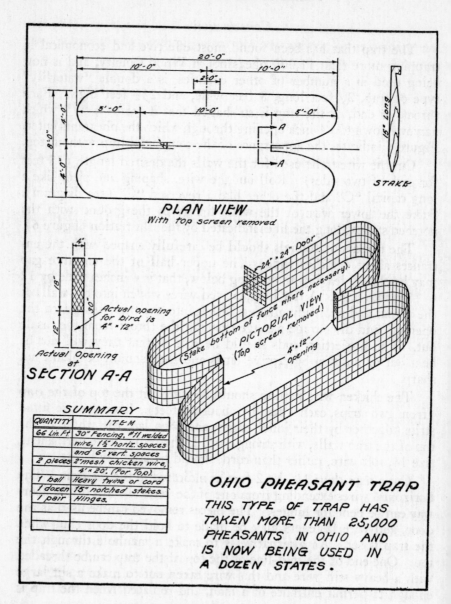

Figure 6.—Ohio pheasant trap.

A forked stick about 4 feet long can be used as a prop in the center of the trap to prevent the top from sagging and to permit more convenient moving about in the trap.

The walls of the trap may tend to bend toward the center. If so, they may be held in the desired position by braces of cord or wire extending from the upper rim of the walls to adjacent trees or stakes.

The finished trap should blend with its environment as much as possible. If properly constructed, it will be firmly anchored to the ground. No tall stakes should be used. The walls should be so flexible that the captive birds in flushing will strike a springy rather than a rigid barrier, thereby reducing the possibilities of injury. Traps with walls 4 feet or more in height are convenient to work in, but are much more likely to result in injuries to the birds. Pheasants are unable to strike the walls with much momentum if the trap is kept low. Chicken-wire netting is quite satisfactory for the tops of the traps, but results in scalping if used for the walls. Fish netting, which would be otherwise suitable for the tops cannot be used on account of squirrels and other mammals cutting through it. Smaller traps will catch pheasants, but a great percentage of the birds escape from them, as the openings through which the birds enter the traps are relatively more conspicuous and easy to locate.

The Ohio pheasant trap (plate 13) is very durable, and if not moved will last 5 or more years. When the trapping season is over, the tops may be unlaced and rolled up for storage and the walls left standing. The whole trap may be taken down and moved in less than 15 minutes.

Baiting

Ear corn is the best bait for general use in pheasant traps. Other baits, including wheat, oats, and soybeans, have been tried but with less success. All corn placed inside the traps should be out of reach of birds from the outside. A small quantity of shelled corn should be scattered in the throats and near the ends inside as leads to attract pheasants to the ear-corn bait. If pheasants do not approach the trap, spread thin trails of corn from the trap for a hundred yards or more in the direction of the parts of the refuge frequented. The escape doors should be left open for a time after the trap is first baited, permitting pheasants to enter, feed, and leave freely. They should be closed only after a sizable group of pheasants is feeding regularly within the trap. The trap can then be closed late in the afternoon and made ready for a catch the next morning.

Shelled corn serves well as bait when there is little or no snow on the ground. On some refuges fox squirrels carry a great deal of ear corn away from the traps. When shelled corn is used, squirrels remove the embryos from some of the kernels but cannot carry large quantities away. As pheasants eat much of the "dehearted" shelled corn, squirrels, therefore, interfere little except when ear corn is used. Where smaller rodents are numerous, it may also be desirable to use shelled corn as bait.

Trapping Season

If a large surplus of pheasants is to be removed from a refuge, an early start is imperative. If the surplus is small and if the refuge area has sufficient natural food resources so that little artificial feeding is necessary, trapping may be deferred. Usually it is best to begin trapping shortly after the close of the gunning season, or as soon as the wariness induced by hunting has diminished. If natural foods are abundant so that the birds do not bait readily, it may be necessary to wait for snow and stormy weather. During mild winters trapping can be done most efficiently late in January and in February. Winter feeding tends to increase and concentrate the refuge population. Failure to feed, or decrease in natural food late in winter, tend to reduce and disperse the refuge population. When large surpluses occur, it is usually possible to trap successfully any time from December 1 to March 1.

Schedule for Setting and Visiting the Traps

Most of the pheasants are trapped during the first half of the morning, although some are taken in the evening or throughout the day. Where practicable, it is best to visit the traps from 9 to 10 a.m. and then only briefly. Refrain from approaching the traps while birds are in the vicinity, or walk slowly so that the flock gradually retreats without flushing. If the catch is removed in midmorning, most of the birds will have been confined for only a few hours. Usually, however, birds held in traps overnight are none the worse for their experience, although the chance of losses to dogs or other flesh-eating mammals is greatly increased. It is imperative that all the escape doors be fastened securely in an open position whenever the trap is not in operation, as predators form the habit of making regular visits to traps where confined birds may be cornered.

Operations may continue as long as the take warrants, usually 3 or 4 days. The escape doors should then be reopened and the trap heavily baited and "rested" until it is again being visited daily by a large flock of pheasants. While traps are being "rested" trappers can shift their activities to other refuges. This alternating use and rest increases efficiency and greatly reduces the cost per trapped bird.

For economy, every effort should be made to trap the entire number of pheasants desired within a relatively few days. This results also in less disturbance to the refuge population. As mortality is proportional to the number of days of trap operation (not to the number of birds trapped), it is greatly reduced by making occasional wholesale catches rather than taking only a few individuals each day. By anticipating stormy weather and having all the traps well baited and ready, larger daily catches can be made, resulting in increased efficiency and reduction in trapping costs.

Methods of Handling Birds

Traps containing pheasants should be approached slowly and quietly to prevent undue excitement of the birds. After the operator has entered the trap, the door should be securely fastened. The birds tend to mass together in one of the rounded corners. Grasp the pheasants, one at a time, over the back and press gently to the ground. Place the open end of a loosely woven burlap sack in front of the bird and gently shove the bird into the sack head first. Thus putting the bird in a dark place ends its struggles. Birds can be so handled not only without injury but usually without the loss of a single feather.

Three to five pheasants can be placed in one sack, which is then tied with an attached drawstring. The sexes should be kept in separate sacks for convenience in handling, distributing, banding, and making records. Pheasants can be weighed, without their struggling, by pushing each bird head first into the large end of a stocking. After weighing, the bird is pushed on through and removed from the small end, the foot of the stocking having been cut off.

Selective Trapping

The location of the trap determines to some extent the representation of the sexes in the catch and makes possible some selection as to sex. Pheasants tend to segregate into flocks or groups of a single sex during much of the winter. A trap placed near a known roost of cock birds will be likely to take a disproportionate number of males. Traps set in heavy cover usually catch a larger proportion of cocks than those in more open situations, as the margin of a stubblefield.

Mortality

A record has been kept each year of the pheasant mortality due directly or indirectly to trapping operations. By proper timing and various precautions, trapping mortality losses can be kept at the minimum, but trapping always involves some losses. The average mortality due to pheasant-trapping operations in Wood County (involving about 10,000 birds trapped during seven winters on three refuges) was 2.5 per cent of the birds handled each year. This loss is considered relatively unimportant as it is less than the known natural mortality in a single month in winter.

Hens are two to three times as susceptible to trapping mortality as are the cock birds. Males make up a fourth of the pheasants trapped, but suffer only 9.3 per cent of the mortality. Attacking birds in the traps, dogs cause about 50 per cent of the total losses, while predators as a group account for more than 90 per cent, leaving less than 10 per cent due to smothering, handling, scalping, or other injuries. When losses are heavy, it is best to reduce greatly the number of hours during which the traps are closed, or even to suspend trapping operations.

It is doubtless impossible to develop a trap that will entirely prevent mammalian predation, as even when predators are unable to enter the trap, they usually succeed in decapitating pheasants, which, in endeavors to escape, thrust their heads through the walls of the traps. Cats, weasels, minks, and opossums occasionally kill trapped pheasants, and, of these, the first two are most destructive. The game protector took 74 feral house cats in box traps on the Liberty Township Refuge during two winters. Great horned owls and several species of hawks, though present in some numbers in the trapping areas, are not known to have contributed to the mortality of trapped birds.

Transportation and Release

Pheasants can be transported in loosely woven burlap sacks or in darkened crates with adequate openings. The crates may be built to fit the rear compartment of an automobile or may be standardized for hauling in the bed of a light truck. Ventilation is very important, not only to prevent suffocation, but overheating as well. Birds should not be released in cold weather unless perfectly dry.

The birds should be released as soon after capture as possible, although it is considered a good investment of time to weigh and band them and make records of the age, sex, and condition. Plantings should preferably include 20 to 35 per cent of males. If the catch does not permit this, surplus birds of either sex can be kept in a darkened crate for a day, or used with birds from other traps or refuges, to obtain the desired sex ratio in each colony. Where the planting is large, or considerable stock already exists in the locality of release, the sex ratio of released birds is of less importance.

Sites for Release

These should be selected and mapped well in advance of the trapping season. They should not be chosen haphazardly, but their selection should be correlated with a permanent stocking plan based on a thorough knowledge of land-use, critical environmental conditions, existent breeding stocks, potential or actual refuges, hunting pressures, and the known pheasant kill in each part of the county or counties to be stocked. Where possible, the landowner should be invited to witness the release so as to stimulate his interest and solicit his cooperation in such management as may be necessary for the success of the plant. Releases should be made where there is an abundance of waste corn, soybeans, or natural food in close proximity to acceptable clover.

As a rule all pheasants trapped have been used to stock other parts of the county in which they were taken. Even though the birds are caught on State refuges, proper encouragement of cooperation by the landowners and township associations in management and controlled hunting usually demands that trapped birds be used to stock only the county in which they were produced.

Mass Plantings

Experience indicates that it is not advisable to release pheasants in lots of fewer than 12 birds, and groups of 50-200 are more likely to produce satisfactory results. Where the potential productiveness of the new range is reasonably certain, mass plants promise most. In 1933 the Perrysburg Township Refuge of Wood County was established to serve a locality which at that time had very little breeding stock. A mass planting of 200 birds resulted in a refuge population during the five succeeding winters of 450, 650, 900, 1,100 and 1,400 birds. Already about 1,800 surplus birds have been trapped on this refuge and distributed. This increase made possible the organization of a large and successful township-controlled hunting association. In 1937, permit holders of this group took an average bag of 6.1 pheasants each during 22 hours of hunting.

Advantages of Pheasant Trapping and Transplanting

Many tracts of land have their brood stock extirpated each year by overshooting, and others are unable to support pheasants in winter. Such lands, if far removed from a dispersal center, remain idle so far as pheasant production is concerned. These require occasional restocking. Then they may be quite productive, as other factors being constant, the yield per unit of brood stock appears always to be greatest where population pressure is least. Tracts with refuge potentialities can be developed into new dispersion centers by mass plantings of trapped birds and in turn, will stock lands within their dispersion zone.

Trapping refuge surpluses makes it possible to obtain quantities of brood stock, the cost of which, if produced by artificial propagation, would be prohibitive. As to stocking value, trapped wild pheasants are decidedly superior to artificially propagated birds. Olds (1941) compiled the banding returns obtained during the 1940 hunting season from 1,169 wild-trapped cock birds released in January-February 1940 and from 3,811 adult game farm cocks released during March of the same year. The wild-trapped birds gave 2.4 times as many returns per thousand as the game farm birds.

The cost per bird trapped decreases greatly as trapping efficiency and the take increase. Based on the trapping records of three prewar winters, the costs per bird are for: Trap materials and construction, 3.6 cents; trapping and distributing, 19.0 cents; transportation of birds and travel expenses of operators, 9.0 cents; bait for traps, feed for refuge, and incidentals, 3.0 cents; a total of 34.6 cents. Usually only 30 to 40 per cent of the birds on a refuge are trapped. Costs of refuge maintenance and management (aside from trapping) should be charged to the remaining birds, about 40 per cent to 70 per cent of the original population, most of which disperse from the refuge the following spring.

The Ohio pheasant refuge and management system and the Wood County system of controlled hunting make possible an average annual pheasant kill of 80 to 120 cock birds to the section for the entire area of the County (612 square miles). Despite this tremendous kill, eight township or local refuges have a total winter population each year of from 8,000 to 10,000 birds. Of these, 1,500 to 3,000 may be trapped and distributed in localities not sufficiently stocked to insure maximum production during the next breeding season. These surplus birds are indispensable to balanced production throughout the county and are a most valuable asset to management.

A certain degree of population pressure usually develops in the vicinity of refuges, as the spring scattering of breeding stock is never complete, unless supplemented by artificial dispersal. Trapping relieves this pressure and puts the excess brood stock to work. Where the buffer zone surrounding the refuge is narrow, considerable crop damage may result unless a part of the surplus population is removed by trapping. Trapping to reduce population pressure also tends to lower mortality, as overcrowded birds may become undernourished or malnourished and thus be more susceptible to disease.

As the pheasant crop is more evenly distributed, hunting pressures even out. This avoids the abuses that develop where numerous hunters pursue concentrations of game, and increases the recreational value of each pheasant produced.

Pheasant trapping also keeps game managers in the field during the most critical months of the year when there is much to be learned concerning management improvements. It makes possible the banding of large numbers of birds and hence the accumulating of data that can be used to check the efficiency of many phases of management. Furthermore, the opportunity to handle and examine all birds trapped and to gather pertinent data concerning them, enables the manager to recognize and heed any danger signals as to quality of the stock.

CONTROLLED HUNTING SYSTEMS

Privately-Organized Hunting Systems

The Wood County, Ohio, Controlled Hunting System, begun in 1930, was developed as a defense against trespass abuses during the hunting season. The following is part of a notice which was issued to hunters at that time by the Plain Church Game Protective Association of Wood County:

As the hunting season approaches, the anxiety of landowners increases. It is a deplorable and well known fact that many who are otherwise law-abiding citizens become outlaws when out hunting. They kill our quail, hen pheasants, poultry, and sometimes our livestock, destroy our fences, and utterly disregard the game laws by trespassing upon our land without permission. Since these laws are so flagrantly violated by so many unscrupulous hunters, therefore, we, as farmers have met and organized ourselves into an association.

Despite a common grievance against trespass abuses and a common desire to end them, organization difficulties might have prevented a cooperative solution had it not been that the township was a natural social unit, that is, the majority of the residents of each township, involved, attended the same school, church, grange, and lodge. Hence, individual differences of opinion were more readily submerged to forward the cooperative plan. The first organization, the Plain Church Game Protective Association, also had another community objective, the raising of money to pay off a mortgage and to build a new church.

For several years the Ohio Wildlife Research Station made careful surveys of each association, and tabulated and analyzed information on some 140 points regarding their nature and progress. This afforded unusual opportunity to observe the development side by side of more or less contrasting systems. Each feature, desirable or undesirable, was carefully appraised as to why it worked or why it failed. As the years passed, the associations tended toward standardization through interchange of features demonstrated to be useful.

No two associations have the same regulations, but the general setup during recent years has been essentially as follows:

The majority of the landowners of the area involved form a game protective association.

Hunting is by association members only.

Landowners, tenants and their children hunt on their own

Plate 8.—Ideal wood-lot cover for pheasants.

Plate 9.—A brushy fencerow serves admirably as a travelway and covert. (Photograph by O. H. Niemyer, Ohio Division of Conservation)

Plate 10.—Drainage ditches are good pheasant retreats, especially in winter.

lands without permit, or elsewhere on association lands with a permit costing 25 cents.

Residents who do not own land can join the association for 50 cents.

Nonresidents become members of the association by purchase of a permit tag costing from $2.00 to $4.50. Depending on the size of the game crop, an upper limit of 200 to 350 nonresident permits is established, or one to about each 50 acres.

Purchase of a nonresident permit, worn on the hunting coat, entitles the holder to hunt on all association lands. A map of the 5,000 to 20,000 acres given with the permit designates the areas open to hunting during the 14-day open season (Nov. 15 to Dec. 1, Sundays excluded). Hunting is restricted to three species, pheasants, Hungarian partridges, and rabbits.

General information about the permit holder is recorded, including name, description, residence, and state hunting license number.

The landowners' interests are protected by prohibition of: Hunting within 500 feet of any building or in standing corn where men and teams are at work; destroying fences or other property; and shooting at protected game. Violation of regulations results in revoking the permit and in prosecution.

Landowners or tenants usually reserve the right to say under what conditions anyone may hunt on their land and to limit the number to 6 hunters to each 80 acres.

Each association elects a president and secretary-treasurer and all arrangements are made through these officers. From 2 to 20 deputies are appointed to minimize violations before, during, and after the hunting season. Each landowner signs up for participation in the coming hunting season. Refuges, and closed and open areas are posted with appropriate signs. Arrangements are made for refuge care, winter feeding, and certain other pheasant management work. Landowners are encouraged to recognize key pheasant-producing areas and to develop and protect them.

Experience of some of the associations as indicated by hunter participation may be summarized as follows for the season of November 1936:

As nearly as could be determined, the hunters in Liberty Township, Wood County, included: 300 nonresident permit holders, hunting on the Liberty Township Game Protective Association lands; 72 resident nonlandowners, 117 resident landowners, and 11 hunters with honorary permits, also on association grounds; an estimated 140 tenants, landowners, or minors hunting on their own lands without permits; besides 210 hunters on the 24 per cent of the township not included in the association areas; a total of 850 hunters on 36 square miles, or an average of 24 hunters per square mile.

In 1937 the average hunting pressure in Wood County was 17, and in 1938, 18, hunters per square mile. In 1937 for every 100 hunters on association lands in Liberty Township, there were 87 on nonassociation lands. In Plain Township the ratio was 100 to 32.

In 1938 in Liberty Township, for each 100 hunters on Game Protective Association grounds (per unit of area) there were only 47 on nonassociation lands. The ratio in Plain Township was 100 to 49. In 1939 in Liberty, Plain, and Portage townships, for every 100 hunters on Game Protective Association lands, there were only 30 hunters on nonassociation lands.

Thus the association lands were carrying a heavier hunting load each year, while hunting pressure on nonassociation grounds tended to remain about constant or to decrease. However, there are compensating factors which we now list.

Advantages of the Controlled Hunting System.—There is an orderly harvest of the surplus crop each year.

Law violations are minimized; unscrupulous hunters avoid controlled hunting areas.

Property interests of landowners are protected; trespass abuses are eliminated.

An adequate brood stock is preserved.

A larger pheasant yield is made possible each year and a given area provides improved hunting for more hunters.

Landowners regard larger game crops as an asset, not a liability.

Landowners modify agricultural operations to favor pheasant management. From 65 to 95 per cent of the farmer-landowners hunt, so look at game production from the sportsman's as well as the farmer's viewpoint.

Improved farmer-sportsmen relationships are encouraged. Sportsmen value their privileges highly and farmers take great pride in the number of birds produced on their farms. Instead of stretches of land posted with "No Hunting" signs, hunters are pleased to see such placards as "Welcome, Members of ———— Township Game Protective Association."

The nonresident hunter is pleased with the system because he is assured good hunting and saves much in time and traveling expenses.

The system is essentially a democratic and a nonprofit one. No one who obeys regulations is excluded. Hunters consider that the small fees merely support the regulation and management upon which a continued game crop depends. This mutually advantageous system prevents the development of exclusive, undemocratic hunting plans.

Income and Expenditures.—A number of associations collect $500 to $1,000 per year or about $20 to $40 for each section of land involved. Officers of the association usually serve without pay.

Funds are spent for printing and mimeographing, posting association lands, affiliating members, and employing the required enforcement officers. There are also disbursements for management measures, refuge developments, winter feeding, and new breeding stock.

Some associations use 10 to 20 per cent of their income to pay for two social events for association members—one before, and one after, the hunting season. These are important in the administration of the system, in smoothing out personal differences, and in promoting community interest in the plan.

A rather typical distribution of the unexpended balance is: One-sixth to the local school, one-sixth to the community church, and four-sixths prorated to the landowners on an acreage basis. The landowners usually feel sufficiently compensated if their receipts cover damage to fences and crops by hunters and to corn by pheasants.

Reasons the Controlled Hunting System Succeeds.—Because of the important advantages to the landowner or operator, previously outlined.

Because the plan produces more pheasants, results in an orderly harvest, protects property rights, causes the landowner to want more game—not less, and results in favorable farmer-sportsmen relationships.

Because the plan recognizes the landowner's pride in his land and what it produces. He likes to have his farm attractive to pheasants and, if possible, harbor more birds than his neighbor's farm.

Because the plan is developed and maintained as a local project with local initiative and local talent doing the work—hence there is local pride and local interest in the results.

Because the pheasant refuge management system is the key to high production yields.

Because of the application of scientific management practices.

Most valuable of all is the contribution of hard-working game protectors with ability to recognize weaknesses and with tact in correcting them without detracting from the community nature of the projects.

Reasons for Failure May Be Listed As.—Inadequate leadership and manpower.

Breakdown of teamwork due to deficiencies in organization or to personal differences.

Passing of control of the system from the farmer-landowners to outside agencies.

Disregard of local initiative, talent, pride, and interest.

Profit-taking when it becomes the primary objective.

Inadequacy of pheasant management and harvesting, as when associations attempt to produce large pheasant crops on lands of low-carrying capacity and with inappropriate land use.

State Organized Hunting Systems

As most hunting in Ohio is of farm game on private land, it is to be expected that numerous problems arise between farmers and hunters. A. W. Short, Chief of the Bureau of Game Management in Ohio, considered the problem (1939) in the light of the following facts: (1) The State holds the trusteeship of all resident wildlife for the benefit of the general public; (2) the land on which the wildlife grows is privately owned and operated; and (3) the hunting population buys licenses with the expectation of having a place to hunt with at least a fair chance of success.

The Bureau of Game Management, which was created in 1937, has been doing commendable work in improving hunting conditions and farmer-hunter relations. The Bureau expanded until it had 27 trained employees in the field in 1940. These men have done much to make the citizens of Ohio "conservation-minded" by working with schools, youth groups, and farmers' and sportsmen's clubs. In addition they have established safety zones, and propagation and supervised hunting areas similar in many ways to those of the controlled hunting cooperatives already in existence in northwestern Ohio.

Benjamin (1941) has described the plan of State-supervised hunting on private lands in Ohio. The main objectives are to: (1) Provide demonstrations of minimum cost hunting for the average hunter under as nearly ideal conditions as possible; (2) protect the landowner from trespass and damage; (3) protect the hunter from exploitation and prosecution for unauthorized trespass; (4) teach the hunter population to obtain written permission to hunt and to safeguard landowners' and farm residents' persons and property, and (5) demonstrate the advantages of proper game management practices over haphazard methods.

The controlled hunting areas vary in size from 800 to 4,000 acres and the number of landowners on each range from 1 to 48. The Division of Conservation and its agents regulate the number of hunting permits issued per day, post the area without expense to the landowners, practice game management, and enforce the game laws with the aid and cooperation of the landowners. The amount of game bagged is learned through the "checking station" system.

Benjamin summarized the State-supervised hunting done in Ohio in 1938, 1939, and 1940 as follows:

Number of	1938	1939	1940
Areas	14	38	40
Counties represented	13	35	39
Townships represented	18	54	78
Acres involved	31,000	180,000	207,658
Landowners participating	253	399	244
Hunters using the areas[1]	2,390	6,819	15,511
Days of hunting	201	519	902

[1]These figures do not include the farmers and their guests, but only those hunters that passed through the checking stations.

These controlled hunting areas are very similar to the cooperatives in northwestern Ohio (Wood, Hancock, Henry, Wyandot, Hardin, and other counties) except that they are under definite supervision of the Ohio Division of Conservation. Like most of the associations, they are operated on a nonprofit basis and an effort is made through limited permits to regulate the hunting pressure so that maintenance of ample brood stock is insured.

The establishment of refuges, including safety zones and game-propagation areas, has been important in connection with the development of the State controlled hunting system. In 1940, Ohio had 581 safety zones (totaling 8,794 acres) in 58 counties. These small areas, closed to hunting, average about 15 acres, and range from 1 to 30 acres, in extent. They are located in districts with favorable food and cover and their chief function is the preservation of brood stock. The safety zones are posted by the State. Landowners and tenants agree not to destroy food or cover within the safety zones. Grazing by livestock is discouraged. Of the game-propagation areas, there were in 1940 about 376, totaling 76,648 acres in 81 Ohio counties. They ranged from 100 to 300, and averaged about 204, acres in extent. They have been of considerable value to date, but with increased brood stock each year, will tend to be even more important in the future.

The Pheasant in Michigan[1]

By HOWARD M. WIGHT

A century has passed since the range now inhabited by the pheasant in southern Michigan was first settled by the white man. The changes that have occurred in this period can perhaps be visualized best by enumerating the animals which have been nearly or entirely extirpated from the southern third of the State.

These include all that are unsuited to areas of intensive agriculture as the wild turkey, passenger pigeon, black bear, timber wolf, porcupine, bobcat, and marten. It now seems evident that some of our finest game birds and mammals cannot be maintained in sufficient numbers to permit general hunting over the altered parts of their former range.

In order to replace the native game under these conditions, the introduction of better adapted species is justifiable. The ring-necked pheasant is one species that is filling such a need. When first introduced, many predicted that it would not survive, but after a comparatively brief period, it has spread far and wide and occupied places where our native birds had almost disappeared. The fear that its competition would still further reduce the number of our native species has not been realized.

RESULTS OF LIFE HISTORY STUDIES

Ecological Factors

Factors of the external environment which may affect the pheasant are either nonliving (physical) or living (biotic). Air temperature and pressure, relative humidity, precipitation, wind velocity,

[1]Condensed by Paul D. Dalke from unpublished manuscripts of the late Professor H. M. Wight.

solar radiation, and electrical and sound disturbances are all atmospheric factors that may affect the pheasant's activities. Also soil structure, composition, and moisture, topography, exposure, and seismic disturbances play a part either directly or indirectly. Likewise the presence of free water in proper amounts is essential. The effects on the pheasant of the living or biotic environment are of equal importance. Plants provide food and protection, and the animal associates may have either beneficial or harmful influences.

The physical characteristics of the environment are readily measurable by instruments, but the interpretation of their effects upon as widely tolerant a bird as the pheasant is difficult. The biotic influences of the environment are not as readily subject to quantitative measurement and only in recent years have satisfactory methods been developed of determining population densities.

The measurement of both physical and biotic influences is an essential part of investigation of the pheasant. An attempt has therefore been made in southern Michigan to measure animal populations, cover, and food supply and to interpret the pheasant's reactions to these factors.

In determining the protective value of cover, the characteristics of each type must be considered and recorded quantitatively and qualitatively for density, durability, composition, height, and stability. Food factors include quantity, quality, and availability.

Internal stimuli, although interesting, will receive only general consideration here. They include all the responses originating from within the organism such as hunger pangs, the nesting impulse, and play behavior.

Pheasant responses take the form of characteristic movements, postures, or sounds. Each act is a part of the daily routine of satisfying physiological requirements. The behavior each day would be monotonously similar were it not for frequent disturbances arising from a changing environment.

The pheasant is apparently exceptionally tolerant to physical stimuli, with a wide range between its maximum and minimum limitations. For instance, its distribution as aided by transplantings now encircles the globe in countries having a temperature range in annual means of from 40° to 74° F. It occurs at elevations between one mile and sea level. It feeds upon an innumerable variety of grains, seeds, fruits, leafy vegetation, and animal matter. Its nests have been found in nearly every type of cover. It apparently is fairly resistant to both drouth and to extreme precipitation. It thrives in the presence of a great variety of cover types but can exist in less diversified conditions. It demonstrates remarkable qualities of self-protection in the presence of predatory enemies, and is apparently less susceptible to disease in the wild than are any of the native upland game birds. For these reasons, accurate evaluation of the effects of environment upon the species is not easy; in fact is possible at all only through careful and continued observations made under various conditions.

Cover Types as Influencing Seasonal Movements

In southern Michigan, pheasants are normally found within one or more of seven general cover types. These are hayfields, mixed herbaceous types (including abandoned fields), woods, brush, cornfields, marshes, and grainfields. Table 5 shows the use of cover types by pheasants for each season of the year on a percentage basis.

The pheasant's range is not stable but rather dynamic or everchanging with the changes occurring so rapidly that only a general analysis of them can be made. Table 5 indicates that in winter more than 50 per cent of the pheasants were found in marshes, while in summer approximately 34 per cent were observed in hayfields. The fall period represents the time of a general population shuffle when variation in choice of cover types is greatest.

The winter months are especially trying for the birds because a combination of conditions often makes the cover, chiefly marsh, inadequate for concealment. At that season the pheasant is affected by three principal stimuli. The first is the increased food requirement for production of body heat and in preparation for reproduction. The problem of obtaining a sufficient quantity is greatly intensified as foods which provide the essential diversified rations are more scarce and difficult to obtain.

A second set of influences is associated with the short winter days and the inclemency of the weather. There is a lag in the time of day when the birds leave their roosting sites in search of food and a hastening of their return to the roosts, both of which are associated with lowered temperature and diminished light intensity. High wind velocity leads them to search persistently for windbreaks, such

TABLE 5.—Percentage of pheasants found in various cover types at different
seasons of the year

Season	Marsh	Mixed herbaceous	Brush	Woods	Hayfields	Cornfields	Grain-fields
Winter	53.7	13.8	13.3	0.6	4.9	13.0	0.9
Spring	30.1	16.1	29.5	5.5	12.1	6.5	0.2
Summer	5.1	19.3	16.4	8.5	34.1	6.6	10.0
Fall	14.7	21.0	19.2	5.1	7.4	32.1	0.5
Averages	15.9	17.6	19.6	4.9	14.6	14.5	2.9

as the protected side of trees, heavy brush cover, lower spots protected by sedges, and weedy places. They definitely avoid exposed positions. It is generally believed that pheasants seek marshlands largely for cover but the temperature factor may also be an important secondary influence in this choice, for it has been demonstrated that the winter temperature may be 19° higher among the marsh sedges than in the grass and mixed herbaceous cover in more elevated locations (table 6). Since, however, movement to the marshes actually occurs prior to periods of extremely low temperature, it seems probable that the chief effect of temperature is to hold the birds in cover already chosen.

The third set of stimuli prompts the pheasant to seek concealment from natural enemies. This response, highly developed in the mature pheasant, seems to be instinctive in the chick, and is increased daily through maternal training and later by experience. It is in fact so strong that pheasants continually seek concealment even when it is apparently unnecessary. In other words, cover is valuable not merely in providing shelter from enemies or from adverse climatic conditions, but in giving a sense of security that may conserve nervous and muscular energy which would otherwise be expended in unnecessary skulking from dangers that do not exist.

As the marsh cover type usually does not provide an exceptionally good source of food, other reasons than food seeking must be sought for the presence there in winter of large numbers of pheasants. As a matter of fact, search for food is apparently the principal reason why the birds leave the marshes.

With the coming of spring more pronounced movements occur. At that season rains flood the marshes so that they are no longer

TABLE 6.—Monthly average difference between the weekly means of maximum and minimum temperature (Fahr.) of various cover types, Williamston, Michigan, 1931 and 1932

Date 1931-1932	Mixed herbaceous and uncut hay		Spruce and huckleberry swamp		Cut-over oak-hickory woods		Leather-leaf bog		Brushy fencerows	
	Max.	Min.	Max.	Min.	Max.	Min.	Max.	Min.	Max.	Min.
Nov. 28-Dec. 25	—3.7	+2.8	—7.7	+1.5	+5.6	—3.1	—.09	—2.7	+0.1	+1.2
Dec. 26-Jan. 22	—6.5	—3.0	—2.4	+3.7	—3.2	—6.9	—6.2	—8.3	—6.1	—5.6
Jan. 23-Feb. 19	—8.3	—7.7	+2.5	+4.7	—3.8	—11.9	—8.6	—14.4	—1.0	—9.2
Feb. 20-Mar. 18	—19.0	—5.7	—6.1	+4.2	—9.8	—13.6	—12.6	—15.7	—16.4	—9.2
Mar. 19-Apr. 15	—16.6	—6.4	—6.9	+3.8	—8.1	—12.7	—6.7	—11.5	—14.2	—6.2
Averages	—10.8	—4.0	—4.1	+3.6	—3.9	—9.6	—7.0	—10.5	—7.5	—5.8

TABLE 7.—A qualitative and quantitative comparison of cover types in winter for pheasants

Characteristics	Marsh types			Herbaceous			Shrubs			Woods	Hayfields	Corn	Grain
	Leatherleaf	Sedges	Bluejoint grass	Sweet clover, goldenrod	Timothy, goldenrod bergamot	Timothy, goldenrod	Rose	Panicled dogwood	Sumac	Red oak	Alfalfa, timothy	Stubble	Wheat stubble
Cover:													
Height	33	33	33	33	33	33	33	33	33	10	5	5	10
Density	20	33	33	10	10	10	15	3	33	5	0	0	3
Stability & durability	22	11	5	22	22	22	22	33	3	3	5	5	22
Total points	75	77	71	65	65	65	70	69	69	18	10	10	35
Classification	Excellent	Excellent	Good	Good	Good	Good	Good	Good	Good	Poor	Poor	Poor	Poor
Food:													
Quantity	0	1	1	2	2	2	2	1	3	3	1	3	3
Quality	0	2	1	2	1	1	1	3	1	3	1	3	3
Availability	0	2	1	2	2	2	3	1	1	0	1	2	2
Total points	0	4	1	8	4	4	6	3	3	0	1	18	18
Classification	Poor	Medium	Medium	Good	Good	Good	Good	Good	Good	Poor	Medium	Excellent	Excellent

KEY TO COVER SCORE (POSSIBLE 99[1])

Density per 2 ft. sq.
1- 5 stalks	0
5- 10 stalks	5
10- 25 stalks	10
25- 50 stalks	15
50-100 stalks	20
100-150 stalks	22
150-200 stalks	33
200-over stalks	33

Height
0- 2"	0
3- 6"	5
7-12"	10
13-18"	22
19"-above	33

Stability and durability
Valueless	0
Poor	5
Medium	11
Good	22
Perfect	33

KEY TO FOOD SCORE (POSSIBLE 27[2])

Quality
Excellent	3
Good	2
Fair	1
Poor	0

Availability
Good	3
Medium	2
Poor	1
Inaccessible	0

Quantity
Abundant	3
Common	2
Present	1
Poor	0

[1] Total points for cover determined by adding scores for each factor.
[2] Total points on food score determined by multiplying scores for each factor.

satisfactory as roosting sites. Further, mating starts during March and the cocks, which generally have remained separated from the hens, now seek mates, and a physiological stimulus of great intensity causes a general breaking up of the winter flocks. With increased plant growth, the pheasants select their nesting sites at greater distances from the marshes until by the first of June they have scattered a mile or more from their winter coverts. The marsh then ceases to function as the most important cover and its place is taken by clover, alfalfa, and other hayfields, where nests and broods are most frequently found. In late June, haying commences and if weather conditions are propitious all of the alfalfa and clover fields are promptly cut, thus depriving the flocks of young pheasants of ideal cover. They are then forced to seek protection elsewhere, and wood lots that have a good underbrush and ground cover, along with brush patches, fencerows, and abandoned fields grown up to herbaceous plants are utilized. The second growth of alfalfa and clover develops rapidly and the pheasants return to the fields for a time but the period is brief because the fields are either once more cut or are grazed by stock.

By that time cornfields offer excellent cover and are much utilized, especially during September and October. By the time the corn is cut, the birds have once more resorted to the marshes for cover, returning to the fields chiefly in search of food. Grainfields surrounded by fencerows which provide good cover are a favorite feeding place through the fall and the open winter period, but convenient dense cover sufficiently high to conceal the bird is a necessary part of the pheasant range at all times in Michigan. Consequently the dense vegetation in marshes, the herbaceous cover in low areas in the fields, and the brush and herbaceous cover of swamps and kettle holes are most sought in winter.

Cover Analysis

A comparison of the value of the various cover types in winter is given in table 7. The summer months are not included as the problem of finding cover is not difficult at that season. Good cover should afford protection both from the elements and from enemies, and should be dense and sufficiently tall to provide ample shelter. Cover, excellent in summer, may be poor in winter because of loss of leaves, or because it may generally fray out and become worn down to a thin stand.

The plan of scoring used in table 7 is based on the quantitative value of each cover type in terms of the pheasant's requirements; each characteristic being graduated according to the requirements of a ground-living animal of about the size of the pheasant.

The evaluation of cover types should also consider the topography of the site as it affects both water and air drainage, while exposure is important as it determines the light intensity. It is also closely associated with wind velocity and temperature.

The scheme considers the various characteristics of the food supply such as quantity, quality, and availability.

Table 6, earlier presented, illustrates the remarkable variation in temperature of different cover types. The information summarized there not only helps to explain the tendency of the birds to remain in the marshes during the winter, but also in part their inclination to avoid exposed leatherleaf bogs and open woods. The minimum temperature for these two types of cover averaged 10.5° and 9.6° less, respectively, than that of the sedge marsh cover type during the period from November 28 to April 15.

The scores given for each characteristic in table 7 were determined in the field as follows: The height was ascertained by actual measurement, and density was evaluated by counting the number of stalks within a space 2 feet square.

Stability and durability are not easily measured but with experience in the field, reliable ratings are possible on the basis of judgment. If the cover has only slight value in these respects, it is scored as 5, if medium in value as 11, and if very good as 22. Tests in the field with trained workers indicated this system to be reliable.

The measurement of density is made at a height of one foot above the ground. This gives a spreading or rambling shrub like leatherleaf, ground juniper, or shrubby cinquefoil a much higher score than if the measurement were made at the surface.

The score for each cover factor was arbitrarily chosen but is based upon field observations of thousands of pheasants and upon measurements of the cover in which they fed, roosted, and sought protection.

It should be mentioned that this system is designed to measure only ground cover and that it was especially developed with reference to the pheasant.

Dispersal of Pheasants

The term dispersal has a meaning quite different from either cruising radius or seasonal range. It is used here to denote the movement of pheasants completely out of an area. The term drift used by Leopold in apparently the same sense seems to carry the idea of movement in a particular direction, while dispersal includes movement to surrounding areas without reference to direction.

There are two chief sources of information on dispersal. The first is the appearance of pheasants in places where they have not been liberated, to which they have simply wandered or been forced. The second is records of banded birds either accidentally killed or shot during the hunting season.

Data from pen-reared pheasants liberated directly from the state game farm do not properly represent the behavior of birds on established ranges. They do, however, indicate the comparative instability of the pheasants liberated in the field. Bands returned to the Conservation Department from 192 birds released in 1932 indicated that the average bird did not move more than two miles. However, the average distance traveled for birds released in the fall of 1931 was 4.3 miles, while the maximum distance was 22 miles. The movements of settled birds have been shown to be greatest in fall, due to the shortage of cover, farming activities, and the hunting season (Leopold, Lee, and Anderson, 1938). That the pheasants reared within a brood territory under the care of the hen become through experience attached to a particular locality from which they do not readily move, is a well established fact. But birds that are forced to shift about by farming activities and other disturbances seem to become more roving in temperament, and the young cock birds, especially after repeated flushing, lose their tendency to return to the home territory. On the other hand, old cocks that have lived within a territory for one or more years do not really leave, and return again and again even though at times they may wander far. In one instance a cock pheasant was observed to make three-mile trips back to the roosting territory from which it had been driven during hunting. Young cocks, however, are often forced several miles from their roosting site, just as are newly released birds.

Food Habits of Adult Pheasants

By PAUL D. DALKE

Adult pheasants usually do not commence feeding as soon as they leave the roost, but wander about, taking little or no food until about an hour after sunrise. In summer their early morning activity consists mostly of playing or exercising, while in winter they usually stand or crouch under shrubby or herbaceous cover.

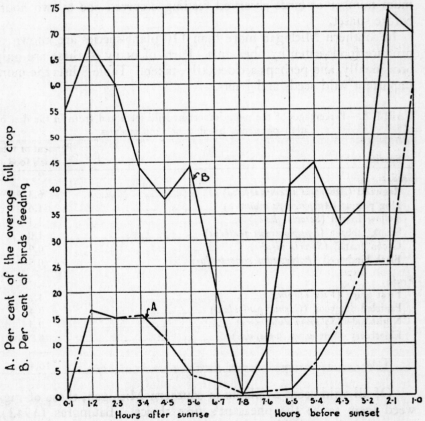

A. Average amount of food in crops of adult pheasants.
B. Distribution of pheasants observed feeding.

Figure 7.—Index of pheasant feeding during the day.

Figure 7 shows the average amount of food in the crops during the course of the day based upon analyses of 352 units. The percentage of pheasants observed feeding throughout the day shown in curve B is based upon 3,832 observations at all seasons. Both curves indicate that the feeding period in the morning is at a maximum between one and two hours after sunrise. In midday most pheasants are inactive and have a minimum amount of food in their crops. The intensive afternoon feeding period begins about three hours before sunset and continues until roosting time. The maximum number of birds observed feeding occurred one to two hours before sunset.

In southern Michigan more than 110 plant species are known to produce foods eaten by pheasants. Parts of many of these are only occasionally, and perhaps accidentally, taken. Table 8 lists the more important wild seeds and fruits.

TABLE 8.—Percentages of the more important wild seeds and fruits in the diet of adult pheasants, based upon crop analyses

Species	Per cent of total year's food
Seeds:	
Ragweed (*Ambrosia artemisiaefolia*)	6.3
Hog peanut (*Amphicarpa monoica*)	1.6
Yellow foxtail (*Setaria glauca*)	1.1
Skunk cabbage (*Symplocarpus foetidus*)	1.0
Green foxtail (*Setaria viridis*)	0.9
Black bindweed (*Polygonum convolvulus*)	0.5
Fruits:	
Frost grape (*Vitis vulpina*)	4.1
Panicled dogwood (*Cornus paniculata*)	0.4
Nightshade (*Solanum dulcamara*)	0.3
Elderberry (*Sambucus canadensis*)	0.2
Total	16.4

Of all wild seeds available in southern Michigan, those of ragweed seem to be the pheasant's first choice. Baumgras (1943), computing the available weed seeds per acre found in several different habitats in Clinton County, Michgian, reported those of ragweed comprised about 50 per cent of the total. Wheat stubble fields were especially productive of ragweed seeds, averaging 205 pounds per acre in October. Stubbles of wheat, oats, barley, rye, and corn are the ragweed's ideal habitat. Its wide distribution, abundance, and accessibility make it the most important pheasant food producer other than the cultivated grains. Seeds of burdock are sometimes an important food in times of deep snow, and constitute an excellent emergency reliance.

The importance of fruits during periods of deep snows was evident from numerous direct observations of the birds feeding on grapes and nightshade berries. Where panicled dogwood is locally abundant, the fruit is gleaned as it drops to the ground. Vegetable constituents amount to 94 per cent of the annual food of adult pheasants, of which corn, wheat, barley, oats, buckwheat, and beans make up 74 per cent. Of the grains, corn contributes 33, and wheat 20, per cent.

Upon first consideration of these figures, it would appear that the pheasant is a rather expensive bird for the farmer to support, but the bulk of grains is obtained from field waste and from manure spread on the fields. The comparatively large proportion (8 per cent) of barley eaten comes from waste grain in newly-sown fields.

The abrupt increase found in the amounts of grass and leaves eaten by pheasants in late winter cannot be explained on the basis of increased availability. Pheasants are in the breeding season by March and this increase in green food may be very likely a seasonal dietetic requirement associated with reproduction.

Insect foods were consumed in the largest quantity in June, the month of maximum insect activity, and consisted mostly of the larvae of Lepidoptera (cutworms and other caterpillars).

Economic Status.—The economic status of the pheasant varies greatly from one agricultural region to another, and it is therefore unsafe to generalize from limited observations. The pheasant is an omnivorous feeder, and is prone to feed upon the most accessible foods. Sometimes that may be something of value to man, but in the majority of cases damage has been more imaginary than real. In areas where vegetables are raised for city markets, however, pheasants have been known to cause considerable loss where they were allowed to become too abundant.

A cross section of opinion as to the economic status of pheasants on farms was obtained by interviewing farmers on an area of approximately 70 square miles in Ingham County. The opinion of

92 per cent of the farmers was that damage was of minor importance. The remaining farmers presented real grievances which should not be overlooked in a pheasant management program. In one case, popcorn planted next to a marsh was extensively damaged by pheasants. One farmer reported loss of melons and grapes, and another of tomatoes. These are typical of the most common complaints and they are among the problems for which scientific wildlife management seeks a remedy.

About a third of the annual food of the pheasant is corn. This appears rather high in view of the fact that in the general farming area where the food study was carried on, corn occupies only 11 to 13 per cent of the improved farmland. The 33 per cent of corn in the annual diet does not appear so out of proportion, however, when the sources of this grain are taken into consideration. They include waste grain which remains in the field, fragments that are dropped by pastured stock, corn carried into the woods by squirrels, and also that which is returned to the field in barnyard manure. This instance in itself makes it clear that the economic status of the pheasant can not be adequately indicated by a mere list of foods eaten.

Breeding Habits of the Pheasant

By PROFESSOR WIGHT

The Sexual Cycle.—Seven phases in the pheasant's annual cycle are recognized:

1. The interphase lasts from late summer until January and follows the summer moult. During this phase, the genital organs are in a shrunken and nonfunctional condition.

2. The premating phase is characterized in the males by rapid development of the testes. It culminates in concerted crowing and fighting among the cocks. They seek the hens but copulation does not take place.

3. The mating phase is characterized by a general breaking-up of flocks of hens, mating of males and females, copulation, and establishment of territories.

4. The laying phase is that during which the nests are built and the eggs are produced; copulation continues.

5. The incubating phase covers the period when the hens are incubating. Copulation does not occur during this period and the male appears to be isolated from the hen.

6. The brooding phase during which the young are constantly attended by the females, and not infrequently by the cocks after the broods are a few weeks of age.

7. The postnuptial phase covers the period when the cock birds are in moult. During this period there is a pronounced and sudden decrease in the size of the testes. The cock becomes solitary, generally stops crowing—behavior which indicates a marked change in his physiological condition.

The interphase comes to an end about the first of the year when growth of the sex organs of the male begins. During the fall and winter there is a general segregation of hens and cocks, although groups made up of both sexes often are observed where roosting cover is restricted or where the birds have congregated because of abundant food.

With the first warm days of February, the cock pheasants begin concerted crowing. Fighting between cocks in the presence of females becomes a common occurrence. The activities of this period appear to be affected by temperature, being conspicuous during warm periods and almost lacking during cold spells. The exact time when the premating phase begins is difficult to ascertain because the pheasant cocks, like domestic roosters, begin to crow while still immature. They continue to crow occasionally throughout the fall and winter, so fighting seems to be the best indicator. It is followed by the breaking-up of the flocks of hens.

When the hens attach themselves to a cock and his "crowing area," they promptly build their nests and start laying their clutches. This activity is followed by the incubating, and finally the brooding, periods. If weather is responsible for a good or poor pheasant year, it must be through its effect upon one or more phases of the sexual cycle.

A summary of the important events in the breeding cycle for the years 1928-1933 is given in table 9.

Table 9 indicates a marked overlapping of the phases of the sexual cycle, as well as wide variation from year to year in the time of the events of the breeding season.

TABLE 9.—Pheasant phenology

	1928	1929	1930	1931	1932	1933
First general crowing	—	—	Mar. 10	Feb. 23	Feb. 10	Mar. 3
First signs of fighting	—	—	Mar. 14	Feb. 23	Apr. 8	Mar. 18
First signs of mating	Apr. 10	Apr. 5	Mar. 18	Mar. 20	Apr. 8	Mar. 16
First nest located	Apr. 12	May 6	May 6	Apr. 12	Apr. 20	May 1
First brood seen	June 1	May 11	May 12	Apr. 23	May 6	—
Largest clutch found	11	16	18	14	20	—
Largest brood observed	11	16	18	14	19	—

Average date of concerted crowing	Feb. 23
Earliest crowing (1932)	Feb. 10
Average date of first fighting	Mar. 16
Earliest fighting (1931)	Feb. 23
Average date of first pairing	Apr. 2
Earliest pairing (1932)	Feb. 27
Average date of first nest located	Apr. 24
Earliest nest (1931)	Apr. 12
Average date of first brood seen	May 11
Earliest brood (1931)	Apr. 23

Largest clutch (1932)	20	Latest nest found (1930)	Aug. 29
Largest brood (1932)	19	Latest evidence of hatching	
Smallest clutch (1932)	5	(1929)	Sept. 24
Smallest brood (1929)	1	Longest proestrum (phase 2, 2 months)	1932

	1929	1932	1933
Average of 22 clutches	11.5	11.8	10.6

Mating Behavior.—Courtship and mating in the field have been seen occasionally and observations in Michigan confirm the description by Townsend (1920) who writes: "In courtship the ear tufts of the cock are erected and the bare skin about the eyes is prominent and very red. He struts before the hens, turning in all directions to display his gorgeous plumage, or walks with an exaggerated bobbing motion." Leffingwell (1928) adds that "The male runs around the female with short steps, usually with the tip of the partly outstretched wing describing an arc on the ground, and stops in front of her. The feathers of the upper back, lower back, rump, and tail are shifted over the side on which the female is, and the tail partly spread. The neck is bent and the head kept low. Apparently the air sacs are partly inflated, for after the pose is held for several seconds, the plumage is allowed to fall back to its natural position as

TABLE 9.—(Continued)

	Number of birds	Per cent of potential fall population
(No. lost)		
1. Winter and spring mortality (19 × 16.6)	317	19.2
(No. lost)		
2. Spring movement off area (16 × 16.6)	264	16.0
Breeding birds left on area 94 — 35 = 59		
3. Unfavorable sex factor (16.6 — 13.2) × 59	200	12.1
Actual sex factor 1 ♂ : 2 ♀ = 2/3 — 0.66		
4. Average eggs per clutch = 11		
Incomplete clutches of eggs		
Theoretical 13.2 — (.66 × 11) × 59 =	350	26.1
Observed (20 — 11) × no. of nests		
5. Destruction or desertion of nests	240	14.5
6. Infertility of eggs (total unhatched eggs in all nests)	3	0.2
7. Mortality of young birds	38	2.3
8. Summer mortality of adults	6	0.4
Total losses calculated on basis of observations	1,418	
Losses unaccounted for	62	3.7
Total losses	1,480	89.5
Actual 1933 fall population	174	10.5
Total potential population	1,654	100.0

the bird gives out a hissing sound." Copulatory behavior strongly resembles that of the domestic fowl.

Territory.—Perhaps no other factor in the life history of pheasants is linked more closely with stocking or determines population more directly than territorial spacing.

The crowing of cock pheasants is one of the common sounds of early spring. The males remain in restricted areas which they protect as individual territories against the invasion of all other cocks. Because these areas are distinguished especially by the call of the cocks, they have been designated "crowing areas," and this term is used here synonomously with "territory" in the technical sense. The spring and summer pheasant range is broken up into many small units, each in the possession of an individual cock bird which zealously protects his "crowing area" by driving off other males and by warning the female and her young of approaching danger.

The method by which the females are attracted to the crowing area is very similar to that of the domesticated rooster. The cock calls them with a low cluck, picks out choice bits of food, displays before them, and frequently lets his powerful voice out in lusty crowing. Many observations lead to the conclusion that the size of the pheasant harem depends more upon the number of hens in the neighborhood at the time spring mating occurs, than upon pronounced polygamous tendencies on the part of the cocks. There is evidence, however, that the cock bird attempts to increase his harem after he has mated with one or more females. Just what determines the establishment of a crowing area, and the approximate time of its selection, is not easily determined. In some instances, the crowing area is retained year after year in the same location and it may be within or near the wintering territory. In other instances where young cock birds have lived together during their first winter, they establish adjacent crowing areas.

If a male is entirely vanquished in his quest for an area, he usually moves out completely, and becomes a wanderer, and is driven from place to place as he enters the territories of other birds. The females and males do not become sexually mature at the same time, hence cocks vanquished by an opponent or slow in maturing become available for females maturing at a later date.

The extent and shape of the crowing areas are determined by the composition, density, and arrangement of the cover. A patch of either brush or woods is an essential part of the cover within a crowing area, although during the latter part of June, hayfields provide sufficient shelter. Herbaceous cover is almost always part of the territory. Thus the crowing area is a unit of land bearing dense, woody vegetation combined with open herbaceous cover suitable for nesting. Its size is controlled to a considerable degree by the random occurrence of these facilities.

Nesting Habits of the Pheasant

The choice of a nesting site is not readily made by the hen during the early spring months as the cover especially suitable for nesting is not yet available. Marshland is wet, the remains of the wild herbaceous plant cover of the previous year is thin, pasture brushland is occupied by sheep and cattle, and weedy cultivated fields are being plowed. Therefore, when the hen pheasants leave the marshes, their choice of nesting sites is limited by cover density governed by seasonal conditions and by the progress of various farm practices.

Hayfields provide the principal breeding ground for pheasants on agricultural land in southern Michigan. Of some 245 nests studied, approximately 60 per cent were found in hayfields, with fencerows a poor second. The choice of hayfields as a nesting site is responsible for one of the greatest hazards to pheasant reproduction. English (1933) has shown that haying accounted for half (37 out of a total of 74 per cent) of all nesting losses (see balance sheet, table 11). Although the laying period extends from April to September, more than 60 per cent of the functional nests were found from June 15 to July 15.

The particular site selected by the hen depends to some extent upon the height, density, and relative accessibility of cover. Shallow gullies, deep furrows, or fencerows adjacent to, or leading into, fields are often followed by females seeking a nesting site, and consequently the nests are often near such strips of cover. Sixty per cent of the nests studied were found within from 10 to 30 feet of an edge.

Pheasant Broods

The brooding period is the most vital of all the phases of the annual cycle. Each moment is full of vicissitude, and constant vigilance on the part of the hen is necessary to successful reproduction.

Young pheasants are precocious. They leave the shell fully protected by natal plumage, and are able almost immediately to move about. The most obvious hazard to the growing young, that of being killed while on the roost by nocturnal animals, is in some way satisfactorily met. Although hundreds of observations have been made of roosting sites, no evidence was seen of young pheasants being killed there. It seems logical to conclude that pheasants, old and young, when quiet on the roost do not throw off sufficient odor to attract enemies. Broods of pheasants repeatedly flushed at night finally flew into trees to avoid disturbance.

Broods are difficult to locate early in the season because they do not flush readily and their cruising radius is not great. During July they are forced from hayfield cover and then are more readily observed. Hayfields and brush and herbaceous types are the most important coverts for pheasant broods in the summer and early fall.

During the first week, the hen pheasant keeps the brood within a few rods of the nesting site if the cover is dense and they are unmolested. The young feed upon small insects and seeds. During this period much time is spent by the mother in hovering the young although they are able to withstand considerable exposure. During two downpours of rain, one following the other with a total of 1.9 inches, 6 nine-day-old pheasants were picked up so helpless they could not walk. Placed beneath a domestic hen they soon dried out and completely recovered.

The hen pheasant is the head of the family and continues to care for the brood long after the cock has sought seclusion during the moulting period. No evidence has been found that the hen rears two broods in one season. She may, however, be forced to start several nests and even incubate two or more clutches in the event of nest destruction and abandonment. When the young are only a day or two of age, the hen will not leave them until she is almost stepped upon, then she flutters off assuming the broken-wing ruse, characteristic of most gallinaceous and of certain other birds. This habit is apparently confined to the first few days after hatching for it has never been observed at other times.

If one of the young is disturbed and utters the distress call, the old bird comes at once, sometimes quite close to the cause of the disturbance. In one case a hen pheasant was seen to rush at a collie dog. Trippensee (1934) observed an open combat between a hen and a weasel in which the former was completely victorious. At the low note of alarm, every young bird in the flock quickly conceals itself. A closer approach causes the hen to run through the cover or flush, flying low and to a distance of only a few rods if the birds are young. When the chicks become older, they seek cover and remain motionless like the hen in the face of approaching danger. Nearly full-grown birds often creep through dense cover ahead of dog or man, scattering in all directions. One by one they are later assembled after which the hen cautiously leads them out of the area where they were molested.

Development of the Pheasant

Pheasant eggs are incubated from 23 to 25 days, following a laying period of about 14 days. Thus they are exposed to destruc-

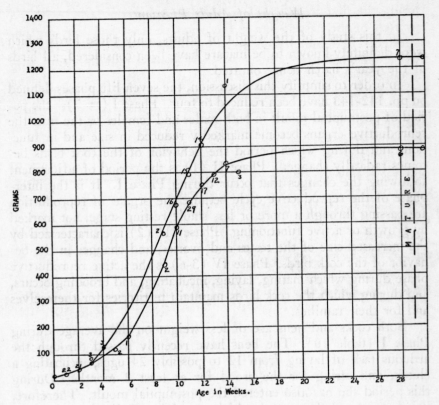

Figure 8.—Rate of growth in weight of pheasants.

tive agencies for more than five weeks. Hatching in the wild occurs within 24 hours. The young almost immediately take food and the crops and gizzards of day-old chicks were found to be completely stuffed with small insects.

The average weight of several hundred day-old pheasants was 21.8 grams (nearly nine-tenths ounce). Figure 8 gives the growth curve for pheasants from one day to maturity. Weight is a fairly accurate indicator of age of growing birds. (In explanation: 100 grams = 4.12 ounces; 500 = 1.33 pounds; 900 = 2.32 pounds, and 1,200 = 3.09 pounds.)

Weight of Adult Pheasants

In this study of the weight of adults, only those birds which were definitely known to be mature have been considered, all birds of the year's hatch being omitted.

In order to simplify this discussion, the seven life phases defined on pp. 142-143 have been reduced to four. Phase I (= 7)—the period of postnuptial moult in both males and females or the time the reproductive organs become markedly reduced in size and in function, and during which period the behavior of the cock birds becomes radically changed. Phase II (1) is the period of adjustment following the changes that occur during Phase I. It is the interphase of the reproductive cycle because the organs of reproduction are passing through a more or less stable resting stage, not marked by growth or active functioning. Phase III (2) is characterized by the increased size of the testes and ovaries, and changes in the behavior of the cock birds. Phase IV (3-6) is the active reproductive phase during which mating, laying, incubating, and brooding occurs, and during which the cock birds maintain territories for themselves and for their families.

Both cocks and hens are of less weight on the average during Phase I (table 10). The hens have recently passed through the arduous task of laying from 12 to possibly 24 eggs, incubating a clutch, and caring for the brood for at least 2 months. During this period she has also entered the postnuptial moult. Therefore, it is but natural that she should lose weight. Following establishment of a territory the cock bird constantly patrolled it and carefully guarded his hens. He has spent hours of his day fighting, during which time he took little food. He also guarded the hens while they fed and sometimes fed them from his own bill. During the incubating period he continued his vigilance over the territory, and when the young were two or three weeks old, he often traveled with the brood, doing the triple duty of patrolling the territory, guarding the flock, and searching for food for the young. Then the moult followed with the added loss of weight which probably accompanies this change. But the pronounced change in the physiological state of the bird during which the testes suddenly shrink from a breeding index of 750 units to only 40 units, probably affects metabolism and may be the most important factor in the average sudden decrease in weight of males.

TABLE 10.—Relationship between physiological condition of the bird, average weights for each phase of the cycle, and condition of environment

Phase	Period	Physiological properties	Av. Weight—grams Males	Av. Weight—grams Females	Relative conditions Cover	Relative conditions Food	Environmental factors influencing activity
I	July Aug. Sept.	Moulting Decrease in size of sex organs Change in temperament	1,231	854	Excellent to Fair	Fair to Excellent	Haying Harvesting Grazing
II	Oct. Nov. Dec.	Dormant condition of sex organs	1,321	949	Excellent to Fair	Excellent	Corn harvesting Grazing Hunting
III	Jan. Feb.	Marked increase in size of sex organs	1,275	971	Poor	Fair to Poor	Snow Sleet Cold Decreased cover
IV	March April May June	Active breeding	1,347	1,118	Poor to Fair	Poor to Fair	Rain, flooding Nest destruction Plowing Burning Grazing

During the second phase, the interphase of the reproductive cycle, both cocks and hens are relieved of parental cares and the sex organs are in a resting stage. The increased demand made on the birds by extra movement associated with hunting and migration to winter quarters is more than compensated for by the sexually dormant physiological condition and the increased food supply. Both cocks and hens increase in weight during the interphase.

January and February, the premating period, are the months with the most severe meteorological conditions in southern Michigan. In the latter part of this phase much time is spent in fighting and in the pursuit of females. Thus it is not surprising that the cock birds lose weight.

The fourth phase is marked by rapid increase in weight by both males and females, that is especially marked in the latter. This condition cannot be explained by either increased food supply or lack of activity. More logically it may be assumed to be the direct effect of hormones associated with the sexual condition of the birds.

The Dust Bath

Dust bathing is an important activity of the day. The birds bathe with energy, lying first on one side and then the other, kicking the dust up between their feathers and rubbing their wings and plumage in the dust in a most thorough manner. Pheasants have been observed to bathe almost constantly for an hour.

The frequency with which both pheasants and other birds use ashes for baths indicates that some characteristic of ashes, either mechanical or chemical, makes them more attractive than is soil. The second choice for dusting seems to be dry muck, and this in turn is followed by freshly exposed soil, often piles or loam thrown up by moles.

The youngest birds observed in dust baths were ten days old. If this is the regular time of starting dusting, it indicates that this habit is closely associated with plumage development, because then the down feathers are being most rapidly shed. The functions of the dust bath are to assist the birds in ridding themselves of dead epidermal cells, to cleanse the feathers of excess oil and dirt, and to help remove old feathers. It may also assist in eliminating external parasites.

Pheasant Mortality

By P. F. ENGLISH

The biotic potential of a species is its capacity to reproduce in a given time in the absence of environmental resistance, and being a constant is useful in calculating the effects of environmental factors in reducing the gross numbers of a species. The biotic potential depends on the rate of multiplication and the sex factor; and pheasant mortality may be expressed in terms of the degree of reduction of the theoretically possible population.

With a sex factor of 0.83^2, a maximum clutch of 20 eggs, the largest number observed to have been successfully incubated, and a single generation per year, the biotic potential of the ring-necked pheasant is 16.66 (per individual of population).

Failure to produce the potential number of fall birds is due to such factors as unfavorable sex ratio, incomplete clutches of eggs, destruction or desertion of nests, infertility of eggs, mortality of adults and young birds, and movement off the breeding area. The average effect of these losses upon a given population is shown in table 11. These figures are based upon field observation.

From this table the relative importance of each factor or group of factors appears in its proper relation to the others, all having been reduced to a common denominator. Some factors are subject to manipulation under management whereas others are not. It seems clear, provided the population is sufficiently large to make it safe, that improvement of the sex factor can be brought about by regulated hunting, that rather heavy winter losses must be allowed for in calculating allowable kill, and that losses due to destruction or abandonment of nests are very important in limiting the pheasant's rate of multiplication. The percentage of successful nests varies from year to year. For example, in 1932, 41 per cent of the nests were successful, and in 1933 only 18 per cent. Weather conditions influencing farming operations contribute materially to the degree of nesting success. About 62 per cent of all the nests were found in hayfields and of these, three-fifths were unsuccessful due to mowing, indicating the great hazard in this type of cover. Plowing, burning, building fence, and cutting brush caused about 10 per cent of

---

[2] Number of females divided by total population.

TABLE 11.—Environmental resistance effects in terms of birds destroyed and per cent of the potential fall population
Area I—680 acres. Williamston, Michigan

	Number of potential birds	Per cent of potential fall population
1932-33 winter population by dog census	94	
Maximum sex ratio observed 1 ♂ to 5 ♀ = 0.83		
Maximum clutch successfully incubated, 20		
Biotic potential 20 × 0.83 = 16.60		
Productive capacity of birds on area 16.60 × 94 =	1,560	
Total potential population 94 + 1,560 =	1,654	
Actual 1933 fall population by dog census	174	
Loss due to environmental resistance	1,480	
1. Winter and spring mortality (19 birds, each with a biotic potential of 16.6)	316	19.1
2. Spring movement off the area (16 × 16.6)	266	16.0
(Breeding birds left on area 94 — 35 = 59)		
3. Unfavorable sex factor (reducing the potential from 16.6 to 13.2) 3.4 × 59	200	12.0
(Actual sex factor 1 ♂ :2 ♀ = 2/3 = 0.66)		
4. Average eggs per clutch—11		
Incomplete clutches of eggs		
Potential 13.2 — (.66 sex factor × 11 eggs per clutch) × 59 breeding birds =	348	20.2
(Observed (20 — 11) × no. of nests)		
5. Destruction or desertion of nests	270	16.3
6. Infertility of eggs (total unhatched eggs in all nests)	3	0.2
7. Mortality of young birds	42	2.5
8. Summer mortality of adults	6	0.4
Total losses calculated on basis of observations	1,451	
Losses unaccounted for	29	
Total losses	1,480	89.5
Actual 1933 fall population	174	10.5
Total potential population	1,654	100.00

the nesting losses. Experimental evidence indicates that pheasant eggs can stand fairly low temperatures prior to incubation without affecting their hatchability. In a test of 500 eggs in 16 different lots held at 10°, 16°, 31°, 68°, and 85° F. from 2 to 6 hours, there appeared no marked difference in either the hatchability or fertility of the eggs. Therefore it seems doubtful if cold weather in the spring is a limiting factor.

Agricultural Practices in Relation to the Pheasant

By PROFESSOR WIGHT

It is generally believed that certain farm crops, particularly corn, because of their food value, are especially important in determining the success and distribution of the pheasant. Although this is not entirely true in Michigan, nevertheless corn and other crops in combination with other still more important factors contribute much to the well-being of the birds. The importance of the combination of various factors is illustrated in Lenawee and Monroe Counties, Michigan, where corn is the principal crop. The habitat in these two counties is probably more ideal for the pheasant than that of the counties farther north where comparatively little corn is grown and where the climate is not so mild. The differences in favor of the counties in the central part of the State are twofold: First, Lenawee and Monroe Counties practice clean farming and secondly, the land types which these counties represent have a low percentage of swamp, marsh, or other submarginal land. It appears that in Michigan, at least, the highest pheasant population densities are confined to areas where clean cultivation is made impossible because of the comparatively high acreage of submarginal land, covered with wild vegetation both herbaceous and woody.

Fire as It Affects Pheasants

The destruction of native vegetation by fire is generally considered a phenomenon almost restricted to the wild forested regions, but that is not the case. The wildlife of the State is probably more inconvenienced, and reduced in number, by fires on agricultural lands than by those in the north woods. Yet fire goes uncontrolled in the agricultural areas of the country while millions are spent to prevent and control it in the less thickly-settled wild areas.

On wild submarginal lands, fires are common but their effects upon the pheasant population are not usually given much consideration by the average landowner. Nevertheless, they are sometimes seriously destructive. The burning over of marshes just prior to spring dispersal is especially harmful. The removal of wild herbaceous cover of abandoned fields or fencerows destroys crowing territories, nesting sites, and general escape cover for the pheasants both in summer and winter. Burning is a widespread practice employed to destroy weed seeds, although evidence indicates that burning wild lands is not an efficient method of eradicating weeds. In fact it encourages some very objectionable species, thistles for instance. Since marsh vegetation is frequently the only early nesting cover, its destruction by fire causes unnecessary mortality of the eggs and may considerably reduce the potential fall population.

Burning to Improve Grazing

It is unfortunate that so many farmers continue the custom of burning grazing land. They do not realize that it destroys the best forage, decreases the fertility of the soil, interferes with the normal tendency toward leveling by filling, and drives out or disturbs the wildlife.

One of the most picturesque sights of southern Michigan each year is the annual "touch off" of many strawstacks. The effect of strawstack burning on pheasant economy is roundabout, but any practice which depletes the soil and reduces fertility, adversely affects the pheasant crop. Conversely the conservation of a rich productive soil contributes to the pheasant's general welfare.

Some of the Direct Relationships Between Grazing and Pheasant Range

Marshland.—Among the agencies operating to change natural succession in marshlands are grazing, fire, and drainage. Frequently fire and drainage are used to improve grazing in marshes. Burning, if consistently practiced, tends to change the sedge marsh to the mixed herbaceous type; drainage has the same effect; and both increase shrub growth. Grazing, if intensive and accompanied by burning and drainage, converts the sedge marsh type to open pasture of sod-forming grasses.

The use of marshland in winter by pheasants depends upon the character of the vegetation and the intensity of use by stock. The

Plate 12.—Good winter feeding station. The cans contain a reserve stock of corn.

Plate 13.—A morning catch of pheasants. This trap is more in the open than is usually thought desirable.

157

Plate 14.—Upper. Storm aftermath. Pheasants killed by a blizzard in Iowa. (Photograph by Iowa State Conservation Commission.)
Lower. Good pheasant range in Iowa. (Photograph by J. R. Harlan.)

ungrazed sedge marsh is ideal roosting cover whereas the grazed marsh may be almost valueless.

Woodland.—Wood lots in some instances provide the only available cover for broods of young pheasants immediately after haying and before the corn is sufficiently high to afford shelter. But when other types of cover are available, whether grazed or ungrazed, they do not seem to be especially attractive to young pheasants except during very hot days. On the other hand, an ungrazed woodland corner is one of the best places for a crowing area and, when used for nesting, it is the safest of sites. Thus, except as a desirable component of the crowing area, woodlands provide only emergency cover and otherwise are little used. But grazing may completely destroy their usefulness. The nature of the damage done to wood lots by stock is manifold. Reproduction is killed by grazing and trampling; young saplings are bent down and trees rubbed and barked. Lutz (1930) found the soil on grazed wood lots compacted, organic debris reduced, and nitrogen in the soil depleted.

Wild Pasture Land.—There are two principal types of wild pasture other than marshland and woods. The first includes: the comparatively open cleared land which may have such poor soil that woody vegetation does not thrive; land partly cleared, burned and for long periods grazed and recleared for pasture; and cultivated land that has been abandoned for growing crops. A second type constitutes an intermediate stage between the open marsh and the hardwoods-tamarack swamp. The open rough pasture land and the abandoned fields turned over to grazing are subject to much improvement for the benefit of the pheasant at a comparatively low cost.

The effects upon the pheasant are indirect but important. Any improvement of the open pasture, which is not good pheasant territory, relieves grazing pressure on the less desirable pasture areas as marshes and, therefore, indirectly benefits the pheasant. The open pastures, however, can be greatly improved for pheasants by planting clumps of evergreens that are stock-resistant and by planting other shrub cover at different spots. This can be done so that it does not greatly interfere with the amount of stock the pasture can carry, which it benefits by shade and protection from flies.

Fall Grazing.—Many farmers who do not sow a field of Sudan grass, sweet clover, or alfalfa especially for their cattle find it necessary to graze nearly all of their hayland after the first cutting. This appears to be a wasteful practice, as no second or third cuttings are possible and it is often necessary to feed grain heavily during the winter months in order to conserve the hay supply. Furthermore, agronomists have found that the next year's crop is greatly benefited if clover or alfalfa fields enter the winter with a stand about a foot high. Thus if the farmer will but follow the most up-to-date methods, pheasant problems created by grazing will cease to exist.

Fencerows.—The brushy fencerow is a part of the southern Michigan landscape that is especially beneficial to pheasants. In the census work it has become increasingly obvious that lands which have comparatively few brushy fencerows generally provide poor pheasant range and invariably have a comparatively thin pheasant population. The fencerow provides the pheasant summer and winter cover when other shelter is not available; it furnishes crowing centers for the cocks, nesting sites for the hens, escape refuge for the young birds, and avenues of communication throughout the year for all pheasants. Lacking fencerows, a farm will almost inevitably be without pheasants.

Routine Farm Practices

The routine farm practices such as plowing, cultivating, haying, and harvesting are so well established that they are not subject to marked change. Nevertheless, they have important effects upon pheasants, sometimes beneficial, sometimes deleterious.

Spring plowing, for instance, destroys much cover and many pheasant nests, but the damage done does not equal the benefit derived from the cover and food that the unplowed land provided during the winter, and will provide later when the crops are harvested. Manure spread on the ground prior to plowing is a valuable source of winter and spring food. Many flocks are kept from wandering away from an area during late winter and early spring by this provision of excellent food just at a time when other supplies are becoming scarce.

Haying is, of course, an essential part of farm economy but it is also most injurious to pheasants. More pheasant nests are destroyed by mowing than by any other cause or group of causes. Haying also removes the chief source of cover and food for the young pheasant broods. Substitute cover then becomes necessary if the birds are to succeed. The fencerows, wood lots, and wild marginal cover alone hold the pheasant broods during late June and early July when the hayfields have been cut. The second hay crop harbors birds for a brief time before it is cut again, and then the corn and grainfields provide the daytime cover, the pheasants returning to the short alfalfa and cloverfields to roost.

Harvesting.—Grainfields are chiefly of value to pheasants after the grain is cut and threshed, although they provide satisfactory cover and food also at the time of late hay cutting. The stubblefield cover is low, usually six to seven inches, hardly enough to afford the feeling of security that the pheasant seems to demand. The repressed herbaceous plants are liberated by cutting and they grow rapidly, greatly improve the cover, and in some fields make almost ideal shelter. This is especially true of ragweed, which usually produces a dense stand in small grainfields after harvest.

From this discussion of agricultural practices, it is evident that here lies the secret of pheasant management. Slight modification may increase the pheasant population manifold in localities where deleterious procedures are in vogue, whereas on other farms almost ideal conditions exist. The various ways by which cover on farms can be improved and practices modified to the benefit of the pheasant are discussed in the following section.

PHEASANT MANAGEMENT

Pheasant Population Studies

The pheasant population of southern Michigan is not like that of the indigenous game species, for being an introduced bird, its distribution depends to some extent upon where and when it was liberated and upon the number of birds released. The first releases of pheasants reared on a Michigan state game farm were made in 1917, and a general open season was declared in 1925.

It has been the purpose of the population studies to obtain definite information regarding the factors that control the numbers of pheasants on various types of range, and to seek an explanation as to how and to what extent they influence the population. These have clearly shown that pheasant density is proportional to the condition of the range, and that the liberation of more birds than are necessary to accomplish establishment fails to affect ultimate numbers. Various other factors that will be considered in the following sections are of far greater importance.

Hunting Pressure.—In some localities, hunting pressure is probably one of the most important factors limiting the pheasant population density, especially on the better pheasant ranges in southern Michigan where management is not practiced. A typical area near Northville provided information on the nature and the effect of hunting pressure on the pheasants. A remarkable consistency in the winter pheasant population was noticed for a three-year period, 1928-1930, but the number of birds dropped rapidly following increased hunting during the season of 1931.

This range of 2,600 acres consistently maintained a winter population of about 150 birds, with a sex ratio of approximately 1 cock to 2 hens. Reckoned on the basis of average clutches of 11 eggs, the fall population, allowing for normal losses, should have been about 416 birds. Actually it was 445 in 1930 or 29 in excess of the expected number.

The total gun-hours for the 2,600-acre tract were 1,350. From the known kill on 320 acres, it was calculated that it took the average hunter 10 hours to kill a pheasant, or a kill per gun-hour of 0.10 pheasant. The Michigan Conservation Department's figures for 1929 and 1930 based on more than 400 reports for each year showed kill per gun-hour of 0.18 and 0.14, from 39 counties in the southern part of the State. The crippling loss closely approximates the ratio of 6 cocks crippled to 10 bagged as given by Leopold (1933). In addition to the legal kill of cocks, there were about 4 hens killed or crippled to each 10 cocks taken. The postseason census showed a sex ratio of 1:12, evidence of the importance of gun pressure as a factor affecting the pheasant population and controlling sex ratio.

The Northville and Williamston areas are representative of the better land types for pheasant range in southern Michigan. The pheasant population of the former tract had stood up year after year under heavy hunting but that on the latter had steadily receded. Only one difference seemed to be in favor of the Northville area and that was the presence of a large, centrally-located sanctuary, which encompassed cover units suited to protect pheasants during the fall and winter months and which also provided a safe retreat during the hunting season. The hunting pressure on both areas, however, far exceeded safe limits. Production on the Northville area, so widely known and readily accessible, already a delicately balanced mechanism, was wrecked by a lengthened season.

That game ranges differ in their ability to support shooting is evident, but it is not always easy to explain why. The principal differences, however, seem to be associated with the cover conditions which make it possible or impossible for birds to escape the guns.

The trend in Michigan during the past decade has been toward greater restriction of hunting by individual farmers. More of their properties are being closed to the public. As a result, gun pressure on the lands where hunting is still permitted has become very heavy; the birds tend to move into the closed areas and hunter success declines as the season progresses. It appears that the closing of lands, creating sanctuary areas at frequent intervals, is the chief reason that the pheasant population has been able to maintain itself.

Comparison of Regulated and Unregulated Shooting.—At Williamston, two sections were hunted simultaneously but by different methods. On one area the only control consisted in regulating the number of hunters. On the other, both the method of hunting and the number of hunters were controlled. The control consisted of the maintenance of small sanctuary units, one-quarter of an acre to six acres in size which were posted against hunting. The signs did not always prevent hunting, and dogs were on occasion sent into the food patches or other coverts to drive the birds out. But this was tolerated by only a few owners, and the intended protection in the aggregate was achieved. The managed area provided 0.56 gun-hours per acre, while the unmanaged area afforded only 0.09 gun-hours per acre.

Table 12 gives data on hunting results for the two areas.

TABLE 12.—A comparison of the hunting conditions on managed and unmanaged game areas, Williamston, Michigan

	Managed	Unmanaged
1. Fall population, acres per bird	3.8	7.6
2. Gun-hours per acre	0.56	0.09
3. Cocks flushed per gun-hour	0.73	1.5
4. Gun-hours per bird killed	9.0	3.2
5. Winter population, acres per bird	6.8	28.5
6. Loss from area, acres unaccounted for, acres per bird	0.56	0.75
bird	0.56	0.75

This table seems significant in a discussion of hunting pressure, for item 1 indicates a population on the managed area capable of withstanding more intensive hunting than that on the unmanaged area, and item 3 indicates that cocks were flushed in a reverse ratio to their abundance. Items 3 and 4 show that hunting on the managed area was more difficult and sporty. Item 5 shows the unmanaged area to have been over-hunted and the managed one under-hunted despite the fact that the gun-hours were more than six times as great on the managed area. The unaccounted for loss (item 6) indicates that notwithstanding heavy hunting, the managed area held its birds better than did the unmanaged tract. This comparison has been given in order to point out that more gun hours can be allowed on a properly managed area with less actual pressure on the population than is exerted by a much lower gun-hour kill-ratio on an unmanaged area. Thus it would seem that hunting pressure cannot be properly interpreted solely in terms of gun-hours.

Food and Cover as a Factor.—Pheasants occasionally disappear from a range where they have apparently become established, even in the complete absence of hunting. This result often seems to be associated with insufficient food or cover. In one instance an unusually heavy winter pheasant concentration was observed in a marsh adjacent to a field of unhusked corn. The following winter in the absence of such food, the marsh was inhabited by only a few birds. A fencerow may attract many pheasants one year and few the next, depending upon the presence or absence nearby of an abundant food supply.

A dense woods may harbor but few pheasants, but if it is cut, the young coppice provides a satisfactory range. When sheep or goats are pastured during the summer in such woods, the pheasants leave. Leopold (1933) has introduced the term recessive establishment for a condition under which pheasants apparently have become well established on a range only to dwindle in numbers until there are only a few stragglers which finally disappear. We may logically seek examples of recessive establishment in areas where a combination of devastating agencies, as disease, severe climate, or increase in the numbers of some natural enemy, combined with more intensive hunting, causes pheasants to decline in numbers gradually until they can no longer meet the increased resistance of the environment. Such a condition has not been observed in Michigan, but failures due to faulty releases or to liberations at points outside the pheasant's normal biotic province have been common. On certain ranges in southern Michigan, isolated releases have been made which have failed to show any great increase over a period of several years, and then suddenly in one year the birds have become definitely established and have spread rapidly. We call this retarded establishment. It is probably the most common type of colonization under Michigan conditions. It occurs instead of complete establishment (in which the release is a success from the start) because of a series of poor years during which small groups of birds face unusually high environmental resistance. For example, ten birds from a fall release survive the following winter with a sex ratio of 1:1. The maximum possible fall population from this group is 65, but due to the usual losses the expected fall number is only 22. In such a small population, a series of showers might kill all the young, or the hens might uniformly select alfalfa fields for nesting sites at about the same time so that all of their nests could be destroyed during the haying season. A more common reason, however, for the failure of the pheasants to become immediately and completely established is the behavior of the birds at the time of release. Liberated pheasants usually become widely scattered and when this occurs, establishment must come from chance union of the cocks and hens resulting in isolated pairs. Often, apparently, the scattered birds do not find mates.

The Relation of Cover and Food Distribution to Movements and Mortality.—Many ranges of large dimensions provide roosting sites for pheasants on one part of the tract and food in abundance on another. On unmanaged ranges, these facilities are sometimes separated by distances of from one-fourth mile to even a mile.

Such an arrangement of these two essentials in the life of the pheasant is particularly hazardous during storms or periods of intensely cold weather and may be responsible for high mortality. The pheasant's movements off of the roost are retarded by decreased temperature, especially during periods of strong winds. When temperatures remain below 10° to 15° F., pheasants usually do not leave marsh cover to feed in nearby cornfields, but take materials available within the margins of the marsh, which may provide only a starvation diet. Of thirty birds that were known to inhabit a certain area, only three, a cock and two hens, visited a cornfield less than ten rods away from the margin of the swamp during a period of severe cold. This illustration emphasizes the importance of having food and essential cover near together and, if possible, contiguous.

Breeding Sites as a Determining Factor in Population Density.— In Michigan, breeding territory is one of the most fundamental factors limiting pheasant population density, and it is the most important one on managed areas where the food supply can be controlled. Where the sex ratio remains constantly low, the productivity of an area depends largely on the number of cocks that it will support. If an area has insufficient cover to attract cock birds, then no territories will be set up and no young will result. The area with the best breeding conditions will produce the highest annual increase, provided sufficient food is available.

Biological Principles of the Pheasant Population Studies.—From the evidence gathered, it seems that breeding sites and sex ratio are the principal positive agents in increasing the pheasant population, while gun pressure and environmental resistance are the principal negative agencies limiting the numbers of the birds. Hunting is legitimate when it removes the excess over the required breeding stock but no more. Environmental resistance is sometimes difficult to control, but can be partially regulated through management of cover and food.

Where stocking is light, it seems unsafe to attempt to increase the sex ratio much above the present proportion of 1:2, but experience indicates that where the birds are plentiful a sex ratio of 1:3 or even 1:5 is safe and will result in maximum production. Therefore, we must attempt in every way possible to build up a stocking which will permit the reduction of cock birds in favor of an increase in sex ratio for that is not only the quickest but is the most economical method. Once the area is provided with a suitable number of crowing territories, an adequate number of cocks can be established; and at the end of the hunting season enough cocks should be left so that in the following spring, allowing for normal winter losses, each crowing area will be occupied.

Management as a Means of Increasing the Density of the Pheasant Population.—The management methods put into operation on the Williamston area in 1931 had by 1933 brought about a much more rapid increase in the pheasant population than had been anticipated. On one of the managed areas, the possible fall population had been increased fourfold, from 85 to 340 birds. During this period, the population on an adjacent check area decreased from 27 to 21 spring breeding birds. These represented a loss to the possible fall population of but 52 birds and a diminution in the expected fall population of only 18 birds because of the increase in the ratio of females to males. This difference in the expected annual increase in the numbers of pheasants on the two areas has been credited to the management practices, and we believe this is a sound conclusion.

Management consisted of increasing cover and food by controlling grazing, brush cutting, and spot burning, by providing additional cover lanes and food patches, setting up small sanctuaries, partially regulating hunting, and limiting the number of hunters.

Management Units and Specific Management Practices

What constitutes a good pheasant management unit seems to depend very largely upon the nature of the range. Even a small tract, 40 to 80 acres, under one ownership which can be made to provide year-round requirements of the pheasant may be satisfactory. But when two or more small adjacent parcels of land are required to meet all needs, it is advisable that the owners cooperate in developing a management plan. Ordinarily, a project should include a section (640 acres) or more if cooperation between owners can be obtained. Nevertheless, individual owners should not be discouraged from making improvements even on restricted areas.

A better arrangement for an extensive management program is provided by a community organization. A township is a logical unit for such a cooperative project. There are many advantages to such a plan, including increased enthusiasm, and opportunity for sponsorship thus lessening the cost of the project, for establishing a system of controlled hunting, and above everything else for adopting a general land-planning scheme whereby better utilization of the land can be obtained. A plan to be successful must take into account first the economic, social, and ecological conditions prevailing in the township and formulated to fit them. The Williamston management program was developed in this manner. There plantings of evergreen trees were liberally used and an attempt was made to save, or to rehabilitate in whole or in part, the abused hardwood wood lots. These improvements increased the number of crowing areas and provided seasonally needed cover.

Wildlife Sanctuary as a Management Unit.—A system of privately-owned refuges has been in effect in Michigan since 1929 when a law was passed permitting the dedication to State use of privately-owned land for designated periods for the purpose of affording a sanctuary for wildlife. Even earlier, in 1926, the State had, by negotiation, acquired 273 units involving 71,622 acres. A survey of these wildlife sanctuaries, made by the author in 1928, revealed that a large percentage of the areas was well adapted to the needs of the pheasant and required only management to make them still more valuable. The wildlife sanctuary system even without specific management provides the State with a means of safeguarding and perpetuating nucleus breeding populations, even under severe hunting pressure. Unfortunately management that would make these areas even more effective has thus far been neglected.

Use of Submarginal Land.—Although pheasants can be managed most profitably on good farms, much can be done to help them on submarginal lands. It is to be expected that present trends will bring about increased utilization of submarginal farms by wealthy owners for estate purposes, with wildlife reckoned as one of the important attractions. A number of such projects are already in operation and they provide the most promising opportunity for developing privately-owned management where expense is a secondary consideration, and recreation may be the primary purpose, in maintaining the estate. Such units should be brought under a sustained-yield plan, to provide maximum production and increased recreation.

On such areas, sportsmanship is usually at a high level, and the number of birds removed is moderate, recreational value being measured in terms of hours of pleasure rather than in game brought to bag.

MANAGEMENT PRACTICES

Pheasant Requirements

The chief requirements of the pheasant have been discussed, but some of the more important points may well be recalled in order that the reasons for the practices recommended may be clear. Management should attempt to accomplish the following things:

1. Provide adequate cover during each month of the year.
2. Arrange the cover in such a way as to meet the largest possible number of requirements.
3. Supply lines of communication which make a greater cruising radius safely possible, and at the same time increase the shooting area.
4. Provide nourishment by protection of natural food, and by supplying artificial feeding grounds, including food strips and food patches, both permanent and annual.
5. Provide rearing grounds where pheasants may nest in comparative safety, rear their young unmolested, and at all times find adequate shelter from their predatory enemies.
6. Regulate shooting so as to reserve sufficient annual breeding stock and maintain a sex ratio conducive to maximum production.
7. Increase the number of crowing areas in order that the maximum population may develop.
8. Provide a good balance between game birds, predators, farm stock, rodents, insects, and song birds, so as to protect the interests of the landowner as well as those of the sportsman.
9. Provide a means of controlling the three major movements of pheasants that occur each year.
10. Provide a plan for removing the crop that will yield the greatest recreation in gun-hours and insure maximum safety to the land occupants and their property.

Although we cannot hope to develop in Michigan a pheasant population equalling that of certain sections of South Dakota, Iowa, and Minnesota, where vast cornfields are left standing throughout the winter, the present population can be greatly increased by the adoption of improved management practices.

Winter Roosting Sites.—During the winter, the preferred roosting sites for pheasants are in marshes or other dense low cover, such as is often found on Michigan farms in kettle holes and other uncultivated depressions occupied by herbaceous vegetation, and in unused odd corners grown up to brush and weeds. Among roosting sites of secondary value are wood lots, fencerows, stubblefields, and uncut hay, especially timothy.

One of the first steps toward increasing the pheasant population is to reserve areas suitable for roosting. So far as practicable, these should be protected from burning, grazing, and in some cases also from hunting. While the average farmer cannot turn over any large amount of his land entirely to pheasants, he will wish to go as far as he can in providing adequate winter roosting sites when he realizes that wild animals, just as domestic stock, suffer if they do not receive the proper care.

On very cold days, pheasants linger near or within the roosting sites, and frequently do not leave the roost at all. Consequently their greatest comfort during a cold winter is derived from a dense roosting site near which a good food supply is available. Often the pheasant population within a comparatively small natural site may be increased from a few birds to 30 or 40 by planting some evergreen trees and preparing an inexpensive food patch nearby.

Spring Roosting Sites.—During the early spring when low ground becomes flooded, pheasants must seek new roosting territory. Unless they can find suitable roosting sites on the particular farm or unit being managed, they may be forced to leave. As a result, they may rear their young on adjacent farms where they will probably remain during the fall hunting period, returning to the original areas only to spend the next winter. The best winter roosting site is one of dense cover not subject to spring flooding.

Summer Roosting Sites.—The summer roosting sites are often in hayfields. A second critical period therefore arises when the hay is cut and the birds are forced to seek new quarters.

Those who wish to retain pheasants on their land throughout the hunting season should provide either one or more fields that are not grazed or mowed, or wild land in which the birds can find suitable cover for summer roosting. If leaving any grassland unmowed is impracticable, some good may be done by rotating grazing and the second cutting of hay so that one or more fields in each 80 acres will at all times provide a cover at least 6 inches tall. The pheasant's ability to adjust itself to frequent changes makes possible the provision of summer roosting sites sufficiently attractive to hold the flocks with but little effort on the part of the landowner. He must, however, employ forethought.

Fall Roosting Sites.—Early fall roosting sites are easily supplied. The more important at that season are ungrazed hayfields, wild grass, weeds, brushy wood lots, fencerows, and stubblefields. Later in the fall there is a general migration back to the marshes and other lowland.

Since grain stubble provides good cover for the birds, it is advisable to adjust the binder cutter so as to add two or more inches to the height of the stubble. It is generally considered good agricultural practice to return the straw to the land, and alfalfa and clover which start the winter with a fairly high stand have a marked advantage over fields that have been grazed or cut close. In these instances, sound agricultural practice goes hand-in-hand with good pheasant management.

Wood Lots and Other Special Roosting Sites.—There are comparatively large areas throughout the Michigan pheasant range that provide few if any winter roosting places, and on such areas very few birds occur. One method of establishing roosting sites is through the improvement of wood lots. Many of these which have been thinned by years of grazing and cutting may be made suitable by underplanting with evergreen trees. This not only affords excellent cover for pheasants, but benefits rabbits and other wildlife. Moreover, it is a good forestry practice that is not expensive and which yields returns in the form of posts, poles, and firewood. Accompanying this improvement of wood lots, plantings of seed-bearing plants should be made in order to supply food near the roosting place.

A practical method of developing intensively farmed land into good pheasant range is through a combination of planting evergreens and shrubs with food patches and food strips. Fencerows may be improved by seeing that they include evergreens interspersed with food-producing shrubs and with open spaces that are permitted to grow up to grass and other herbaceous plants. Adjacent to wood lot or fencerow cover, there should be patches of food or strips of grain reserved along the edges of fields. Such a combination of shelter and food provides a complete pheasant environment. The degree of its success depends upon the extent and intensity of the practices required.

Cultivated orchards may be turned into excellent roosting sites by planting during July a cover crop of Sudan grass, millet, and buckwheat. These furnish cover and an abundant supply of food, and furthermore make a quick late growth which dies down and may be plowed under as early in the spring as desirable.

Crowing Areas.—The reproductive season for the pheasant really begins in late winter, when each cock selects an area which he defends against the intrusion of other males. The family consists of one cock and one or more hens with their young and its members seldom enter the territory of another. As previously shown, the population on a given area will, other things being equal, be proportional to the number of crowing areas, and this number in turn is determined by the frequency and density of brushy cover. Practices which increase the number of crowing areas are thus fundamental to effective management. Some of them are:

1. Protecting fencerows from cutting and burning so as to keep them dense and brushy.
2. Protecting wood lots from grazing, thereby permitting increase in undergrowth and in natural reproduction.
3. Underplanting open wood lots with evergreens, thus establishing mixed hardwood and evergreen coverts.
4. Protecting kettle holes from cutting, burning, and grazing.
5. Permitting certain fence corners, stone piles, abandoned gravel pits, or other bits of waste land to grow up naturally; or better still, planting them to trees which may later be utilized as fence posts, Christmas trees, or lumber.
6. Planting eroded gullies to trees, shrubs, and herbaceous plants which will provide cover and stop erosion.
7. Setting out evergreen and deciduous trees and shrubs as a combined game and forest planting.

Crowing areas need not be large, but their number and general distribution probably more than any other one thing determine the production of pheasants. It is desirable that the individual family territory be reasonably compact so that as many cocks as possible may be accommodated on a given area.

It is now believed that the extent to which the cock is polygamous is determined in part at least by the number of hens present. The cocks fight over the possession of hens, but after the fighting is ended the conqueror cannot possess the hens unless they are ready to mate. Naturally the larger the flock the more hens there will be ready for mating to the victorious cock.

Therefore, spring conditions which keep the hens together in flocks may affect the number of hens comprising the family and indirectly determine the number of young pheasants that will be produced in a "crowing area." Thus it is important that provision be made for good roosting cover, which will continue to stand into the spring and prevent the hens from scattering before the breeding season. Maintaining compactness by combining winter and spring cover, roosting and nesting sites, and food in an area of a few acres, is the secret to producing an ideal crowing area.

Nesting Cover.—One of the most difficult phases of pheasant management is provision for safe nesting sites. This is because the pheasants, like domesticated hens, make their nests in the most unexpected places. It has been found that the safest place for a hen pheasant to nest is within a wood lot, but it unfortunately is true that she prefers to nest in dense alfalfa or clover fields, where the nest, if not her own self, is likely to be destroyed by a mowing machine.

The nests are built within or near the crowing area and thus the nature of that tract sometimes determines the success of the nesting activities. A brushy wood lot or an evergreen and shrub planting, for instance, provides a crowing area in which nesting is comparatively safe. On the other hand, the nest of a female whose cock has chosen a fence for his crowing place is commonly either near the fence or within an adjoining hayfield. Both locations are hazardous as the nest in the hayfield may be cut over prior to the hatching period, and the fencerow nest, because it lies in the natural path of men, dogs, and predatory animals, is subject to disturbance and may be abandoned or destroyed.

The following practices are suggested as a means of reducing loss during the nesting period:

1. Develop brushy wood lots for crowing areas.
2. Plant evergreen trees and shrubs in groups in suitable places.
3. Protect properly located small areas of wild clover.
4. Control and restrict so far as practicable early spring grazing, especially in wood lots and brushy spots.
5. Leave uncut hay strips along the edges of fields.
6. Remove the excess of predatory animals at the season of primeness for their fur.

7. Utilize each stone pile, gully, and odd corner as sites for tree and shrub growth.
8. Keep farm dogs tied up throughout the nesting period, except when they are being used for specific duties.
9. Take precautions during the haying season to save as many nests as possible. One is the use of some mechanism that will flush the pheasant before the cutter bar reaches the nest. For illustration of a flushing bar, see plate 2 (lower).

Controlling Critical Movements

Flock Detention.—Pheasant broods, if not disturbed, tend to remain on the family territory until the hunting season. If, however, they are daily molested by farming activities, they may change their territory frequently. This brings about such a marked movement that many farms which have produced several broods of pheasants have only a few stray cocks left when the hunting season starts.

The practices necessary to retain pheasant broods on the areas where they were hatched include the following:

1. Wood lot management, consisting of restricted grazing and underplanting.
2. Reservation of brush and wild grass areas sufficiently large to provide concealment and protection while the birds are resting.
3. Provision for fencerows that are sufficiently wide and dense to afford opportunity for quick escape from enemies.
4. Rotation of grazing and second cutting to provide a cover suitable for concealment at all times.
5. Cutting grain stubble several inches higher than usual to provide better roosting and feeding cover.
6. Leaving narrow strips of hay and grain along the margins of the fields.
7. Providing food patches designed to afford protection as well as food.
8. Using evergreens and shrubs in special plantings.
9. Protecting vegetation from cutting, burning, and grazing in and about kettle holes or other spots of dense cover.

Fall Dispersal.—Pheasants on the average Michigan range are almost constantly disturbed. The mowing machine, the binder, the corn harvester, fall grazing, plowing, and finally hunting, in turn, interfere with their normal activities. As a result, the sexes become segregated, because the females sneak from poor to better cover and finally congregate in the dense cover provided by marshes, whereas the cocks more frequently seek safety by flight, and return time and again to their familiar strongholds, where they take whatever cover they can find.

Management practices, already outlined for flock detention, control equally well the fall dispersal, except that these practices should be planned to attract the hens to the marshland where they may be protected during the hunting season. The cocks will be left more generally distributed where they may be hunted in the open. Fortunately the natural differences in the behavior of the sexes provide a basis for such a plan. The following suggestions will prove helpful, although each area must necessarily be treated to meet its particular requirements:

1. Lanes of cover through which the hens may sneak should end near, or lead into, suitable cover for winter roosting.
2. Food patches should be provided near the marsh roosts so that the hens need not move far from them.
3. Special evergreen and shrub plantings, associated with dense low cover and a food patch, should be provided, within which young pheasants may be reared and from which they may never be forced to move.

Protection During the Hunting Season.—The failure of many good pheasant ranges to produce good shooting is frequently due to the fact that the sportsmen do not realize that the next year's crop depends upon the number and sex of the birds left on the area after the hunting season. Until the sportsmen appreciate fully that one of the most important phases of pheasant management is the regulation of hunting, the full value of management cannot be obtained. Despite protestations that the gun is not responsible for the decrease of game, in the case of the pheasant at least, it is clearly one of the most destructive factors.

The following suggestions are pertinent in this connection:

1. Hunting should be regulated if the pheasant range is to yield its maximum of sport and birds. Such regulation consists of properly limiting and distributing the hunters. The entire

range should not be hunted at one time and the average range should not be completely hunted over during any season. A careful analysis should be made prior to the hunting season and a plan should be developed which will provide sporty shooting but at the same time protect the birds from constant flushing. Such a plan will tend to keep the birds localized on their original range.

2. The common practice of hunting swamps and marshes should be abandoned as these areas provide natural sanctuaries for hen pheasants.

3. Evergreen and shrub plantings should not be hunted, unless they have been planned especially to improve hunting by encouraging the cock birds to remain outside the marshes and swamps.

4. Food patches planted to provide winter food for pheasants should not be hunted.

Many of the improvements previously recommended are designed not only to increase the supply of birds but to expand the area that can properly be shot. Overgrown fencerows, lanes of hay, grain, and other food plants, and frequent patches of brush and weeds tend to keep the birds scattered and thus add to the uncertainty as to when a bird will be flushed, which is one of the chief pleasures in pheasant shooting.

Management of Cover and Food

The best means of supplying satisfactory food and cover for the pheasant are determined by the interests of the owner, the amount of money available, and the character of the particular area being managed. Methods that can ordinarily be used to advantage are discussed in the following pages. These will not seriously interfere with accepted agricultural practices, but rather fit into a modern farm management plan. In each case the reasons for recommending the particular type of improvement have already been presented.

Evergreen and Shrub Plantings.—On the average farm, little space can be devoted to the planting of trees and shrubs but nearly every farm has unused corners which could be used for this purpose, without reducing the annual income from crops and stock.

Evergreen and shrub plantings have certain advantages over

the other types of improvements. They are more permanent, and their value for game increases annually for many years. They are particularly suited to small pieces of land not well adapted to other uses. They improve the general appearance of the farm and increase its value. They attract various useful birds which would not otherwise inhabit the farm. And finally they will produce a crop of lumber, Christmas trees, fence posts or firewood.

The ideal site for evergreen plantings is close to a marsh or some other lowland that may be protected from grazing, and which is bordered by fertile land that may be utilized for a food patch. Evergreens should be planted in groups so that the dense growth of grass and herbs that will occupy the open spaces between the evergreen patches will afford satisfactory roosting and nesting cover. In each of these instances the four vital requirements are cared for—food, roosting cover, nesting cover, and "escapes." Ordinarily the evergreens should be combined with food-producing shrubs, trees, and vines.

Figure 9 maps an experimental area of six acres in which the following trees, shrubs, and vines were used, which will become increasingly valuable in meeting the above mentioned requirements:

Norway spruce	Elderberry	Oriental bittersweet
Scotch pine	Rugose rose	Common bittersweet
Corsican pine	Japanese rose	Wild grape
Black locust	Raspberry	Matrimony vine
Mulberry	Blackberry	Honeysuckle vine
Mountain ash	Coral berry	Woodbine
Highbush cranberry	Snowberry	Hawthorne
Willow	Red-berried nightshade	Japanese barberry
Panicled dogwood	Bush honeysuckle	Cherry
Spirea	Euonymus	Red-osier dogwood

The area planted need not be as large as that illustrated, nor is it necessary to use all of the trees, shrubs, and vines suggested. Several small patches of one-half acre to one acre each are of more value for game birds than is one unit of an acreage equalling their combined area.

Source of Planting Material.—Some of the material for planting may be obtained on the farm. A wide variety of plants may be readily transplanted by the use of root suckers. Prepare these by cutting the tops from the wild plants, turning a few furrows through

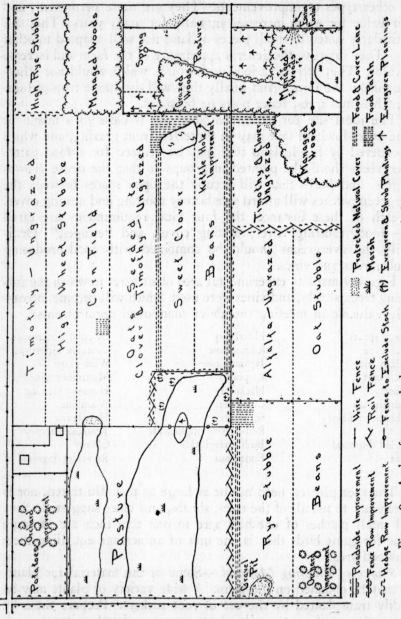

Figure 9.—A plan for general pheasant management on a typical farm unit. Nearly all of the suggestions given in this chapter have been followed in this plan (see opposite page).

the roots, and picking out suitable transplants with a fork. These should immediately be covered with straw, dirt, or leaves, and thoroughly wet down. Shoots will be produced which later may be set out in suitable spots. Wild grapevines are frequently found growing in cultivated fields next to fencerows, where large numbers can easily be dug up. Red-berried nightshade plants are usually abundant in buttonbush swamps. Small well-rooted plants make the best growth, but cuttings (about 12 inches in length) will succeed under favorable conditions.

Many shrubs and vines, such as raspberries, blackberries, roses, wild grapes, woodbine, and matrimony vine, may be multiplied rapidly by layering. This is a simple process consisting of placing dirt on the long branches but permitting the tips to protrude. Roots form under the soil which serve to nourish the tip when it is cut off and transplanted.

Planting stock may also be purchased from commercial nurseries at reasonable prices. This is especially true if lining-out or young stock is used, the price of which is often less than the cost of growing it privately in small quantities. Several state forestry departments can supply evergreen planting stock at low prices. Care should be used in selecting plants suitable for the site on which they are to grow. Spruce and Norway pine, for instance, should be planted in moist places, whereas Scotch pine will grow well on much drier sites.

Planting.—Evergreens and shrubs may be planted either in the spring (April and early May) before growth has started, or in the fall after it has stopped. The operation is simple, but in order to avoid losses, the roots must be kept constantly moist. It is therefore advisable to be ready to plant so that the stock can be set out immediately after receipt. It may, however, be heeled-in for a period in moist soil, providing it is not permitted to dry out or start growing.

Planting may be done in various ways, but one of the most economical is to plant by the slit method in scalps. Remove the sod from a patch two feet on a side, with a grub hoe and plunge a heavy long-handled dibble into the ground near the center of the square. Push the handle forward to open up a slit. Then drop the dripping wet roots of the plant, taken directly from a pail of water, straight down into the hole spreading the roots as much as possible. Insert the dibble a few inches behind the open hole and close the earth around the roots by pressing firmly forward again. Finally, press the heel against the opening left where the dibble has been removed, and by the same movement fill the hole with dirt. When the operation is finished the plant should be slightly deeper in the ground than when it grew originally. Two or three men working together increase efficiency, but one man can set out several hundred plants a day even while working alone.

Subsequent Care.—The plantings require but little care except for protection against grazing and burning. It will help, however, if they are kept from becoming covered with grass and weeds, and an application of fertilizer will hasten their growth.

Food Patches

For many years corn and buckwheat have been recognized as good game-bird food when allowed to remain unharvested, or when they are cut and left in the shocks. They are both ideal food plants for pheasants but both have their weaknesses. Unless corn is left standing in large quantities or used in combination with other plants, it does not provide satisfactory cover. Furthermore, the expense involved in the planting and cultivating corn and its susceptibility to attack by the corn borer are disadvantages. Nevertheless, it is the best single pheasant food that has yet been found. Buckwheat makes an excellent early fall crop, but the seed soon shakes out and the plants break down. It is, therefore, of value chiefly in the fall and does not provide good food and cover in winter when those facilities are most needed.

More than 50 different plants have been tested at Williamston in an attempt to determine food and cover combinations that are best suited to meet the requirements of the pheasant. The following is a list of food plants which proved satisfactory under the conditions existing there: Sudan grass, early-maturing sorghums, various true millets, Siberian millet, various buckwheats (including Tartarian when mixed with supporting plants), flax, corns, cowpeas, and soybeans. Although sunflowers provide a good food, they are usually stripped early by other birds so that they are of little value to the pheasants.

While sweet clover is not a good food plant, it is very valuable for cover and for that reason should be included in a planting program. It is beneficial to the land, both because of its nitrogen-fixing qualities and because of the rapidity with which it adds humus to the soil. It should be used freely in eroded areas and in idle places to replace obnoxious weeds. Sweet clover used on a dairy farm for summer pasture is not only a profitable source of cattle feed, but also meets essential pheasant needs. It provides shelter, even while it is being grazed, and also reduces the necessity for intense grazing in grass pastures and pastured wood lots, thus conserving the cover there.

Ordinarily it is a mistake to select a site on poor soil for a food patch, but even on the better spots, production will vary. Hence the list of plants mentioned herein is only suggestive. The patch should be made up of a mixture of species for best results, and care must be used to select mixtures that will grow together under the existing site conditions. For these reasons, it is impossible to suggest a universally suitable mixture.

Preparation and Planting.—In southern Michigan the farmer is constantly busy from early spring until after the harvesting period. Spring grain is no sooner planted than the land must be prepared for corn; following corn planting comes bean planting; and quite often before the beans are in, the corn must be cultivated. Then alfalfa is ready to cut, and the haying season has arrived.

Thus the time element is a most important factor to consider in planning the food patch. Food patches should be planted during any brief lull occurring in June. Experimental plantings of each variety have been made at various periods to determine their ability to mature before the fall frosts. The buckwheat, millets, Sudan grass, proso, and flax may generally be planted safely from June 15 to July 8. It is best to plant corn, soybeans, cowpeas, and sorghum not later than the third week in June, although they may sometimes mature successfully if planted later, and always provide valuable cover.

The seedbed should be carefully prepared as for all small grains, and if possible given a liberal coating of barnyard manure. Fertilization will improve the food patch just as it will any farm crop.

Broadcasting in Mixtures.—Certain of the plants, as flax, Sudan grass, millets, soybeans, cowpeas, sunflowers, sorghum, buckwheat, and corn, grow well when combined, provided they are not planted too thickly. Ten to twelve pounds of seed per acre give the best results. This has made the best mixture thus far tried. The sunflowers should be used sparingly and the corn should be hoed once or twice in July. There is always more danger from planting too much, than too little, seed and the tendency is to cover the seed too deeply.

Broadcasting in Individual Patches.—This method has been especially helpful in providing opportunity to determine pheasant preferences. It is well adapted to the needs of the birds and produces a heavier yield of food. With the exception of cowpeas, buckwheat, and millet, each of the food patch plants previously mentioned stands up well and provides good cover.

Small Grains Broadcast in Corn.—This has proved to be the most economical method of providing corn in dense cover. The corn may be cultivated up to the middle of July. At the time of the last cultivation, buckwheat, millet, and Sudan grass is sowed broadcast along head lands or the edges of fields, where the corn is to be left standing for the pheasants. Often the growth of the Sudan grass is rapid and luxuriant that it actually tops the corn. If soybeans,[3] sunflowers, or cowpeas have been planted with the corn, the combination is greatly improved and an excellent food patch results.

Drilling along the Edges of Cornfields or Beanfields.—When beans and corn are planted by the use of grain drills, the outer edges may be sown to any one of the game foods, or to such combinations as may be used in the drill without extra machinery, or without the additional time and expense that would be involved in extra preparations.

Food and Cover Strips

Successful food and cover strips must fit in with the farm layout and management. They should either be prepared in connection with small grain sowing or should consist of strips of small grains, corn, or hay left uncut. The plans should not call for such lanes in fields which are to be fall plowed, and only plants which are stock resistant, such as flax, should be used in fields that are to be grazed. Flax or field peas may be sowed along the edges of fields that are being seeded. The sowing consists of either drilling with oats or

---

[3]Care should be taken to use varieties of seeds that will mature under local conditions.

barley, or broadcasting a strip one drill wide along the edge of the field.

Small grains as wheat, barley, or oats may be left uncut in the corners of the field and along the edges; a strip four feet wide usually is of as much value as a wider one. Hay strips are valuable as lanes, and may be left in a similar way.

Fencerow and Hedgerow Improvement

Although this type of improvement is subject to certain objections, it is one of the most important because it meets so many of the requirements of the pheasant. Farm practices have tended toward larger fields and fewer fences. Each year considerable attention is given to clearing up the fencerows by cutting and burning. This practice has been greatly increased by the availability of steel fence posts. There are obvious reasons for this practice, and there are also reasons against it. One of the most important things to consider is the attraction and protection which brushy fencerows furnish for both song and game birds. Plants which harbor injurious insects or dangerous plant diseases should not be used in fencerows.

Fencerows contribute to pheasant management by providing:

1. Avenues of escape or places of safety in which the birds may seek refuge.
2. Crowing areas.
3. Food in both winter and summer. Wild grapes and shrub fruits are especially sought.
4. Lanes of cover which safely increase the pheasant's cruising radius, hence the general distribution of the birds.
5. Travelways that lead from the pheasants' roosting sites to their feeding grounds.

The practices used in the Williamston Wildlife Management Project to improve fencerows have consisted of planting food and cover-producing trees and shrubs, as mulberry, mountain ash, snowberry, wild grape, oriental bittersweet, and sweet clover, and by protecting them from annual cutting and burning.

There is still a third system of developing a hedgerow which may come into use more and more. This consists of preparing a strip of land as for fall wheat, and broadcasting the seeds of various hardy plants which are easily propagated from seeds, as black locust, hackberry, cherry, wild grape, and oriental bittersweet.[4] If these are sown in the fall, they germinate the next spring and make considerable growth the first year.

A combination of sowing and planting will probably prove to be the most efficient and economical method of developing hedgerows when large areas are involved.

Hedgerows and fencerows are improved by cultural practices. At first the important consideration is to increase their density. This may be done by topping or pruning to cause them to spread out, or by lopping trees and permitting sprouts to develop from their trunks.

After a few years the method must be reversed and thinning will be required to release the valuable food plants from shade so that they may grow and produce fruit. Fence posts, firewood, or even Christmas trees may be obtained during such thinnings. Grape or other vines that grow above the reach of the game birds for which they were planted may be pulled out of the trees and trained in low-growing shubbery, or the tree may be cut down, bringing with it the tangled vines. The increased fire hazard which results if the brush is permitted to remain until decayed is in many instances so great that it is advisable to pile the branches or other material away from the fencerow or hedgerow and burn it.

Wood Lot Improvement

The rather general practice of heavily grazing and cutting wood lots not only leads to their ultimate destruction, but in the meantime greatly decreases their value for wildlife. It is therefore decidedly worth while to protect at least a part of the wood lot from grazing and if the woods has been abused, either to allow natural reproduction to grow, spot plant with seeds or seedlings of hardwoods, or underplant with evergreen trees. The last practice produces a dense mixed evergreen and hardwood type which affords excellent winter cover and provides crowing areas and nesting sites for pheasants.

Roadside Improvement

The following suggestions are offered for improving roadsides for pheasants:

---

[4]Native bittersweet is hard to grow from seeds, and it is usually necessary to propagate it in a hothouse.

1. Cooperation between the road commission and landowners to insure that necessary cutting and burning of brush will be done in a manner and at a time that will least affect pheasant nesting activity.
2. Encouragement of low-growing shrubs that do not interfere with vision on curves, but increase the attractiveness of the scenery, reduce the expense of cutting and burning, and favor the bird population.
3. Protection of fruit-bearing plants, as red-berried nightshade, bittersweet, and wild grape, from being taken by those who pick them for bouquets, jelly, or wine.
4. Adoption of a plan of cutting which will include only the taller species that affect safety through decreased visibility or otherwise bear upon the upkeep and care of the road.
5. Utilization of herbaceous plants in places where shrubs are undesirable.

Kettle Hole Improvement

The pheasant population is frequently proportional to the area of marsh and smaller areas of lowland, such as kettle holes (Spencer, 1940). These areas provide valuable winter cover, and their reclamation for agricultural purposes is detrimental to the pheasant and other wildlife.

Almost any kettle hole may be improved so as to increase the game and song bird population on a farm; in fact no area is more easily improved for this purpose. The average farmer cannot be expected to follow the practices outlined here to a point beyond which there are no returns either in money or pleasure, but neither can he afford to cut, burn, and finally level the only spots on his farm where wildlife can find shelter, if the final results yield him nothing but the satisfaction that he is maintaining clean cultivation.

The condition of the kettle hole will determine the appropriate treatment to improve it for wildlife. If the area has been heavily pastured, the first measures would be to fence it against grazing, and to protect it from cutting and burning. If the kettle hole is of the typical buttonbush type, wild roses, spireas, and highbush cranberries may well be planted. Red-berried nightshade, if not present, should be introduced. Frequently redistribution of the plants is beneficial. Nightshade plants may be easily lifted up with a spade and replanted in more advantageous places. A few mulberry trees about the edges increase the value of a kettle hole. When a kettle hole in a cultivated field is irregular in shape, so that short rows and extra turnings are necessary, it may be squared advantageously by planting clumps of evergreens at the corners. That portion least subject to flooding may well be cleared of woody plants so that dense herbaceous growth will develop and make a roosting site.

Each kettle hole should be provided with a food patch of about an eighth of an acre. A few rows of corn in which soybeans and sunflowers have been planted may be left standing along one edge, and in July, just before the cornfield is cultivated for the last time, Sudan grass may be broadcast.

Orchard Improvement

In some sections of the United States, orchardists have grown wild cherries in fencerows adjacent to cherry orchards on the theory that they decoy robins and other cherry-eating birds away from the cultivated varieties. This practice fits in well with pheasant management, for such fencerows provide excellent cover and food, crowing areas, and avenues of escape. It is not, however, considered good by experienced horticulturists, and should be used only where the pheasant is more favored than the orchard or where one more fencerow of this type would not add to the insect and plant disease problems.

The orchard itself may be made to provide excellent winter headquarters for the pheasant by planting a food patch among the trees in July. Plants which may safely be recommended for this purpose are millet, Sudan grass, buckwheat, and proso. These may be turned under in the spring. This type of improvement has in some instances, where Sudan grass was used, provided winter roosting sites as well as food and protection.

Use of Fences

Fences are used to protect wildlife food or cover from stock. They need not be expensive. In the work at Williamston, woven wire has been used because of its safety to stock, but a less expensive barbed-wire fence is equally effective. The type of fence depends on the kind of stock which it must hold and the selection can best be left to the judgment of the owner.

A small patch of a few square rods of brush which is of little value for pasture may increase the pheasant population by an entire flock. Similarly a stone dump, a small kettle hole, or a small marsh is of great value to pheasants. Every farmer who wishes to increase the bird life on his farm should carefully consider the possibility of fencing such areas as these from stock.

Predator Control

Control of predatory animals is regarded by the average sportsman as of prime importance. Despite this widespread belief, investigations indicate that the wild reared pheasants in most localities are not seriously depleted by predators. Other agencies more often cause pheasant nests to be abandoned or destroyed, and both the young and the mature birds reared in the wild seldom fall before the attack of either ground or aerial predators.

Although not so important as generally supposed, predatory animals are, nevertheless, responsible for a slow constant drain. Those which have been found to be especially troublesome include the great horned owl, the Cooper's hawk, and the crow. The latter breaks up a large number of nests during early spring before the nesting cover becomes dense. Cooper's hawks are hard to control, but those nesting or wintering on a managed tract can finally be eliminated by shooting if they are consistently pursued. Great horned owls, which are particularly injurious during the winter months, can be shot if their nests can be located. Overpopulations of avian predators cannot be tolerated, but the damage caused by only a few of these birds is so little that it is compensated for by the destruction of rodents and by the esthetic value of the predatory birds themselves.

The damage to pheasants by ground predators seems to be hardly worthy of serious consideration. Because of the value of their skins, the fur-bearing animals are usually not allowed to become numerous, and there has been no proof to date that it is not a good practice to grow an annual fur crop simultaneously with a pheasant crop on the same managed tract. Conditions vary, however, in different localities, and it is quite possible that individuals of any of the several kinds of ground predators may become more troublesome than has been found under Michigan conditions. One of the best illustrations of variation in this respect was afforded by an intensive study of the food habits of the skunks inhabiting seventy-eight different dens. A high percentage of the damage to game birds by this large group came from the inhabitants of only a few of the dens.

The increased cover that will result from the practices recommended herein, the systematic removal of the fur crop each year, and a diligent attempt to reduce the excess of Cooper's hawks and great horned owls will usually provide ample protection for pheasants

Erosion Control

Southern Michigan offers abundant evidence of the dangerous and costly effects of erosion. In regions where small grains are the principal field crops, gullies develop which rapidly deepen and frequently cause the abandonment of large areas for agricultural purposes.

Such gullies can be avoided and remedied to some extent by the practices recommended by the various state experiment stations and by the Soil Conservation Service, U. S. Department of Agriculture, but often they become so deep that they are beyond reclaiming for cultivated crops. These gullies should be planted with such trees as black locust, wild cherry, and hackberry and with shrubs that grow rapidly and have extensive root systems, thus retarding further erosion. Sweet clover and alfalfa may be used in combination with the tree and shrub plantings to good advantage, thus providing excellent pheasant cover.

CONCLUSION

The importance of keeping in mind the year-round requirements of the pheasant for food, shelter, and reproduction cannot be overemphasized. Neglecting to meet any one of these requirements at any season may cause failure of the entire management plan. The size of the population will be determined by the amount of the essential requirement that is least adequately provided.

All requirements may be easily met on the average farm without entailing much trouble or expense. The various methods presented herein have been suggested with the thought continually in mind that they must fit in with sound farm practices. Nevertheless, in generalized suggestions it is impossible to make recommendations to fit individual cases. If, however, the principles here set forth are kept in mind, it should be possible to adapt methods to any tract of land where pheasant management is desirable, without interfering with wise farm practices.

The cost of pheasant management will vary greatly under different conditions, depending upon the amount and arrangement of natural cover. The areas under management at Williamston are typical of much pheasant range in southern Michigan and the cost of management on other similar areas should not differ greatly from those prevailing in that locality. The cost of all improvements at Williamston average less than 10 cents per acre per year, or 47 cents per bird.

Success in pheasant management depends primarily on recognizing and satisfying the basic needs of the birds in such a manner that they can always find in as small compass as possible, all of the kinds and quantities of food and cover they require.

The Pheasant in the Northern Prairie States

By PAUL L. ERRINGTON

Pheasant hunting in South Dakota began to draw national attention about 1925, and since that time a great deal has been said or written of the remarkable spread and increase of the introduced ring-neck over the northern prairie region of north-central United States. The Huron-Redfield-Clark-DeSmet area was the scene of South Dakota's first spectacularly heavy pheasant populations. The choice "pheasant country" now includes eastern South Dakota, southwestern Minnesota, and northwestern Iowa. Dependable census figures are difficult to find, but, from available data, it would appear that fall average densities of from 6 to 50 birds per 100 acres—and even exceeding a bird per acre—may be expected in good pheasant counties. Hundreds, indeed thousands, of birds may be seen at times about a single tree claim, weed patch, or marsh—particularly a vegetation-choked dry marsh surrounded by cornfields—but these represent local concentrations and may be misleading in indicating numbers living on large expanses of land. The great success of the birds in most of this area appears to have depended upon practices as to harvesting corn that leave considerable residues in the fields. Bags by the pheasant hunters have been large, from half a million annually in most of the states to from three and a half to four and a half million in South Dakota in some years (plate 7).

From the main center of their abundance in the northern prairies, pheasants may be found north to southern Manitoba, and south into southern Iowa and northern Missouri. While North Dakota and Nebraska have some excellent pheasant range, a tremendous proportion of the area of these States probably cannot be occupied by the birds. In western South Dakota, vast areas (as the semi-arid

Plate 15.—Upper. Sandhill river valley supporting a substantial pheasant population. Lower. Nebraska sandhills; sandhill sunflower in foreground. The seeds of this plant are an important food of pheasants and other wildlife.

191

Plate 16.—Upper. Pheasants feeding with cattle; this is a good way to get insects. Lower. Pheasants and sharp-tailed grouse at a feeding station. They shelter in the marsh in the background.

plains extending a hundred miles in all directions from Faith, Meade County) are almost devoid of pheasants. Other extensive tracts, comprising groups of counties, have few pheasants except along watercourses where some land is under cultivation or in similar places where living conditions are more or less favorable. Northwestward in southeastern Montana, pheasants are essentially restricted to irrigation districts.

THE NORTHERN WINTER AS A FACTOR LIMITING PHEASANT POPULATIONS

It would seem that shortage of winter food alone is sufficient to prevent any material spread of pheasants into the forests of northern Minnesota. Birds that require concentrated foods (grains) for winter sustenance (Errington, 1937) cannot be expected to thrive in woods, especially where the cold is intense for weeks or months and fluffy snow accumulates to a depth of several feet. There is surprisingly little difference, however, in general appearance between nearly pheasantless parts of southern Manitoba and some of the best pheasant range of the James River counties of South Dakota. Immense acreages of both areas are devoted to wheat, and while corn was a principal cultivated crop in the flatlands of Spink and Beadle Counties, South Dakota, during the years of pheasant ascendancy, these counties were scarcely considered in the "corn belt" during the droughts of the early 30's. Wild sunflowers of the Dakota prairies furnish an important food for pheasants, and in the dry years, wintering pheasants were said to have subsisted largely upon seeds of Russian thistle. In many localities there was not much other available plant food.

The pheasant has the knack of scratching for, and pecking out, food—notably ear corn—that is beneath crusted snow or is partially imbedded in ice or frozen ground. Furthermore the prairie winds, while covering much ground with drifts, leave large spaces exposed, so this bird is unlikely to go hungry. Moreover, it can endure fairly protracted fasting in cold weather and quickly recover lost weight when food is again available (Errington, 1939).

That food shortage can be critical in winter on the northern prairies was brought out by Beed (1938), who wrote of a situation observed on the Waubay National Waterfowl Refuge in Day County, South Dakota.

"The winter of 1936-37 in northeastern South Dakota was very severe. Over seventy inches of snow fell and this snow was constantly being shifted by high winds. No grain crops were raised in this section during the 1936 season, and most natural food plants that had been able to mature seed were buried deep in snow. All upland game birds were faced with extreme food shortage and temperatures as low as —30° Fahrenheit.

"Early in December, ring-necked pheasants began to die from starvation and exposure. This loss continued through March, 1937, and conservative estimates placed the loss at eighty per cent of the pheasants entering the winter. The stomachs of one hundred twenty-six pheasants found dead on the refuge were examined. One hundred four contained no food whatever. Eight contained coralberry seeds. Three contained blue grass sprouts and nine contained some barley. The barley was grain that had been placed at the shelters. In all cases the gizzards contained gravel in sufficient quantity for digestion."

There is evidence that sheer severity of the winter climate alone may delimit pheasant populations on the northern edge of their prairie range (plate 14, upper). Green (1938) recorded loss of pheasants in northern Iowa through starvation in the extraordinarily severe winter of 1935-36, when the mortality was drastic enough to reduce the population to approximately half of its early winter, postshooting level.

"A large part of the loss of pheasants was attributed to freezing and choking which seemed to be very closely related. Two blizzards and three drift storms, each lasting one to two days and coupled with temperatures of zero to —35° F., wreaked havoc among the pheasants. Birds, caught in drift storms and blizzards away from dense escape cover, almost invariably turned their tails to the wind and crouched on the snow. The body feathers of such unfortunate pheasants were ruffled and the driven snow was packed under the feathers. Body heat melted the snow and the severe cold caused the water to freeze and thus encase the birds in ice. Many of the ice-encased birds probably froze to death, for their bills and nostrils appeared to be clear of bloody or excessive exudates, and of the head not more than the eyes were covered with ice. . . .

"After those storms it was a common occurrence to find pheasants, heavily coated with ice and snow, that would not fly at the approach of the observer. Such birds ran a short distance and then stopped in a crouching position.

"Following those five drift storms numerous pheasants were found with the bills or nostrils, and in some cases both of these parts, covered with ice. . . . Probably in such cases the birds died of choking, although some of them were also encased in ice."

In his summary, the same author states:

"Survival was highest in the flocks that roosted in dense cover of willows and groves adjacent to an available food supply that required little ranging to obtain. Survival was less in the flocks that roosted in dense cover but which were required to range over long distances to obtain food. Losses were highest in the flocks that roosted in open cover but which were required to range over long distances to obtain food. Losses were highest in the flocks that roosted in open cover and that were forced to range some distance in feeding."

In fact one must conclude that pheasants in the less suitable parts of the western and northern Dakotas and the southern Prairie Provinces may be confronted nearly any winter by fatal hazards like those recorded by Beed and Green.

THE ENIGMA OF THE IOWA-MISSOURI PHEASANT FRONTIER

What determines the limits of habitability of the southern and southwestern fringes of pheasant range in the prairie region is highly debatable. For one thing, the status of pheasants appears to be changing year by year, and there is scant basis for concluding at this time exactly where the boundaries of the habitable range lie. In southern Iowa, pheasant populations of river bottomlands have shown a pronounced increase in the decade following Aldo Leopold's (1931) survey. Of the several explanations advanced to account for repeated failures of pheasant plantings, most are about as lacking in either proof or disproof as they were years ago. Bennitt and Nagel's (1937) statement "that even adult pheasants in Missouri have met with unusual environmental resistance—through what factors we do not know" may therefore be endorsed as being still valid.

The recent history of the southern Iowa pheasants suggests that the earlier populations may not have been dense enough to have reproduced efficiently, which would be in keeping with the results of

Allee's (1931, 1938) studies of population behavior. Some continuation of the current southward expansion of the pheasant range may occur, but its rate looks slow and damped in comparison with that observed in east-central South Dakota, where the birds, hardly getting a start before 1920, by 1927 had attained astounding abundance.

POPULATION MECHANICS

Two major field investigations of pheasant reproduction have been made in Iowa. The first, 1933-35, by Hamerstrom (1936), was planned to obtain data on as many nests as possible in typical environment; the second, 1939-41, by Baskett (1941, 1942), covered intensive research in one locality.

Both studies revealed heavy losses of nests, particularly from causes associated with human activities, but a large proportion of the losses were plainly offset by subsequent renestings. Only 23.1 per cent of 445 nests Hamerstrom had under regular observation were to any degree successful, but analysis of the data suggested that between 70 and 80 per cent of the hens ultimately hatched out a brood for the season (Errington and Hamerstrom, 1937). Thus substantial nesting losses had little influence on final productivity.

In communities where early nest failures result in large numbers of hens renesting in such inviting midsummer cover as alfalfa fields, the dangers from mowing machines increase and involve more than the losses of replaceable clutches of eggs. Attempts to calculate the percentage of incubating hens killed or maimed by mower sickles have their own pitfalls, for one reason because of overrepresentation of this conspicuous type of loss in the field notes. Not only may remains of mowing victims readily be seen but the operator of a mower is more apt to notice when he strikes a hen than when he cuts over an unattended nest. From the existing data, an estimated annual loss through mowing of 10 per cent of the pheasant hens nesting in Iowa should not be wide of the truth.

During the breeding season, remains of pheasants may be found in varying numbers in the den debris (including scats) of red foxes (Errington, 1937) and in the nest debris (including pellets) of great horned owls (Errington, Hamerstrom, and Hamerstrom, 1940). However, the heaviest pressure was commonly borne by pheasant populations of such high density that the net effect upon reproduction may not have been great. In northwestern Iowa localities where adult pheasants were serving as staple food for foxes and horned owls under observation, the pheasant nesting seemed to continue much as usual, and these localities were among those well known to sportsmen for the excellence of the pheasant hunting they supplied.

Mortality of young pheasants from predation and other causes may be similarly spectacular in northern Iowa counties but much of it has little effect on total populations. There were 577 items of vertebrate prey recorded for marsh hawks in the vicinity of Ruthven in the three summer periods of 1933-35. Of these, 24 were pheasants from about one day to 12 weeks of age (Errington and Breckenridge, 1936), yet counts on the favorite hunting grounds of the marsh hawks and on neighboring lands outside the usual hunting scope of known marsh hawks brought out no perceptible relation between the conspicuous preying of the local hawks and the seasonal shrinkage in size of pheasant broods (Errington and Hamerstrom, 1937). In short, from trends shown by hundreds of brood counts—counts that are valid, as a rule, until wholesale mixing or breaking up of the brood units about the middle of August—it is apparent that the decrease in average brood size progressed much according to patterns that were largely independent of differences in predation factors.

Data have been gathered also on spring-to-fall rates of increase of north-central bobwhite populations (Leopold and Errington, 1942). On areas under observation occupied nearly exclusively by this species, population recovery tended to be in inverse ratio to breeding density. Within certain limits, the heavier populations produce fewer young per adult than do the lighter populations, seemingly irrespective of the usual variables associated with predation, weather, and agricultural practices. In extremes of the 1934 drought productivity of quail seems to have been affected, and their recoveries were retarded in 1936 (and in 1937 on some areas) coincident with the "trough of the cycle" of grouse and hares. How much recovery rates of north-central pheasants were impeded cannot be ascertained by any known data. Mixed populations of pheasants, bobwhites, and other gallinaceous species have shown the same recovery phenomena as have nearly "pure" populations of bobwhites, with rates of increase of the birds collectively being in inverse ratio to their collective breeding densities, one species thriving about as the others fail (Leopold and Errington, 1941). While species other than the pheasant do most of the adjusting that is done in mixed populations, it should not be assumed that the pheasant is invariably the dominant bird. Prior occupancy of the land by better-adapted bobwhites may be one reason for pheasants not maintaining themselves in some parts of southern Iowa and northern Missouri.

One should be cautioned against judging relations of animals on a basis of hostile displays, competition for food, and other outward appearances. When the adjustment processes operate in a manner that is both automatic and governed by properties of the species itself, it may not make much difference from the standpoints of population and management just how ordinary losses occur. If about so many young are due to die, exceptionally heavy mortality early in the season is likely to be made up for by lessened mortality later. If the losses from weather are lower, those from predation may be higher and vice versa. If certain losses are added to those one may normally expect, then the influence on population levels is greater. For example, the "Armistice Day Blizzard" of 1940, which killed large numbers of pheasants (plate 14, upper) in northwest Iowa counties (Scott and Baskett, 1941) occurred after populations had already passed through their main phases of self-adjustment, thus doubtless cutting down some local populations below levels that otherwise would have been maintained.

Juvenile mortality in the northern bobwhite, including predation losses, seems broadly to be correlated with numbers of the young birds, essentially in conformity with the principle of proportional predation that has been emphasized by McAtee (1932). As the birds mature and winter comes on, natural losses (except those due to storms and emergencies unrelated to density) tend to become less dependent upon numbers than on thresholds of security (i.e. fit of the birds to the environment). Parts of populations not well situated are decidedly more susceptible to predation than are the birds that are well-accommodated by their habitats and tolerated by their fellows (Errington, 1941).

The finding of pheasant remains in but 6.4 per cent of northwestern Iowa horned owl pellets in 1934–35 suggests that the pheasants "may have been wintering at densities near some sort of threshold of security" (Errington, 1938). In the preceding winter, when pheasant densities were higher, remains were listed for 20.5 per cent of the horned owl pellets. The 1934 and 1935 spring and summer representations of pheasant remains in 36.7, and 23.1, per cent of the pellets may reflect predation fairly well in proportion to the respective densities of the pheasants.

The question is still unanswered as to what extent the frequently severe depredations of wild flesh-eaters may actually bring about lowering of pheasant productivity or force populations below security thresholds. Even hunting by modern man (whose equipment, ingenuity, and selectiveness give him unique status as a predator) may chiefly replace some other loss if its pressure is borne mainly by pheasants of an annual biological surplus. The toll from human hunting, when neither excessive nor ill-timed, may only supersede much of the otherwise inevitable mortality from "natural" agencies.

MANAGEMENT SUGGESTIONS

Disregarding possible political demands for pheasant stocking or management, one must first be sure that pheasants in greatly increased populations would really be desirable in areas where it is said "that something should be tried." The game manager should be very cautious about encouraging pheasants where serious competition with such native species as prairie chickens and quails would result or where the pheasants might prove to be agricultural pests. Not all complaints made against pheasants are without foundation or necessarily exaggerated. It should be frankly admitted that the pheasant's own powers of recovery and intolerances alike serve to make futile some management practices intended to benefit the bird. In the northern prairie "pheasant country," pheasants have a way of thriving, to a large extent irrespective of the attention man may, or may not, pay them; elsewhere, around and outside of the fringe of proved range, literally hundreds of ambitious and costly pheasant programs have been undertaken with nearly uniform failure. Granted that pheasant responses may be variable enough in some places to warn against free generalizations, better understanding of fundamentals should be gained by considering what is good or poor "pheasant country." Superior pheasant range (plate 14, lower), with its richness in grains and weeds of cultivation and cover afforded by swales and thickets, marshes and hay lands, has very limited counterparts in such areas as the Ozarks of Missouri or the sagebrush plains of Wyoming. The heavy pheasant populations of eastern South Dakota and adjacent states—once the birds had been established—were a result of the environment happening to be favorable rather than a triumph of game management.

Clearer distinguishing of the types of mortality that govern, from those that merely accompany, the increase and decrease of populations is very desirable in connection with management endeavors. It is particularly desirable as background for the appraisal of projects concerning predators because claims made by sporting groups as to the value of their compaigns against "black-listed" animals do not as a rule hold up under critical examination. The usual assertions that every crow, fox, or other flesh-eater killed means so many more pheasants for the hunting season are not based on careful field studies.

Without minimizing the possibilities of reducing losses through management, it should be remembered that, as long as a species exists in great numbers, in great numbers it must die. Increased predation upon pheasants occurs at the same time as increased mortality through motor traffic and miscellaneous causes, and all together may only reflect rising populations. Much of the mortality in good pheasant range is to be expected because of the abundance of the birds, and may be welcomed as evidence of the presence of a shootable surplus, rather than deemed a warning as to the need of "control" measures.

It is possible that locally pheasants might be able to maintain greater year-round densities and produce greater numbers of birds that would be available during the hunting season if predators were selectively destroyed. Management gains so made are not to be calculated, however, on the basis of saving bird for bird the victims attributed to predation, if only for the reason that a substantial proportion of these victims would soon meet some other fate. Even in instances where the desirability of reducing local predators is apparent, as when such egg-eating mammals as ground squirrels and skunks reach peaks of abundance, it is better to think in terms of increasing pheasant productivity through enemy control by perhaps 15 to 25 per cent rather than by the much higher percentages that are such a temptation to predict.

Ordinarily, the present of "normal" populations of predatory species in the north-central region need not be considered a major threat to pheasant production. One should beware of fallacious slogans to the effect that natural enemies hunt 365 days of the year and heed no game laws, for predation by and upon wild creatures is subject to laws of availability and compensation that operate more strictly than man-made statutes. Popular campaigns against predators—even when centered upon known pheasant exploiters as crows, horned owls, and foxes, in addition to being of dubious usefulness, are often objectionable because of the excesses that may attend them. Predator control for purposes of pheasant management is ethically defensible so far as it is conducted by responsible persons, according to local needs, and in ways neither endangering rare species (including predators) nor risking undue destruction of fur resources and other outdoor values.

While pheasant losses during severe blizzards may largely be beyond man's power to prevent, winter starvation of the sort described by Beed (page 194) should at least in part be averted by organized feeding programs. In mid-range pheasant management, greater emphasis should be placed upon being prepared to carry on emergency feeding when and if required than upon regular feeding in localities where waste grains and weed seeds adequate for the nourishment of pheasants are commonly available. In emergency feeding, care should be taken to distribute food where hungry birds can readily find and use it—as in the shelter of habitually frequented thickets.

Given the essentials of good range, established pheasant populations in the north-central region seem to take "in stride" so many of the variables associated with land use that it is uncertain how responsive they may be to environmental manipulations. Nevertheless, it is sound procedure to advocate all feasible correlation of game management with erosion control. Fencing of gullies to protect soil-holding brushy and herbaceous vegetation from livestock, stabilizing of stream banks with willow plantings, leaving erodable parts of fields in grass, all may improve the quality and distribution of either or both nesting cover and winter shelter for pheasants. One should not be disappointed if all such practices do not prove to be of very noticeable benefit to the pheasants; it is imperative that our soils be conserved, and even modest incidental gains should be wholly acceptable.

Simple thoughtfulness may at times be more important than elaborate plans in pheasant management. A farmer who has more cropland than he can plow in the fall can leave unplowed until spring those tracts that lie next to pheasant retreats, in order that the birds may have opportunities to feed during the winter on the exposed waste grains and weed seeds. If lowlands or weed patches are to be burned, this may preferably be done in early spring, before the nesting season but after the pheasants have had full use of the winter cover. Mowing of roadsides and wild hay may frequently be postponed until July, when the peak of the nesting season has passed. The use of cheap and practical flushing devices on mowing machines may save considerable numbers of hens, though losses of nests from mowing may continue to be heavy.

Restocking north-central "pheasant country" with artificially propagated birds has merit if done following drastic overshooting (as in the vicinity of a large city) or to offset some catastrophe. It may be fruitless if done indiscriminately and may have further disadvantages of being expensive, giving a false impression of accomplishment, and diverting attention from basic problems. When restocking is really needed, birds preferred are those live-trapped from suitable wild populations or obtained from reliable game breeders. In North-central States, sportsmen are usually unwilling to pay for stocking to build up supplies immediately available for hunting.

The individual hunter has a responsibility in pheasant management. It is expected not only that he will behave decently on the landholder's property and obey the conservation laws, but that he will also do what he can personally to eliminate unnecessary wastage in the harvesting of game. Studies made in Iowa show that about one pheasant escapes wounded to die, or is killed but not found, for each one to two brought to bag (Errington and Bennett, 1933). Although trained dogs may be useful in searching for birds shot down, especially in dense vegetation, by far the best single precaution the hunter can take against undue crippling is to shoot only at birds that are near enough to be killed cleanly. For cock pheasants this is generally within 35 yards for choke-border 12-gauge guns loaded with proper ammunition.

However, the hunter can make even more positive contributions to the "farmer-sportsman partnership." He should realize that the "key man" in pheasant management is the landholder, to whom may fall a greater share of the burdens than of the satisfactions. A little contributed labor to relieve a farmer at busy times of the year may be much more effective than a farm visit just before and during the hunting season. Help given in digging post holes to fence off an eroded area, unused corner, or stream bank, may be more appreciated than the usual "glad hand."

The Pheasant in the Sandhill Region of Nebraska

By WARD M. SHARP and H. ELLIOTT McCLURE

The sandhills of north-central Nebraska cover approximately two-fifths of the State, or more than 20,000 square miles. They appear to have been formed by winds sifting the finer dirt particles from a great plain, depositing them as loess in the Platte and Missouri valleys, and leaving the coarser sand piled up in rolling dunes. These dunes, of varying heights, are interspersed with valleys having a general southeast-northwest direction. The region has an altitude of 2,000 feet at the southeast and 3,500 at the northwest. Drainage, through three river systems, is to the southeast by the Elkhorn and Loup Rivers, and to the northeast by the Niobrara River. Annual precipitation ranges from 16 inches at the west to 24 inches at the east. The mean annual temperature ranges from 46° at the northwest to 50° at the southeast. There are between 130 and 150 days without frost. It is a region of high winds both summer and winter, with rapid changes in temperature and humidity. The windiest months are March and April with occasional 40 mile-an-hour winds.

Although extensive in area and seemingly uniform in composition, the sandhills offer a variety of habitats for upland game birds. The dunes are covered by grass and vegetation except in more exposed and disturbed areas, which develop into blowouts. In the valleys between the dune ridges, different species of grasses grow because more water and fertile soil are available there. Interspersed throughout the hills in protected pockets are plum thickets and dense growths of rose and chokeberry. Rivers flow between meadows of varying widths which are mowed for hay (plate 15, upper).

Along the banks of the streams dense growths of willow are common. The valleys whose outlets have been obstructed by low sandhills are occupied by lakes and marshes. Though many of them are spring-fed, the depth and extent of these lakes vary with the annual rainfall. Many which had dried up during the droughty 1930's are now refilling from increased spring rain. Usually the lakes do not fill their respective valleys, and their margins support a dense growth of meadow grasses, including bluegrass, which is mowed each year. Mowing practice has varied with the owners, some cutting so close to the water's edge that no willows could grow, others leaving the growth of willows to increase wildlife habitat.

In the interior sandhill area, ranches average over 2,500 acres in extent, and ranches of 30,000 acres or more are not uncommon. It has been customary for ranchers to plant in the vicinity of buildings, groves of cottonwood, plum, or jack pine (plate 15, upper). These serve as windbreaks for the buildings and shelter for cattle, so that it is not necessary to build cattle sheds. Although no intention was involved, one result of these plantings has been to create suitable cover to which sharp-tailed grouse, prairie chickens, and pheasants flock in winter. These windbreaks and groves are veritable wildlife oases and are an extremely important part of the upland game bird habitat.

Because of the sandy soil and the necessity for prevention of blowing, very little of the region has been cultivated. Even peaty soil in the spring-fed marsh areas that was cultivated during the homestead era is no longer plowed, and in general ranching has replaced farming. The largest areas of cultivation are near the edges of the sandhill region, and even there they have caused many blow-outs and ruined much soil. Some ranchers within the hills have patches of corn or small grain in valleys where there is sufficient moisture. Toward the center of the sandhills, such cultivated areas are scarce.

OCCURRENCE

Ring-necked pheasants occur in varying numbers throughout the region. They were introduced in the decade previous to 1910 and slowly spread until now nearly every habitat that will support them is occupied. The birds have passed through more than thirty generations in the sandhill region and have developed a strain that is highly successful even though access to cultivated areas is at a minimum.

Yet the densest populations occur at the edges of the sandhills where the acreage of cultivated land is greatest and where waste grains are available. The fewest birds are found in parts of the central sandhills that have no streams or marshes. The greatest concentrations in the heart of the sandhills occur along streams, about marshes, at the shelterbelts, and on the small cultivated areas. Population densities range from no birds to more than a hundred per section, but large areas are entirely without pheasants. About marshes, numbers run from 25 to 70 birds per square mile, as in the vicinity of the Valentine National Wildlife Refuge. Around the edges and in the cultivated areas along the streams the pheasant population may exceed 100 per section.

WEIGHTS

Sandhill pheasants weigh about the same as do those raised in cultivated areas where grain food is plentiful. They rapidly increase in weight during September, October, and November, the cocks reaching an average of three pounds and four to six ounces by the middle of December, and the hens two pounds, six and two-tenth ounces.

Winter survival is high except when there are unusually adverse weather and food conditions as in the winter of 1942-43. In January, 1943, it was noted that the cocks were losing weight although hens had retained theirs. By the last week in February, both sexes were falling off and by the middle of March a large proportion of the population had died or was starving. By the middle of February, males had lost 11.4 per cent of their weight, and by the middle of March, their average weight was down to two pounds, five and seven-tenths ounces, a loss of 30.4 per cent. The hens showed a loss of six per cent by the middle of February, and by the middle of March, their average weight was down to two pounds, a loss of 16.2 per cent.

GENERAL HABITS

In the spring, pheasants disperse from their concentration areas to the surrounding hills. They range to distances as great as 10 to 15 miles from where they wintered. Some remain near the rivers and marshes, but the spread is large enough so that each cock may set up a crowing and nesting territory. These territories often have as their hubs, plum, willow, chokecherry, or rose, thickets. The males crow in the vicinity of these coverts and sally forth to fight in the meadows or open fields with males from adjoining territories. When not thus engaged, they loaf in the thickets and in the morning and evening feed out from them over the surrounding meadows or hills.

Courtship takes place in the open away from the thickets, and the hens in the courting season make less use of the thickets than do the males. In choosing a nesting site, the hen may settle in the edge of a marsh, at the base of a nearby hill, in meadow, or in a hollow among the hills. Along streams and marshes, the birds nest in the willow thickets or in the hay meadows. Away from the vicinity of water, nests may be made in the thicket serving as the center of the territory or at the bases of yucca plants, Russian thistles, or other clumps of cover nearby.

With the approach of the nesting period, there is a progressive dispersal of the birds. They become more secretive in their habits and fewer and fewer are seen except at the early morning or early evening feeding hours. When incubating, the hen leaves the nest only at those times and feeds in company with the male.

During the summer, after the young have hatched, the female leads them about the cock's territory, eventually bringing them to the thicket where they rest in the shade during the heat of the day. The rooster spends part of the time with the hen and the brood.

Pheasants back in the hills keep close to their headquarter thickets until the young are more than half grown. Birds that have nested on, or in the vicinity of, hay meadows make use of the tall grass until it is cut in mid-July, then they are forced to seek cover in thickets bordering streams or marshes.

With the approach of fall, there is a gradual movement of the pheasants from the hills toward the valleys and winter concentration areas. By September, they collect in mixed groups of all ages from eight weeks to adult and in numbers from five to fifty. These flocks feed in favorable areas, sun or preen themselves on haystacks or in trees, and roost in tall grass bordering the meadows or in thickets in the valleys. By the end of September, the hills are almost completely devoid of pheasants and the valleys are full of them. From then on until heavy snows, the birds continue to concentrate at places where food is abundant. These wintering areas are along marshes and streams that have willow thickets and adjacent meadows, the shelterbelt areas and adjacent cultivated fields, and cattle feed lots if there is woody cover nearby. The pheasant populations in the sandhills can be thought of an expanding and contracting over the hills and back as the seasons come and go.

FEEDING RANGE

The success of pheasants in the largely grainless sandhills makes it desirable to consider thoroughly the feeding range and food habits of the pheasants to bring out what the birds depend upon as substitutes for the usual grain diet.

The feeding range was observed to include five plant communities which, with minor modifications, are as characterized by Tolstead (1942). These were:

1. Springy marshes with black peaty soil, which, as a group, are a most important or even indispensable pheasant habitat. The springs remain open during the coldest weather and the marshes are a winter source of water, food, and cover. These areas are vegetated with marsh willow (*Salix petiolaris*), river bulrush (*Scirpus fluviatilis*), soft-stem bulrush (*Scirpus validus*), duck potato (*Sagittaria latifolia*), bur reed (*Sparganium eurycarpum*), water plantain (*Alisma subcordatum*), jewelweed (*Impatiens biflora*), beggar-ticks (*Bidens cernua*), smartweeds (*Polygonum coccineum, P. lapathifolium,* and *P. hydropiper*), bluejoint (*Calamagrostis canadensis*), spike rush (*Eleocharis*), wild millet (*Echinochloa crusgalli*), witchgrass (*Panicum capillare*), common reed (*Phragmites communis*), marsh sunflower (*Helianthus grosse-serratus*), chufa (*Cyperus esculentus*), rice cutgrass (*Leersia oryzoides*), and sedges (*Carex*), of which there are several species.

2. The meadow communities comprise three zones: namely, the wet meadow, medium moist meadow, and the true prairie. The wet meadow is flooded during the spring months of the wetter seasons. Typical plants here are the sedges, bluejoints, marsh smartweed (*Polygonum coccineum*), marsh milkweed (*Asclepias incarnata*), and reed canary grass (*Phalaris arundinacea*). The medium moist meadow contributes the bulk of the vegetative parts eaten by the pheasants. This community is characterized by Indian grass (*Sor-*

ghastrum nutans), bluestem (*Andropogon furcatus*), slough-grass
(*Spartina pectinata*), timothy (*Phleum partense*), bluegrasses (*Poa
pratensis* and *P. arida*), redtop (*Agrostis hyemalis*), dandelion (*Taraxacum officinale*), red clover (*Trifolium pratense*), alsike clover
(*Trifolium hybridum*), sour dock (*Rumex*), and sweet clovers (*Melilotus alba* and *M. officinalis*). Each year hundreds of acres of bluegrasses are stripped for seed which is used to plant other areas.
Gradually bluegrass, dandelion, and sweet clover have largely taken
over the hay meadows. The weeds and western wheatgrass of the
true prairie contributed to the food of pheasants. Characteristic
plants of this community in addition to those introduced are: Switchgrass (*Panicum virgatum*), western wheatgrass (*Agropyron smithii*),
Canada wild-rye (*Elymus canadensis*), balsam sage (*Artemisia gnaphalodes*), western ragweed (*Ambrosia coronopifolia*), and prairie
sunflower (*Helianthus rigidus*).

3. The sand dune communities are upland grassland (plate 15,
lower). This area contributes substantially to the food of pheasants
chiefly in the form of dry and fleshy fruits. Pheasant populations are
light among sandhills where lakes and meadows are absent, indicating that this community alone does not have a balanced annual carrying capacity. Typical plants of the sand dune communities include:
Sandhill reedgrass (*Calamovilfa longifolia*), sandhill lovegrass
(*Eragrostis trichodes*), sandhill dropseed (*Muhlenbergia pungens*),
sandhill sunflower (*Helianthus petiolaris*), tumbleweed (*Cycloloma
atriplicifolium*), sandhill rose (*Rosa arkansana*), soapweed (*Yucca
glauca*), ragwort (*Senecio riddellii*), prickly pear (*Opuntia tortispina*), puccoon (*Lithospermum gmelini*), ground cherries (*Physalis
lanceolata* and *P. heterophylla*).

4. The shrub community consists of thickets on the lower, north-facing slopes of the sandhills. Common woody plants are: Wild
plum (*Prunus americana*), chokecherry (*Prunus demissa*), wolf- or
coral-berry (*Symphoricarpos occidentalis*), Virginia creeper (*Psedera
quinquefolia*), wild grape (*Vitis vulpina*), bittersweet (*Celastrus
scandens*), poison ivy (*Rhus radicans*), wild rose (*Rosa woodsii*),
and occasional hackberry trees (*Celtis occidentalis.*) This community
is valuable to the pheasants in providing both food and cover.

5. Areas where the native grassland has been destroyed by overgrazing, trampling, cultivation, or burning are dominated by weeds.
Prominent among them are: Knotweed (*Polygonum ramosissimum*),

lambsquarters (*Chenopodium leptophyllum*), pigweed (*Amaranthus retroflexus*), sunflowers (*Helianthus annus* and *H. petiolaris*), Russian thistle (*Salsola pestifer*), ragweed (*Ambrosia elatior*), Ellisia (*Ellisia nyctelea*), dock (*Rumex venosus*), horse weed (*Iva xanthifolai*), and beeplant (*Cleone serrulatum*). Trefoil (*Acmispon americanus*) and wild bean (*Strophostyles leiosperma*), found on areas disturbed by flooding during periods of high water, also are valuable in supplying pheasant foods.

FOOD HABITS STUDY

Collections.—A selective method was used in taking pheasants for this study. The senior author found early in 1938 that birds taken between sunrise and 3 o'clock in the afternoon contained very little food. Birds killed in the forenoon, as a rule, had their crops less than 25 per cent filled, while those taken during the midday hours, in a majority of cases, had no food at all in the crop. In order to conserve birds, the policy was adopted of collecting only after 3 o'clock when the crops usually were full.

Pheasants were collected from groups observed feeding in all of the plant communities, and in as nearly equal numbers as possible from each community every month. However, a bird taken in a marsh might be shown by gizzard analysis to have obtained its previous meal from a habitat on higher ground and the reverse was true. Crop contents usually had been derived from the immediate vicinity in which the bird was collected.

Plant Foods.—Plant items comprised 82.81 per cent by volume of all foods consumed by the sandhill pheasants examined. Seeds and dry and fleshy fruits composed 44.07 per cent of this amount and vegetation and introduced plant foods the remaining 38.74 per cent. Table 13 shows the frequency and volume of occurrence of the plant foods identified in 160 pheasant crops and gizzards collected from September to April inclusive, 1938 to 1941. It also indicates the volumes of animal foods.

Seeds and fleshy fruits were the most important items, those of 101 species of plants being determined. Seventy-five of these species were each represented by quantities less than .01 per cent of the total volume and were lumped as miscellaneous with a total of 2.62 per cent. Sixteen of the species, listed as found in 10 or more crops each, contributed the great bulk of all the seeds and fruits eaten. These

TABLE 13.—Foods from crops of ring-necked pheasants collected in the Nebraska sandhills listed in the order of importance by percentage of total volume

Common name	Scientific name	Times found in 160 crops	Volumetric percentage	Totals
PLANT FOODS:				
Seeds and fruits:				
Sandhill sunflower	*Helianthus petiolaris*	56	4.28	
Knotweed	*Polygonum ramosissimum*	48	4.02	
Jewelweed	*Impatiens biflora*	21	3.93	
Western ragweed	*Ambrosia coronopifolia*	11	3.93	
Russian thistle	*Salsola pestifer*	21	3.77	
Wolfberry	*Symphoricarpos occidentalis*	11	3.14	
Beggar-ticks	*Bidens cernua*	13	2.52	
Lambsquarters	*Chenopodium leptophyllum*	27	1.98	
Tumbleweed	*Cycloloma artiplicifolium*	11	1.38	
Nodding smartweed	*Polygonum lapathifolium*	11	1.25	
Common ragweed	*Ambrosia elatior*	17	1.15	
Virginia creeper	*Psedera quinquefolia*	10	.85	
Prairie trefoil	*Acmispon americanus*	21	.80	
Horseweed	*Iva xanthifolia*	12	.64	
Beeplant	*Cleome serrulata*	7	.60	
Sandhill lovegrass	*Eragrostis trichodes*	4	.54	
Water smartweed	*Polygonum hydropiper*	14	.28	
Water plantain	*Alisma subcordata*	20	.25	
Sweet clover	*Melilotus officinalis*	5	.25	
Soapweed	*Yucca glauca*	5	.10	
River bulrush	*Scirpus fluviatilis*	6	.09	
Prairie sunflower	*Helianthus rigidus*	8	.08	
Ellisia	*Ellisia nyctelea*	6	.05	
Pigweed	*Amaranthus retroflexus*	6	.04	
Sandhill reedgrass	*Calamovilfa longifolia*	5	.02	
Witchgrass	*Panicum capillare*	6	.01	
Miscellaneous, 75 species			2.62	
Grain: Corn, wheat, barley			5.51	44.07
Vegetative parts:				
Bluegrass, blades	*Poa pratensis*	33	14.00	
Dandelion, leaves	*Taraxacum officinale*	7	5.73	
Clovers, leaves	*Trifolium and Melilotus*	10	4.42	
Sour dock, leaves	*Rumex*	7	4.33	
Dandelion, flowers	*Taraxacum officinale*	2	2.15	
Duck potato, tubers	*Sagittaria latifolia*	6	1.46	
Artichoke, tubers	*Helianthus grosse-serratus*	2	1.03	
Spike rush, blades	*Eleocharis*	1	1.00	
Ragwort, young shoots	*Senecio riddellii*	2	.35	

TABLE 13.—(Continued)

Miscellaneous, leaves, roots, etc.		27	2.02	
ARTIFICIAL FOODS:				
Cottoncake		1	1.00	
Garbage		1	1.25	38.74
INSECTS:				
March flies	Diptera, Bibionidae		5.76	
Grasshoppers	Orthoptera, Locustidae		4.67	
Beetles	Coleoptera		4.30	
Miscellaneous insects			2.00	
Harvestmen	Phalangida		.25	
Snails	Mollusca		.13	
Spiders	Araneida		.08	17.19

foods attain importance in the fall and winter in the area through: (1) Prolific yield, (2) great abundance, (3) constant annual production, and (4) apparent high food value. A species that bears heavily only in the most favorable years is too erratic to be an important factor in the survival of any species of resident wildlife. Many of the 75 species listed in the miscellaneous group produced only light crops of fruits.

Plant foods taken during the months included in this study fall into five, more or less, natural groups. This seasonal classification, used in Table 14, is as follows: (1) September, (2) October-November, (3) December-January, (4) February-March, and (5) April. Foods consumed in September are not greatly related to those eaten in the winter, and show less variety than those for other months, except April. The October-November period is represented by the widest variety; at this time the maximum abundance of fruits is available. Foods for December and January are much the same but the supply of fruits being depleted, the seeds of Russian thistle, lambsquarters, and tumbleweed are substituted. The February-March period reflects a still greater shortage of food, although the plant items of importance are much the same as in the preceding two months. April, like September, is in a class of its own. The lack of variety then may be best explained by consumption during previous months, or by germination of the remaining seeds. Pheasant crops collected in April contained an abundance of germinating seeds or small seedlings. In addition, the pheasant at this time includes a considerable proportion of insects in its diet.

TABLE 14.—Food-producing species of greatest importance by seasons. This is based upon a four-year average from 1938 through 1941

	September	October-November	December-January	February-March	April
1.	Sandhill sunflower F	Dandelion V	Jewelweed F	Bluegrass V	Dandelion V
2.	Virginia creeper B	Western ragweed F	Bluegrass V	Knotweed F	Bluegrass V
3.	Common ragweed F	Clovers V	Russian thistle F	Russian thistle F	Knotweed F
4.	Jewelweed F	Sour dock V	Wolfberry B	Lambsquarters F	Sandhill lovegrass F
5.	Beeplant F	Wolfberry B	Spike rush V	Clovers V	Prairie trefoil F
6.	Knotweed F	Sandhill sunflower F	Prairie trefoil F	Tumbleweed F	Common ragweed F
7.		Beggar-ticks F	Sandhill sunflower F	Wolfberry B	
8.		Knotweed F	Lambsquarters F	Prairie trefoil F	
9.		Bluegrass V	Knotweed F	Sweet clover F	
10.		Nodding smartweed F	Common ragweed F	Horseweed F	
11.		Jewelweed F	Beeplant F	Jewelweed F	
12.		Common ragweed F	Horseweed F	Ragwort V	
13.		Beeplant F	Tumbleweed F	Common ragweed F	
14.		Tumbleweed F			
15.		Horseweed F			
16.		Sandhill lovegrass F			
17.		Pigweed F			
18.		Water smartweed F			
19.		Russian thistle F			
20.		Prairie trefoil F			

B—Berries F—Dry fruits T—Tubers V—Vegetative parts: leaves, flowers, etc.

TABLE 15.—Food-producing species of greatest importance by years based upon volume and occurrence of their products in the crops of 160 pheasants.

	1938		1939		1940		1941	
1.	Western ragweed	F	Jewelweed	F	Dandelion	F	Bluegrass	V
2.	Dandelion	V	Duck potato	T	Sour dock	T	Russian thistle	F
3.	Jewelweed	F	Bluegrass	V	Bluegrass	V	Knotweed	F
4.	Beggar-ticks	F	Sandhill sunflower	F	Russian thistle	F and V	Wolfberry	B
5.	Sandhill sunflower	F	Lambsquarters	F	Clovers	V	Sandhill sunflower	F
6.	Knotweed	F	Clovers	V	Wolfberry	B	Jewelweed	F
7.	Wolfberry	B	Virginia creeper	B	Knotweed	B	Western ragweed	F
8.	Spike rush	V	Artichoke	V	Lambsquarters	V	Common ragweed	F
9.	Bluegrass	V	Common ragweed	V	Sandhill sunflower	F	Prairie trefoil	F
10.	Tumbleweed	F	Horseweed	F	Tumbleweed	F	Clovers	F
11.	Prairie trefoil	F	Knotweed	F	Beggar-ticks	F	Ragwort	T
12.	Sandhill lovegrass	F	Russian thistle	F	Duck potato	T	Beggar-ticks	F
13.	Virginia creeper	B	Nodding smartweed	B	Horseweed	F		
14.	Common ragweed	F	Dandelion	V	Pigweed	V		
15.	Nodding smartweed	F	Beggar-ticks	F	Nodding smartweed	F		
16.	Prairie sunflower	F	Sandhill lovegrass	F	Common ragweed	F		
17.			Prairie trefoil	F				
18.			Prairie sunflower	F				

B—Berries.   F—Dry fruits.   T—Tubers.   V—Vegetative parts: leaves, flowers, etc.

The importance of the plant species contributing to the pheasants' diet varied from year to year. As shown in table 15 seeds of Russian thistle were fourth in importance in 1940. In January and early February of that year the ground was covered by 8 to 12 inches of snow and these seeds were then consumed in considerable quantity. Jewelweed was an important food-producing species in 1938, 1939, and 1941, but was unrepresented in 1940 when unfavorable weather conditions prevented it from fruiting. Such fluctuations from year to year are best explained by variations in the abundance of fruits produced, due in part to weather conditions. Bluegrass blades were a rather constant item through the four years because of their constant availability in abundance.

Fleshy fruits of importance in the crops were those of wolfberry (*Symphoricarpos occidentalis*) and Virginia creeper (*Psedera quinquefolia*). Seeds of poison ivy (*Rhus radicans*) and wild roses (*Rosa arkansana* and *R. woodsii*), along with those of the first two species mentioned were prominent in the gizzards throughout the study. Virginia creeper fruits were used during the fall months, chiefly in September, when most abundant. Song birds and other forms of wildlife shared, and helped to deplete, the crop. Wolfberries appear to be unpalatable to song birds, raccoons, and other fruit-eating forms of wildlife during the fall months. Hence there is still an abundant crop of this fruit in winter. Pheasants begin taking wolfberries in October, and increase the amount consumed until January, the severest winter month. The amounts taken after January decline rapidly as heavy consumption exhausts the crop. Fruits of ground cherry (*Physalin lanceolata*), prickly pear (*Opuntia tortispina*), and ball cactus (*Mammillaria vivipara*) occurred in the crops and gizzards chiefly in October and November. The annual yield of these is light and scattered, and is soon exhausted as coyotes and raccoons also feed freely upon them. Ground-cherry fruits are so frequently attacked by insects that the crop is sporadic and local. Errington (1937) shows that single foods of this type do not provide nutriment enough to support pheasants through the winter. The present studies, however, indicate that a mixture of such foods is sufficient for winter sustenance. Wild pheasants trapped at monthly intervals in the winter of 1941-42 showed a mean loss in weight of only .8 gram.

Cultivated grains made up only 5.50 per cent of all foods present in the crops. These, including sorghum, buckwheat, corn, barley, and wheat, were all obtained from experimental food patches and from winter feeding stations. The pheasants took grain from only well-established stations within their cruising radius where feeding had been continued for several winters. In areas where no permanent winter stations were maintained, after deep snows fell and prolonged subzero weather ensued, the birds starved practically within sight of places where emergency food was available.

The vegetative portions of plants found in the food of pheasants comprised: (1) Grass blades, chiefly those of bluegrass; (2) leaves of dandelion, clovers (*Trifolium, Melilotus*), spike rush, and sour-dock; (3) tubers of duck potato and rootstocks of miscellaneous species. Blades of bluegrass and western wheatgrass were two of the most important vegetative materials in the food of the pheasants from October to April. Grasses comprised 14 per cent of the total food. Greatest utilization occurred in December, January, February, and March. Leaves of clover, dandelion, and dock, of greatest importance during October and November when other foods were abundant, came into prominence again in April. Crops taken on hunted areas during the open season yielded the bulk of these leaves. This was especially true where hunting was heavy. The birds, having to keep on the move, apparently filled up with things that could be snatched while trying to evade the hunters. At temperatures below freezing when snows are on the ground, pheasants congregate at open springs in extensive marshes and may be found wading in the shallow water. The crops of such birds have been found to contain snails, and the vegetative parts of duck potato, sago pondweed, and other aquatic plants.

The importance of leafy vegetation in midwinter cannot be overestimated. Basal sprouts of bluegrass, dandelion leaves, and the leaves of clover are important sustaining foods in conjunction with seeds available in the surrounding hills. Rootstocks of grasses and other plants are taken throughout the winter.

Artificial foods of vegetable origin were represented by cotton-cake and garbage. The cottoncake was obtained from that supplied for range cattle. Garbage occurred in crops collected in January, 1940, during a period of heavy snow and subzero temperatures. It was taken from refuse at an abandoned CCC camp.

Relative Importance of the Plant Communities.—All of the five plant communities described under "Feeding Range" (pp. 207-209) are indispensable in supporting a good pheasant population in the sandhills where no cultivated grains are grown. Ready availability of each of these cover types undoubtedly is important as the birds customarily feed in three or more of them daily. If the weather is warm, they may leave the marsh in the morning, range through all of the plant communities, and roost in the sandhills. Some return to the marsh, the only source of water, during late afternoon of the same day. During cold weather, pheasant activities, greatly influenced by the temperature, are usually confined to the meadow and weed communities. The percentages of the food gleaned in each plant community are approximately as follows: Meadow 34.89, weed 13.05, marsh 11.82, sandhill 6.67, and shrub 3.99.

The meadows contribute almost as much food as do the other four communities combined. Being mowed regularly, however, they do not afford year-round cover. The weedy areas are second in importance to the meadows as a source of food, but the shelter they give is also important and their combined food and cover value at least equal that of the meadows. Since the acreage of weeds is only in the proportion of one to about every twenty of meadow land, it is precious. Weed patches scattered among the sandhills produce an abundance of sunflower achenes which are a valuable fall and winter food. The marsh areas rank third in yield of food but their tall dense cover is very valuable as shelter in winter and as a refuge during the hunting season. Springs remaining open in the marshes during cold weather are a source of both food and water. Winter losses are always lower about marshes than in other areas even where there is little surface water except near the springs. Marsh areas near the lakes that are flooded freeze over in winter and are then useless. The shrub communities on the whole are significant sources of food only during the fall when fruits are available. Areas that produce wolfberries and wild rose hips, however, are of material value throughout the winter. Unfortunately these plants are less common than other shrubby species. As the acreage of shrub cover is less than that of any other plant community, its contribution of 3.99 per cent of all foods must be ranked as relatively high. The sandhill communities (plate 15, lower) have importance as pheasant range, especially in fall and spring when insects are abundant. Pheasants seek the sandhills also as a refuge during the hunting season and as a result, the kill is light. The sandhills include about 63 per cent of the total acreage of the plant communities here discussed.

The marsh, meadow, weed, shrub, and sandhill communities, when considered on the basis of all their facilities, are of about equal value in making up a balanced pheasant range. Pheasant numbers are about in direct proportion to the balance of the habitat. Dads Lake valley, for example, with a lake, but no marsh, and very little meadow, supports approximately 30 birds. Pelican Lake valley, located 2 miles to the north and of similar size, but having all of the plant communities, harbored a thousand birds during the winter of 1941-42. Pheasant numbers have been maintained in about the same ratio in these valleys since 1938. The population that can be accommodated in the former valley is definitely limited by lack of balanced habitat.

Wide Variety of Plant Foods.—Thirty-three plant families, sixty-seven genera, and 101 species were represented by the food determinations made in this study of 160 crops and gizzards. Foods taken from the filled crops and gizzards of 58 birds represented an average of 5.3 plant families per pheasant. The highest number exemplified in one crop was 13 and the lowest, 2. Representation of plant genera averaged 6, and of species 6.5, per bird. The greatest number represented in any one bird was 15 genera and 18 species and the lowest, 2 and 2, respectively.

A wide range of species of native plants provides foods that are palatable to pheasants and are available in fall and winter. To glean the variety of plant foods they take almost daily, the pheasants must visit more than one of the plant communities. Apparently almost every seed or fruit the birds find is eaten, even the most minute not being overlooked. The smallest noted in the stomachs were the seeds of sandhill lovegrass (*Eragrostis trichodes*), which average 1,240 per cubic centimeter (about ¼ teaspoonful). Fifteen cubic centimeters, or approximately 3¾ teaspoonfuls, the greatest volume of these seeds found in one crop, therefore, comprised about 18,600 seeds. The stones of wild plum (*Prunus americana*), sand cherry (*Prunus besseyi*), and Russian olive (*Elaeagnus angustifolio*) were the largest bony seeds swallowed but entire berries of ground cherry (*Physalis*) also were gulped. Pheasant liking for fruits, both dry and fleshy, appears to be unlimited, but choice of vegetative parts is selective and is confined almost exclusively to plants of the sunflower, pea, and grass, families.

The most important of the 33 plant families producing the food of the sandhill pheasants are here listed in the order of their percentile contributions.

1. The sunflower family (Compositae) was first in importance. Eight species of sunflower, beggar-ticks, ragwort, and dandelion genera contributed 16.14 per cent of all foods. Vegetative parts and seeds were used in about equal proportions.

2. The grass family (Gramineae) rated second place chiefly through the volume of the blades of bluegrass and other grasses taken; these composed 14 per cent of the entire diet. Seeds of reed, love, and witch, grasses composed only 0.57 per cent of the subsistence.

3. The buckwheat family (Polygonaceae) ranked third and contributed 5.55 per cent of the food through seeds of the knotweed and smartweed genus (*Polygonum*) and 4.33 per cent through leaves of sour dock (*Rumex*).

4. The lambsquarters family (Chenopodiaceae) produced 7.13 per cent of all foods. Seeds of Russian thistle, lambsquarters, and tumbleweed were of most importance.

5. The ragweed family (Ambrosiaceae) was represented by the seeds or achenes of two genera, namely, ragweed and horseweed, which made up 5.72 per cent of the food. No vegetative material of this family was eaten.

6. The pea family (Leguminoseae) was represented chiefly by the leaves of clover (*Trifolium*) and sweet clover (*Melilotus*), the volume of which was 4.42 per cent of all foods. Seeds of prairie trefoil and sweet clover contributed 1.05 per cent to the total diet. Due to their very local occurrence, wild beans (*Strophostyles*) and milkvetches (*Astragalus*) were taken in only limited amounts.

7. The jewelweed family (Balsaminaceae) was seventh in importance, with the seeds of one species, the spotted touch-me-not (*Impatiens biflora*), composing 3.93 per cent of the total crop contents. This species grows in the moist black soil of the willow marshes, more of which is exposed when lake levels are low, as in the dry years 1938 to 1940.

8. Two berry-producing families, namely the grape (Vitaceae) and the honeysuckle (Caprifoliaceae) alliances, contributed 3.99 per

cent to the total volume of food through their fruits. Representing these families were the berries of Virginia creeper and wolfberry; the latter alone made up 3.14 per cent of all foods and was sixth in rank among all food-producing species. Seeds of poison ivy (*Rhus radicans*) of the sumac family and of wild roses were prominent in the gizzard contents.

Plant Foods Represented in the Gizzards.—The seeds of 37 species listed in table 16 are ranked in the order of their frequency of occurrence in the gizzards, but their status in the crop contents also is shown. Good agreement in the rankings for crop and gizzard are illustrated by those of knotweed, sandhill sunflower, common ragweed, prairie trefoil, and several others.

Animal Foods.—Animal foods taken during the fall, winter, and early spring made up 17.19 per cent of the total volume of the pheasant diet. Of the 12,557 specimens represented in 160 crops, 12,400 were insects. The others included 68 aquatic and terrestrial snails, 31 harvestmen or daddy-long-legs (*Phalangida*), 55 spiders (*Araneida*), and 1 mite (*Acarina*). Most of the insects were recognizable, 122 species being identified. The kind most frequently taken was larvae of the March fly (*Bibio*). These made up a third of the animal food, and 5.76 per cent of the total volume of all foods. The next most important item was grasshoppers, 4.67 per cent, many of them doubtless obtained when the pheasants fed among grazing cattle (plate 16, upper). The remaining 6.76 per cent was about a fourth beetles and included smaller amounts of ants, bugs, and others.

The most important of the grasshoppers eaten was *Melanoplus mexicanus*, which is widely distributed over the sandhills and is especially conspicuous on the mowed meadows. Of the true bugs (Hemiptera), the ubiquitous tarnished plant bug (*Lygus pratensis*) was taken most frequently. Of the planthopper alliance (Homoptera) not many were eaten, probably because of their small size; there was an exception, however, as one bird had gorged itself on plant lice of the genus *Delachnus*. This study began with September when many species of insects rapidly became unavailable to the pheasant through death, movement into hibernating quarters, or change into some quiescent stage. For example, the spittle insects (*Lepyronia gibbosa*) were very common up to and through September and pheasants were noted eating them, but because of their

TABLE 16.—Rank and frequency of occurrence of seeds in gizzards and crops

Common name	Scientific name	Rank Gizzard	Rank Crop	Number times found in Gizzard	Number times found in Crop
Wild rose	*Rosa*	1	29	86	4
Knotweed	*Polygonum ramosissimum*	2	2	57	48
Sandhill sunflower	*Helianthus petiolaris*	3	1	36	56
Ellisia	*Ellisia nycetelea*	4	19	36	6
Nodding smartweed	*Polygonum lapathifolium*	5	9	34	14
Common ragweed	*Ambrosia elatior*	6	8	33	17
Prairie trefoil	*Acmispon americanum*	7	6	32	21
Poison ivy	*Rhus radicans*	8	33	31	3
Lambsquarters	*Chenopodium leptophyllum*	9	3	27	27
Bur reed	*Sparganium eurycarpum*	10	58	22	1
Western ragweed	*Ambrosia coronopifolia*	11	12	20	11
Western chokecherry	*Prunus demissa*	12	42	20	2
Water smartweed	*Polygonum hydropiper*	13	13	18	11
Wolfberry	*Symphoricarpos occidentalis*	14	14	16	11
Prickly pear	*Opuntia tortispina*	15	32	14	3
Water plantain	*Alisma subcordatum*	16	7	14	20
Sago pondweed	*Potamogeton pectinatus*	17	36	11	3
Russian thistle	*Salsola pestifer*	18	5	10	21
Tumbleweed	*Cycloloma atriplicifolium*	19	15	9	11
River bulrush	*Scirpus fluviatilis*	20	22	8	6
Sand cherry	*Prunus besseyi*	21	0	7	0
Ground cherry	*Physalis lanceolata*	22	38	7	2
Virginia creeper	*Psedera quinquefolia*	23	16	7	10
Witchgrass	*Panicum capillare*	24	21	7	6
Beggar-ticks	*Bidens cernua*	25	10	6	13
Horseweed	*Iva xanthifolia*	26	11	6	12
Corn	*Zea mays*	27	13	6	10
Jewelweed	*Impatiens biflora*	28	4	5	21
Sweet clover	*Melilotus officinalis*	29	24	5	5
Prairie sunflower	*Helianthus rigidus*	30	17	5	8
Wild bean	*Strophostyles leiosperma*	31	31	5	3
Swamp smartweed	*Polygonum coccineum*	32	57	5	1
Yellow puccoon	*Lithospermum gmelini*	33	34	5	3
Pigweed	*Amaranthus retroflexus*	34	20	5	6
Beeplant	*Cleome serrulata*	35	18	2	7
Sandhill reedgrass	*Calamovilfa longifolia*	36	23	3	5
Bear-grass	*Yucca glauca*	37	25	4	5

rapid disappearance with the approach of cool weather, they were not found in any of the birds collected. The two groups of beetles most commonly taken were ground beetles (carabids) and weevils (curculionids). The sandhills support many large and medium-sized species of the former group, which because of their surface-crawling habits, are easy for the pheasants to find. Of the 733 beetles removed from the crops, 174 were carabids, representing 16 species; 346 were curculionids, of 14 species; 141 were leaf beetles (chrysomelids) with 9 species; and the remainder were members of 12 other families. The presence of the dock flea beetles (*Disonycha triangularis* and *Halicta bimarginata*) indicated that the pheasant taking them had been feeding among the patches of the so-called wild hydrangea (*Rumex venosus*) in disturbed areas at the base of the sandhills away from the subirrigated meadows. A pheasant crop containing leaf beetles, *Haemonia nigricornis*, indicated that the bird had been feeding in marshes, since this species feeds on pondweeds (*Potamogeton*). Insects of the butterfly and moth order (Lepidoptera) were not important in the fall and winter diet, but with the approach of spring and the emergence of cutworms from hibernation, these were eaten extensively. The dark-sided cutworm (*Euxoa messoria*) was an important food during April. Adult flies were not often taken, although during their spring flights, some midges (chironomids) were eaten. The most important single animal item in the diet of the sandhill pheasant was the larvae of March flies (*Bibio*). These maggots collect in large numbers beneath logs or mats of vegetation among the willow thickets along the edges of the marshes. Hence when a pheasant discovers a group, it can eat all it desires for one, or possibly several, meals. *Bibio* larvae not only appeared often in the diet, but also usually were taken in large numbers. As many as 1,900, measuring more than 100 cc. (25 teaspoonfuls), were removed from a single crop. Ants were not important in the diet of the period studied except in early spring, when they were taken during their nuptial flights.

Though mollusks in the form of snails do not bulk large in terms of the total food, they probably have special importance at certain times. Snails (of the genera *Gyraulus*, *Helisoma*, *Physa*, and *Stagnicola*) are sought by the pheasant hens when they are laying eggs. Crops of hens have been examined, the contents of which were almost entirely snails.

The proportions of animal food recorded in table 17 for each month indicate that the volume of this part of the diet decreased steadily from September to February, except for December. In birds

TABLE 17.—Animal food in the diet of sandhill pheasants

	Sept.	Oct.	Nov.	Dec.	Jan.	Feb.	March	April
Number crops examined	14	51	18	14	5	22	23	12
Average volume of crops (cc's)	15	31	52	42.6	61.7	44.8	34.4	33
Average volume of plant food in crops (cc's)	12.5	26	44.6	32.6	56.6	44.1	31.5	24
Average volume of animal food in crops (cc's)	2.5	4.6	7.3	10	5	.7	2.8	9
Per cent of volume made up of animals	19.4	18.2	17.5	28.1	9.7	1.5	9.7	33.5

Groups important in the diet

Common name	Scientific name	Sept.	Oct.	Nov.	Dec.	Jan.	Feb.	March	April
Grasshopper	Melanoplus mexicanus	X	X	X	X				
March fly larvae	Bibio	X	X	X	X	X	X		
Leaf beetle	Haemonia nigricornis					X		X	
Ant	Formica rufa obscuripes						X	X	
Dark-sided cutworm	Euxoa messoria								X
Midge	Chironomidae								X

collected in December, due to some great find, the volume and numbers of *Bibio* larvae were so large as to bring the average percentage of animal food to a point almost as high as that for April. After February, the volume of animal food rose rapidly with increased availability. Table 17 also lists the more important kinds of insects taken in each of the 8 months of the observation period.

Grinding Materials.—There were some seeds that were found regularly in the gizzards but not in the crops, indicating that they were held in the former organ for a period during which the crop was repeatedly filled and emptied. For example, the seeds of wild roses ranked first in frequency of occurrence in the gizzard but twenty-ninth in the crop. It became evident as the study progressed that hard seeds as those of wild roses (*Rosa arkansana* and *R. woodsii*), Ellisia, poison ivy, bur reed, prickly pear, sago pondweed, Virginia creeper, chokecherry, and sand cherry, which were common in the gizzards but not in the crops, were retained as abrasives for grinding other foods. In the sandhills there are hundreds of square miles with neither gravel roads nor any natural outcroppings of gravel, or even deposits of sand coarse enough to serve as grit. It is apparently necessary for the pheasants to use these hard seeds instead.

During a food habits study made in Washington, Beer and Tidyman (1942) found a similar relationship between the inorganic and organic grinding materials in the gizzards. They noted that when the grit content of a gizzard was as great as 6.2 cc., there was no appreciable volume of hard seeds; but when the amount was as low as 1 cc., stony seeds, averaging 2.7 cc., were present. They concluded that during periods of deep snow, hard seeds of berries of woody plants were more available than grit.

The findings of the present study as to the ratio between the average number of particles of inorganic grit and of grit seeds are summarized in table 18. The average number of pebbles was 290, and of grit seeds, 66. Considering only those gizzards having more than 290 particles, we find that the average was 587 pebbles to 28 seeds (21:1) and only those gizzards having less than 290 pebbles, there were 84 pebbles to 106 seeds (1:1.26).

On the Valentine Wildlife Refuge, at places where pheasants congregate in the winter, feeding stations have been established and a pile of gravel dumped at each. Birds collected as far as a mile from these grit deposits had their gizzards supplied with normal

TABLE 18.—Ratio of grit seeds to pebbles in 113 gizzards of pheasants collected over a four-year period

Items		Numbers			
Common name	Scientific name	Average	Above Average A	Below Average B	Ratio of A to B
Pebbles		290	587	84	7:1
Seeds of:					
Wild roses	*Rosa spp.*	68	26	83	1:3
Ellisia	*Ellisia nyctelea*	36	24	40	1:2
Poison ivy	*Rhus radicans*	41	2	64	1:32
Bur reed	*Sparganium eurycarpum*	15	2	24	1:12
Chokecherry	*Prunus demissa*	6	3.4	7.6	1:2
Prickly pear	*Opunia tortispina*	24	4.7	33	1:7
Sago pondweed	*Potamogeton pectinatus*	52	0	52	0:52
Virginia creeper	*Psedera quinquefolia*	33	28	44	1:1:5
Sand cherry	*Prunus besseyi*	1	1	1	1:1
	Averages	66	28	106	1:5

numbers of pebbles. The average quantity of grit was: 290 in number, 5.1 grams (a little less than a fifth of an ounce) in weight, and .4 cc. (about half a teasponful) in bulk. Maximum intakes ranged up to 1,200 or more pieces and in weight up to 22 grams (nearly eight-tenths of an ounce). Some gizzards on the other hand contained not a single pebble.

Miscellaneous hard substances found in the gizzards included: Broken glass, shot, cinders, and coal. Dalke (1938) listed similar items found in young pheasants of Michigan. On the Valentine Refuge, the birds get these oddities about ranch buildings. In the past, marshes and lakes now within the refuge were heavily hunted and at present, similar marshes outside of the area are much resorted to by hunters. During the past 10 years, many marshes have dried, and with their drying, followed by wind erosion, have exposed lead shot scattered there by the shooting. These are occasionally taken by pheasants and although they are a potential source of lead poisoning, the small numbers (2-3) found in single gizzards had apparently caused no ill effects.

Water Supply.—In the spring and fall, sandhill vegetation has an early morning accumulation of dew. On the other hand, for many weeks in the heat of the summer, dew rarely occurs. Although the pheasant appears to require considerable water, it may at certain seasons be able to exist on dew. However, the greatest concentra-

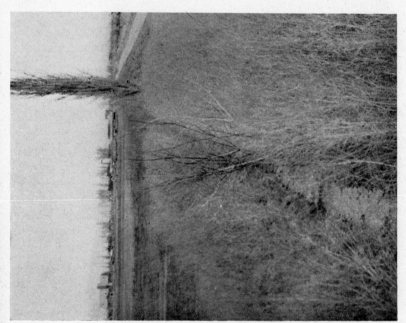

Plate 17.—Left. Mostly herbaceous cover along irrigating ditch. Box Elder County, Utah. (Photograph by William T. McKean.)

Right. Effect of winter's snows upon herbaceous cover along irrigating ditch. Box Elder County, Utah. (Photograph by William T. McKean.)

225

Plate 18.—Upper. Salt grass meadow, cover much frequented by pheasants if near cultivated fields. (Photograph by William T. McKean.)
Lower. Heavily-grazed irrigated fields in winter; cover for wildlife practically destroyed. (Photograph by Lee Kay.)

Plate 19.—Upper. Food patch of small grain and wild sunflowers. (Photograph by Lee Kay)
Lower. Food patch of corn and small grain bordered by good winter cover. Weber County, Utah. (Photograph by Lee Kay)

Plate 20.—Upper. Peterson's Butte, Linn County, Oregon, near which in 1881 the first successful colonization of ring-necked pheasants was made.
Lower. Typical cover in the Willamette Valley, Oregon.

tions and highest populations are found where water is accessible. Even in the dead of winter, open water is of importance to the birds, perhaps more as a source of food than of drink.

FACTORS ADVERSE TO PHEASANT SUCCESS

Unbalanced Habitat.—A pheasant population in the sandhills of north-central Nebraska develops in direct ratio to a balanced habitat. The range must include marsh, meadow, weed, and shrub communities within the daily cruising radius of this upland game bird. The sand dune communities comprise about 80 per cent of the sandhill area included in this study. Consequently this element is never lacking. However, the sand dunes are of value only when the four vegetational types referred to are present.

In areas not balanced by variety, for example if only two fully developed communities, meadow and sand dune, are available, with perhaps a scant representation of weeds, pheasant populations fluctuate from year to year. The instability of the populations apparently is due to great variation in the supply of winter foods. Such an unbalanced range does not have a steady year to year carrying capacity. Weather also affects carrying capacity, dry years, for instance, cut down the winter food supply. Extremely wet years also are detrimental as the marshes are filled with water, freeze over as soon as winter arrives, and exclude pheasants from normally important feeding grounds. Winter kill of the birds is always very severe during periods of heavy snowfall on areas that have a limited food supply.

Intolerances.—Sharp-tailed grouse have often been observed chasing pheasants from winter feeding stations. An occasional male pheasant will attempt to hold his ground; in that event, the grouse assumes a crouched position and, after a few feints, routs the pheasant. No combats were observed between grouse and pheasants except at the feeding stations. Each species is very tolerant of the other during the spring months. The greater prairie chicken has been observed in combat at winter feed stations with both the sharptail and the pheasant. It has never been observed to win and is soon chased away by the grouse. Pheasants do not appear to be aggressive during the winter. On one occasion a male pheasant was observed chasing a male prairie chicken during late May when the females of both species probably were nesting. The prairie chicken would fly a short distance and alight only to be flushed again by the pheasant. The chase continued for more than half a mile.

Communal Nesting.—Pheasants lay some of their eggs in the nests of upland-nesting wild ducks. During an annual duck nest survey each season from 1936 to 1939, inclusive, on the Valentine Refuge, it was not uncommon to find one to three pheasant eggs in a nest. The nests of all upland-nesting species of ducks, including the mallard, pintail, teal, and shoveler were involved. No pheasant egg was observed to hatch in a duck's nest and no nest was deserted as a result of a pheasant egg intrusion. There was also no record of pheasant depredation on duck eggs.

Competition for Food.—Pheasants compete with sharp-tailed grouse for the foods produced by native plants. Sunflower seeds are very much sought by both birds. A heavy pheasant population in areas inhabited by sharp-tailed grouse reduces the food supply for the latter, not only in sunflower seeds but also in fruits of wild rose, wolfberry, and poison ivy. The extent of the inroads on grouse foods by pheasants was not specifically determined but it is doubtless important.

Competitors with the pheasants for food are: (1) Insects, (2) blackbirds, (3) rodents, and (4) livestock. Larvae of the sunflower plume moth (*Oidoematophorus helianthi*) often attack the heads of sandhill sunflowers and destroy the achenes. Yucca seeds are almost completely destroyed by the yucca moth (*Tegeticula yuccasella*), while in dry years rose hips, as well as other fruits, are consumed by grasshoppers. Red-winged blackbirds assemble in countless thousands during the autumn months in the vicinities of the lakes and marshes and take a great portion of the seeds of the sandhill sunflower and other plants. The sandhill kangaroo rat (*Perodipus montanus richardsonii*) is abundant and its hoarding of dry fruits takes a toll of pheasant foods. Overgrazed areas do not produce any winter food because the flowering parts of plants are eaten by livestock. This is a factor of importance in some areas, but less so in others where sound range management is practiced by the more progressive ranchers.

Winter Killing.—Sandhill pheasants are always in a more precarious position during the winter than are those inhabiting cultivated areas. If the season is adverse for the production of seeds, and those seeds that are present are harvested by migrating flocks of blackbirds and other granivorous birds, the pheasant may have to face the winter with a greatly reduced food supply. Heavy snows hardened by winds and subzero temperatures prevent the birds from getting to the ground for food, and winter kill occurs within 15 days after such weather begins. Pheasants also become inactive at subzero temperatures, do less foraging, and may soon succumb to freezing. Such a combination of circumstances brought about starvation of as much as 50 per cent of the birds in some parts of the sandhills in the winter of 1942-43.

Predation.—Pheasants have no serious predator in the Nebraska sandhills country. Golden eagles, duck hawks, and prairie falcons have been observed to kill pheasants during the fall and winter months; the losses, however, are unimportant. Predation by these species is greatest when the pheasants have been weakened during periods of heavy snowfall.

The most conspicuous and commonest hawk is the marsh hawk, which is apparently of no importance as a pheasant predator. Marsh hawks may take some chicks, but they have not been seen attacking adults. The prairie falcon is a spring and fall migrant and in some localities may be an important predator of pheasants and especially of sharp-tailed grouse. On several occasions prairie falcons have been noted attacking pheasants, often only to be forced to release their prey to some Swainson's or American rough-legged hawk. These latter hawks then get the blame for the kill. These slow and more easily observed species also are accused of pheasant predation because they are seen feeding on birds that have died from gunshot wounds.

A study of the food brought to the nests of the great horned owl on areas of heavy pheasant population indicates negligible predation by this nocturnal bird. Coyotes take very few if any adult pheasants. Our observations indicate that the coyote picks up crippled birds or those that have died of starvation.

Depredation on pheasant nests in the sandhills is confined to those by bull snakes and striped skunks. Western bull snakes destroyed about 35, and skunks about 14, per cent of all duck nests on the Valentine National Wildlife Refuge in 1939. In later years the loss has been reduced by the application of control measures. It was interesting to note that no pheasant nests were robbed by bull snakes after the hen began incubation. Pheasants keep these snakes routed from the nest during this period by inflicting punishment by their strong sharp beak. The male pheasant has also been known to kill a bull snake.

Injuries, Diseases, and Parasites.—Because of reduced farming operations and fewer power, light, and telephone wires in the sand-hills, it would be expected that pheasants would be less subject to physical injury than in typical agricultural areas. Five cocks have been captured, each of which had lost a leg at or just below the knee. This maiming could have been caused by mowers or by mink and muskrat traps. One would think that such an injury would hamper the birds in feeding but these cripples were normal in weight.

During trapping operations at the Valentine National Wildlife Refuge, more than 800 pheasants were taken. Thirteen of the males, or 3 per cent of the total, had foot injuries ranging from the loss of one joint of one toe to loss of all toes on both feet. No hens were so maimed. There is no known reason why only cocks should suffer from foot injuries. Three males and no females had shank injuries, leaving lumps or scars. Five of the cocks were blind in one eye, scars indicating that the condition may have resulted from fighting. Other types of injuries included a healing wound on the back of a female, an old injury that was completely covered except for a few pin feathers over the cheek of a male, a severe body tear over the right leg of a female, and a very severe body and breast injury on a male. All of these birds had their injuries healing when caught or healed them in captivity.

Although more than a thousand sandhill pheasants have been handled alive or dead, none have shown a heavy infestation of bird lice (Mallophaga). It was common, however, to find one or two specimens about the head or throat of a bird.

The eye worm, *Oxyspirura petrowii*, infests as many as 26 per cent of the sandhill pheasants in some districts. This parasite appears in the fall in the eye, especially beneath the nictitating membrane. Here they mate and spend the winter. In the spring they pass down the tear duct into the throat and thence through the digestive tract. They also deposit their eggs beneath the eyelids and the eggs later pass out of the body in the same way that the worms do. The complete life history is yet to be determined, but it is conjectured that the eggs are ingested by grasshoppers in the intestines of which they hatch, forming the primary stage, which reaches a host if the grasshopper is eaten by a bird.

MANAGEMENT SUGGESTIONS

Developing Weed Patches.—These may be created in the immediate vicinity of marsh, meadow, and shrub communities by plowing small plats and planting them to corn, rye, buckwheat, or sorghum, or even by letting the broken ground lie fallow. Sunflower, ragweed, knotweed, and other food-producing weeds invade these areas and continue to dominate the site for four or five years after which they are replaced by native grasses.

Pheasants profit little from the planting of food patches as the hordes of red-winged blackbirds that gather in the marshes during August and September strip the patches of their grain, even in the milk stage. It was soon realized that the weeds which volunteered on the plowed plats were of greater value to upland game birds than was the cultivated crop. Food patches distant four or five miles from a marsh had a greater chance of retaining some of their grain than did those nearby.

Supplying Grit.—Coarse grit is not available in the sandhills and to make up for the lack, piles containing 2 to 3 cubic yards were placed at favorable locations on the Valentine National Wildlife Refuge during 1936 and 1937. Observations as late as February 1943 revealed that the pheasants were still visiting these deposits. Birds taken as far as a mile from a grit pile had in their gizzards grinding material obviously derived from the introduced supply.

Winter Feeding.—Emergency winter feeding stations (plate 16, lower) must be put in service before the appearance of heavy snows and subzero weather. If the stations are baited lightly in late November or early December, the birds will learn where to go for food in an emergency. From 7 years of observation on winter feeding in the Nebraska sandhills, the senior author deems that it is a waste of time and grain to start distributing feed after the birds are already dying from starvation and cold. To be of real help at that late time, one must find and feed each individual covey.

The Pheasant in the Intermountain Irrigated Region

By D. IRWIN RASMUSSEN and WILLIAM T. McKEAN

The pheasant's usual close association with agriculture causes it to be classed as a farm-game bird, and nowhere is its dependence upon farming practices more direct than in the irrigated regions of the West. In these areas, agricultural activity has resulted not only in the production of a great variety of crops, but has caused distinct changes in the vegetation of localities that were formerly desert or semidesert, resulting in the creation of habitats suitable for the ring-necked pheasant. Following their introduction, pheasants have become generally established on many of the irrigated areas of the intermountain region and are at present the most important terrestrial game bird.

They occur in large numbers on irrigated areas at elevations near sea level in the Sacramento Valley of California to an altitude of 7,800 feet in the San Luis Valley of south-central Colorado. They have not, however, been established in the southern Rocky Mountain region in either Arizona or New Mexico, although they are found in the Imperial Valley in extreme southern California. Their general absence in western Wyoming and eastern Nevada is due primarily, it is believed, to the very small amount of intensive agriculture. Their distribution in Colorado, Idaho, and Utah is local, but shows a close correlation with fertile soil, intensive agriculture, and moderate winter snow. In each of these States there are localities where pheasants are abundant and large numbers are taken during the hunting seasons.

The occurrence of pheasants in irrigated areas, however, is not a new development. Beebe (1936), in describing their original range, tells of their close relation to, and dependence upon, the irrigated paddy fields of eastern China.

Irrigation and cultivation in the arid western states have resulted in extreme local modification of the quality and variety of the vegetative cover. Here, where the natural annual precipitation of from 5 to 20 inches has been supplemented with an equal, or more often greater, amount of water supplied to the cultivated areas during the summer, great changes have inevitably taken place. There is no evidence that alteration of the ground cover has resulted in any climatic modification, but there is no question that near the surface of the ground and among the cultivated plants the temperature and particularly the humidity have been markedly affected.

Because of limitations as to soil, topography, and available water, the extent of the irrigated lands in relation to the total land area of the region is comparatively small. In Utah only 2.5 per cent of the State's total acreage is under irrigation, and in Idaho, 4.1 per cent. In each of these states, however, the acreage of irrigated land constitutes more than 50 per cent of all lands under cultivation.

Pheasants are not limited to the irrigated fields, but they are almost entirely dependent on them for food. The birds also use both irrigation and drainage canals and their bordering vegetation in many ways. The islands of uncultivated lands in the farming districts and the other areas not suitable for irrigation, as low foothills, ridges, rocky outcroppings, pot holes, and especially stream beds, river bottoms, and marsh areas, support much of the cover for the pheasants during the entire year.

The so-called "dry-farming" areas of the region, consisting of lands cultivated primarily for small grains without irrigation, generally lack water in summer and food and cover in winter. These factors prevent pheasants from becoming abundant.

In the intermountain region, pheasants are often reported to be extending their range and adapting themselves to the arid foothills. In most instances, however, they have been driven to these areas by hunting and their presence above the irrigated fields appears to be more striking than significant. Throughout the arid West, all large pheasant populations are dependent upon irrigated lands.

HISTORY

Private plantings were responsible for the original introduction of pheasants into the intermountain area. The release in 1895 of "about four dozen" birds, originally obtained from Oregon, by a bird fancier, started the pheasant in Utah. The birds were turned loose a short distance southeast of Salt Lake City, and this planting was so successful that a seven-day open season allowing two male birds per day became necessary in 1917 after repeated complaints of damage to cultivated crops. This was several years before the State began a pheasant planting program. Commencing in 1923, pheasants were propagated by the State Fish and Game Department and released; 2,500 to 6,500 have been planted annually and in all counties of the State. The first open season of three days was held in fifteen counties in 1928. Each year since 1928, a short season of three, four, or five days with a limit of from 2 to 4 male birds per day, varying with the locality and year, has been the rule. Pheasants are of fairly state-wide distribution on the irrigated lands, but have found extensive areas with conditions favorable enough for attaining large numbers in only seven or eight scattered counties. An estimated 100,000 birds were taken in Utah during the 1941 hunting season.

In Idaho the first reported planting of 22 birds from Oregon was made privately in 1907. These were released near Buhl in Twin Falls County and at nearby Hagerman Valley. In 1909, according to the Third Biennial Report of the Idaho Fish and Game Warden, 1,000 birds were purchased from Oregon. These were received in September and distributed that fall and the next spring to 39 localities in 24 of the State's 44 counties. The results of this planting were variable. In some areas the pheasants did well, in others they reproduced but did not become abundant, and from most places they disappeared entirely. However, those that became established, multiplied, and began to do serious damage to crops. As a result, Idaho had its first 10-day pheasant season, with a two-bird daily limit, in November 1916. Subsequently, for a number of years, a regular open season for the entire month of November, with a limit of four birds per day of either sex was held in several western and southern counties without apparently depleting the pheasant numbers.

In 1924, Idaho's first game farm began propagating and releasing pheasants, averaging approximately 4,500 birds each year. A second farm began operating in 1937 and this has released from 15,-000 to 25,000 pheasants annually for the past five years.

About 1927, because of the increased number of birds, in the vicinity of Twin Falls, the season was extended to 60 days. This prolonged season, with an increased number of hunters, and the taking of both sexes, resulted in a definite decrease in the population. Since that time, a 30-day season has prevailed each year, with a bag limit of four birds of either sex per day, until 1941 when the limit was reduced to three birds, only one of which could be a hen.

During 1941, 15 of the 44 Idaho counties, in the central and lower Snake River Valley had a 30-day season; 9 in the Upper Snake River a 15-day season; in 3 scattered counties the open season was for 10 days; and 9 northern or "panhandle" counties had an 11-day staggered season. One hundred and ten thousand licenses for hunting of pheasants were sold and an estimated 300,000 to 500,000 birds were killed.

Pheasants were first planted in Wyoming in 1917 by the State Game and Fish Commission. A game farm was established in that State in 1936. The better pheasant ranges are the low, intensively-cultivated areas of the north and east central portions of the State where many thousands of birds are reported taken each year.

Beginning in 1894, large numbers of imported pheasants were released in Colorado near Denver, and south and west of that city. Most of these plantings, other than in the vicinity of Denver, were unsuccessful. About 1908, birds were introduced into northern Colorado in what is now the leading pheasant section. An estimated 20,-000 birds were killed in that State during the 3-day season of 1941.

California began introducing pheasants in 1889, when 140 birds costing $10 per pair were released. The first open season was for six days in 1933. During the 1940 season, 167,035 were reported taken, a large majority of which came from irrigated farms in the Sacramento Valley. Two thousand birds were reported killed in the Imperial Valley, an irrigated district in extreme southern California. Part of this valley is below sea level; it has extremely high summer temperatures and an average annual precipitation of less than four inches.

In Nevada, an estimated 12,000 to 13,000 pheasants were taken during the 1941 season. The important hunting areas are in the west-central part of the State.

FACTORS INFLUENCING PHEASANT PRODUCTION

The past two decades have seen either farm-raised or wild-trapped pheasants released one or many times in practically every county of each state in the intermountain region. These releases have in the main been made upon request by local sportsmen's groups and not necessarily because the localities were suitable for the birds. This procedure has resulted in pheasants being released at varied elevations, under different climatic conditions, on different soils, and where all types of agriculture were being practiced. Having been tried almost everywhere, the present abundance and distribution of pheasants can well be interpreted as indicating the degree of suitability of the various localities. The planting failures, usually attributed to insufficient stocking, poaching, or predation, probably have mostly resulted from deficiencies in the habitats.

Climate.—While the better pheasant populations occur only on areas with favorable land use, a review of climatic data for pheasant localities of high and low population in the western irrigated regions indicates that the numbers of the birds are greatly influenced by certain climatic factors. Winter snow conditions appear to be especially important, with light to moderate snowfall favoring high populations. Winter is the period of maximum precipitation in much of the intermountain region and the presence of deep snow that accumulates evenly and completely covers the ground characterizes many mountain valleys. Such deep snow makes almost all of the waste grain unavailable and covers a large part of the greens and weeds as well. The distress the pheasants show during prolonged periods of deep snow supplies evidence in the field of the importance of this factor. Snow conditions are apparently a more serious factor than differences in elevation and winter temperatures.

Land Use.—Irrigation permits the growing of a wide variety of crops and generally results in intensive agriculture. The most universally-grown crop is alfalfa and this is present throughout the irrigated intermountain region. Small grains, particularly wheat, with some oats and barley, are the most common cash crops, but sugar beets, potatoes, beans, peas, miscellaneous vegetables, fruits, and hays (other than alfalfa) constitute important crops in various localities. Corn, as a rule, is grown only as a minor crop and much of it is harvested while green for ensilage. The growing of peas, clover, alfalfa, and corn for seed is important in Idaho. In certain parts of Utah, producing alfalfa seed is a major farm business.

Land use data, as customarily presented, does not contain information on the minor types and cultural developments that field studies show most directly affect wildlife distribution and activity in irrigated districts. Observations on a 640-acre tract in Box Elder County, Utah, part of Utah's original controlled pheasant hunting area, showed that it included eight acres of fencerows and roadsides and 13.83 acres of land occupied by irrigation ditches or canals and their banks. The average width of irrigation ditches and their banks is 8 feet and of drainage canals, 18 feet. There are 2.43 miles of drainage canals in the pastured land and 8.92 miles of irrigation ditches in cropped land. Thus approximately 5.25 acres of the pastured land and 8.5 acres of the cropped land are occupied by either ditches or drainage canals and their banks. There are 8.92 miles of irrigation ditches used to irrigate 281 acres. Assuming that the same ratio would apply to the entire section, there would be 20.3 miles of ditches per cultivated square mile of irrigated land. The ditches and ditch banks (plate 17) are of extreme importance in pheasant production in all irrigated regions. They furnish resting cover, and travel and escape lanes and serve to vary living conditions in the uniform fields. Along fencerows they are especially effective in providing a variety of the conditions that pheasants require. In the very level fields, characteristic of irrigated lands, the banks furnish protection from wind and provide sunning areas.

As a general conclusion applying to the irrigated lands of the intermountain area, the prevailing types of cultivation result in food for pheasants being sufficiently plentiful, but the degree to which fields are bordered or interspersed by coverts (plate 18, upper) largely determines the number of birds that can live there. These coverts may fringe streams or ditches or may cling to ridges, corners, and other waste lands. Clean farming is not favorable to pheasants and large areas of alfalfa harvested for hay definitely are not desirable range for the birds.

In the Unitah Valley of northeastern Utah, the valley bottom is very uneven, consisting of small hills, benches, and depressions that cannot be irrigated, and of numerous areas of soil unsuitable for cultivation because of gravel or alkali content. The result is a very spotted arrangement of small cultivated fields, idle and fallow land, an abundance of interspersed rank herbaceous native cover, and patches of native shrubs, primarily greasewood (*Sarcobatus vermiculatus*), rabbitbrush (*Chrysothamnus*), willows (*Salix*), and sagebrush (*Artemisia tridentata*). This district of comparatively poor soil but with exceptionally favorable cover conditions and moderate snowfall has an abundance of pheasants.

Alteration of land use in the irrigated interior valleys of California have recently produced marked changes in pheasant numbers. Officials of the California Division of Fish and Game report that formerly there were few birds in Sacramento Valley, which was not considered good pheasant country. Development of rice culture there has produced suitable areas for pheasants and there has been an enormous increase in the number of the birds. Pheasants have never been abundant in the San Joaquin Valley alfalfa district and there has been no material change during a corresponding period.

Agricultural Practices.—Those agricultural and irrigation practices of the intermountain region known to affect pheasant populations adversely are: (1) Heavy fall and winter grazing of irrigated fields and adjacent or interspersed waste lands; (2) growing of extensive areas of alfalfa which is cut for hay, resulting in heavy nest and hen destruction; and to a lesser degree: (3) flooding of cultivated crops during irrigation; (4) fall plowing; (5) burning of marsh and waste areas; (6) burning of vegetation of ditch and canal banks to aid in cleaning them; and (7) utilizing as ensilage a large part of the corn. These practices are discussed in the following paragraphs.

Grazing.—Grazing of irrigated fields by sheep and cattle during the fall and early winter is a common practice throughout the intermountain region. Standing alfalfa and sugar beet tops remaining after harvest are the most important, although not the only crops utilized in this practice. The grazing animals consist usually of herds that spend their summer on nearby mountain range land, and are fed on the farms and ranches during the winter.

The degree of grazing on the fields determines also the amount of herbaceous cover of the fencerows, ditch banks, and waste areas. Under extreme use (plate 18, lower), almost all of it is eaten. This not only removes shelter but may seriously deplete the supply of winter food available from standing vegetation, food that is so essential during periods when the ground with its waste grain and weed seeds is covered by snow.

Often associated with the irrigated fields are bottomlands utilized as spring and summer pastures. These consist of meadows, marshes, flood plains, and other similar lands, which if ungrazed are of great value to pheasants because of the winter cover they provide. In the general absence of woody cover on or bordering the irrigated fields, these bottomlands with growths of woody native species as willow, rose, hawthorn, sumac, buffaloberry, dogwood, and the introduced tamarisk often provide the only extensive cover. The herbaceous growth even of grazed pastures which is unpalatable or inaccessible to livestock, also provides winter shelter.

In addition to the bottomland pastures on good soils, there are often extensive areas within, or adjoining, the cultivated fields that have saline soils and support a highly characteristic native plant cover. These alkali lands are as a rule poorly drained and in addition are often flooded by waste water and subirrigated from the irrigated fields. On the drier tracts, rabbitbrush (*Chrysothamnus*), greasewood (*Sarcobatus vermiculatus*), and saltbushes (*Atriplex*), with an understory of annual brome grasses and salt-resistant herbs form dense stands. On the moister places, salt grass (*Distichlis spicata*) makes a solid sod (plate 18, upper), or where water is ponded and of sufficient depth, small marshes of tules (*Scirpus*) and cattails (*Typha*) develop. In the vegetation of this type, pheasants find some of their best shelter and cover during all seasons of the year as well as considerable food. These tracts are usually grazed but because of the lower palatability of their forage are not closely cropped and a goodly plant cover ordinarily remains.

Growing Alfalfa.—Alfalfa, the major irrigated crop in the intermountain region, is cut two, three, or even four times per year. It makes very attractive nesting cover, but a majority of the nests and a large number of the hens upon them are destroyed in haying operations.

On the Corinne, Utah, tract, in 1941, alfalfa cutting began June 9; the second cutting was 36 days later on July 15, and the third followed in another 24 days on September 8. On the 87 acres of alfalfa comprising 38.2 per cent of the cultivated crops, 66 nests were destroyed during the first cutting. This took place at the height of the nesting season and newly-hatched, young broods that escaped the mower were exposed to predaceous birds. A small number of nests also were destroyed during the second cutting.

Survey of the fields did not indicate a concentration of nests in any selected portions of the fields or in relation to the ditches and fence-rows, their distribution appearing to be at random.

Differences of a few days to two weeks in the time of mowing would result in entirely different degrees of loss. The use of flushing bars may lower hen mortality and save some chicks but it cannot materially change the amount of nest destruction. The chances of a cut-over nest hatching even if provided with an island of cover are very small because of the disturbance to the bird in possession, and in addition of predation by gulls and magpies which commonly forage behind the mowers. Recent substitution of power mowers for horse-drawn machines, increasing their speed, has resulted in a higher mortality of hens. It is apparent that maintenance of large acreages of alfalfa hay together with the associated farm practices constitute a definite hazard to pheasant populations in irrigated areas—one that will doubtless continue and about which little can be done.

Irrigation.—In the great majority of irrigated districts, water is supplied at one end of a field and floods it by following small parallel furrows. This practice results in no great accumulation of water and does little harm to nesting. The loss of nests due to flooding by irrigation water on the Corinne area was 3.45 per cent.

In some very level districts as parts of the Snake River Valley in Idaho, a "border strip system" of irrigating is used. Under this method, water is conducted to different parts of the field, held in large shallow pools by a system of low dikes until it soaks into the soil, and impounded at various depths up to 10 inches. Such an application of water to alfalfa or other nesting cover floods and destroys nests.

Fall Plowing.—Unplowed grain stubble provides pheasants with their most important source of fall, winter, and early spring foods. Fall plowing, a general practice in many irrigated areas as a moisture-conserving measure, covers much food as waste small grains and weed seeds and destroys all cover on the fields.

Burning.—Burning, which is usually limited to the waste lands and marsh areas, appears to be generally detrimental to pheasant welfare. Late fall burning destroys winter food and shelter; early spring burning eliminates nesting cover and forces more birds to nest in the alfalfa where the hazard is great; and burning in early summer takes a big toll of nests and nesting birds.

In Utah County, Utah, early summer fires have in certain past years burned over areas of several square miles of very desirable nesting cover between Utah Lake and the cultivated lands. This has resulted in a noticeable decrease in the number of birds at hunting time.

Burning of weeds and woody plants from ditches, a practice usually done in the spring, appears to be harmful mainly in restricting growth of shrubs and willows.

Growing Corn.—Corn is a minor crop on irrigated areas, and the major part of that grown is cut green and used for ensilage. Corn left standing can be utilized in times of deep snow by pheasants more efficiently than any of the other cultivated grain crops. Observations in the field indicate that even small stands of corn left in the field have a very marked effect in concentrating the birds in winter and aiding in their survival.

FACTS IN THE LIFE HISTORY OF THE PHEASANT

Pheasants appear to be well adapted to live in irrigated areas. Limitation of their numbers on this kind of land is due to land use and climatic factors rather than to irrigation itself. Nonirrigated cultivated lands in the intermountain region have not proved to be favorable pheasant range.

Lands under irrigation have extensive development of canals, ditches, and often drainage outlets. These provide lanes of cover, resting and sunning grounds, and travel and escape ways for the pheasants. Plants growing along these ditches are important also as a source of food, particularly during winter. Man plans to have the ditches reach all fields and their benefit to pheasants extends over all irrigation districts and to all parts of them.

Food.—A study of pheasant food habits in irrigated regions shows they do not differ materially as to staples taken from those prevailing in most other areas. Analyses of stomachs collected in Utah County from 1927 to 1936 and in Box Elder County in 1941 and 1942, from areas where pheasants were abundant, showed that small grains (primarily waste) and weed seeds constituted the bulk of the food. Insects were the major food of the very young birds.

In the 1935 and 1936 samples, taken on Area A in Utah County, small grains made up 59.5 per cent of the total diet and consisted of barley 30 per cent, wheat 16 per cent, corn 4 per cent, and oats 3 per cent. On Area B, small grains constituted 81 per cent of the food, wheat 61 per cent, barley 18 per cent, and oats 2 per cent. Corn was a minor crop on Area A and almost entirely absent from Area B.

Weed seeds included those of both introduced species as knotweeds (*Polygonum*), sunflower (*Helianthus*), sweet clovers (*Melilotus*), wild lettuce (*Lactuca*), mallows (*Malva*), and various chenopods (Chenopodiaceae); and native species as ragweed (*Ambrosia*), (*Cleome*), and others. Seventy-five kinds of weed seeds were present in the 76 stomachs taken in 1935-36 from the two areas, but only 8 of them formed more than one per cent of the annual food of either area. Native species of shrubs as rose (*Rosa*), hawthorn (*Crataegus*), oak (*Quercus*), sumac (*Rhus*), dogwood (*Cornus*), wild currant (*Ribes*), and saltbrush and shadscale (*Atriplex*) provided seeds and fruits.

The greens of all the analyses consisted primarily of alfalfa leaves, but included some grass and other plants. Sugar beets made up most of the remaining plant material. This was taken both in the fall from standing plants, and in winter and spring from waste beets.

Insects, including both native and introduced species, made up 13 and 2 per cent, respectively, of the summer diet on Areas A and B in Utah County, but contributed extremely little during the remainder of the year. In order of abundance they were: Hymenoptera (ants), Lepidoptera (butterflies and moths), Diptera (flies), Coleoptera (beetles), Orthoptera (grasshoppers and crickets), and Hemiptera (true bugs).

The food of young pheasants was studied in Box Elder County in 1941. Stomach analysis showed 76.7 per cent of the food of nine young pheasant chicks 3 to 8 weeks old to be insects. The bulk of the insect material was butterfly larvae and pupae, with smaller amounts of grasshoppers and beetles. In the 9 chicks, 10 to 13 weeks old, insects, consisting almost entirely of grasshoppers, composed only 2 per cent of the food. In both cases the important weed seeds taken were those of bristle grass (*Setaria*), redroot (*Amaranthus*), and knotweeds (*Polygonum*). The younger birds ate some barley and the older ones nearly equal amounts of wheat and barley and 4.2 per cent green alfalfa leaves.

Field observations and analysis of stomachs of a series of pheasants taken in northern Utah during the winter of 1941-42, a year of heavy snow, revealed pheasants as freely utilizing seeds and fruits from the following plants: Roses (*Rosa*), Russian olive (*Elaeagnus angustifolia*), redroot (*Amaranthus retroflexus*), ragweeds (*Ambrosia*), knotgrasses (*Polygonum*), dock (*Rumex crispus*), sunflower (*Helianthus annuus*), teasel (*Dipsacus sylvestris*), and cultivated barley and corn; and as making lighter use of: Russian thistle (*Salsola pestifer*), sweet clover (*Melilotus alba*), burdock (*Arctium minus*), sedge (*Carex*), and cultivated wheat. Vegetative material taken consisted of alfalfa (*Medicago sativa*), various grasses, dandelion (*Leontodon taraxacum*), and roots and tubers of marsh plants. It was evident that the pheasants became more dependent upon food other than waste grain as the snow cover increased.

There is common complaint of pheasant damage to crops in the intermountain region and although corn is not grown extensively, the pulling of newly-sprouted corn in the spring appears to be the most widespread and serious charge. In certain Utah and Idaho localities, this depredation has been successfully curtailed by feeding corn along the field borders during the short vulnerable period. Young sugar beets are eaten in the spring, and at times this loss can be serious; some mature beets are pecked in the fall but this is of minor importance. Under irrigation, many truck crops and fruits are grown, and often there is damage by pheasants to beans, berries, watermelons, cantaloupes, and tomatoes. In 1941, the loss on a 5-acre tomato patch in the Corinne tract was 252 pounds, or at the rate of $3.36 per acre. In the early spring, pheasants cause trouble by scratching and filling the small irrigation furrows in grainfields. Some complaints are made of damage to mature grain but under present agricultural practices, this is of little importance.

Weight.—November weights of 280 legally-killed male birds from three Utah counties varied from 1 pound, 5 ounces, to 3 pounds, and averaged 2 pounds, 8 ounces.

Nesting.—On the Corinne tract during the 1941 nesting season, records were obtained on 154 nests in a density of 24 per 100 acres. Of this number, 56 (36.36 per cent) were successful and 93 (60.39 per cent) failed, records for five being incomplete. The 56 successful nests hatched an average of 7.6, or a known total of 425, chicks. Sixty-six of the 93 unsuccessful nests were destroyed by the first mowing of the 87 acres of alfalfa hay. Thirty-two clutches in the alfalfa had hatched previous to the time the hay was cut (June 9). Shrubby growths of greasewood (*Sarcobatus vermiculatus*) with an understory of annual brome grasses, proved to be the most valuable nesting cover in this tract.

A study was made of the relation of the 154 nests to irrigation ditches and their banks and of the effects of flooding. One hundred and thirty-two of the nests were within 300 yards (92 of them within 20 to 100 yards) of the main ditches. The average distance was 67.93 yards.

There was no evidence that the physical characteristics of the ditchbank itself attracted nesting birds, for only 16 nests were within ten yards of a ditchbank. The influence of adjoining types of crop cover was far greater in determining where the nests were located. One hundred and sixteen of the 132 nests were so placed that they were in danger of flooding. However, only four (3.45 per cent) of these were actually deserted because of inundation.

Of eight nests found within five yards of the ditchbank, only two hatched; six of these were destroyed by predators which appeared to use the ditches as travel lanes.

Predation.—In 1941, on the Corinne tract, man, his domestic cats and dogs, and skunks were the principal causes of nest and bird losses. Five farm dogs on the area were all observed harassing pheasants at times during the entire year. Cats were known to have killed two hens on their nests.

The Great Basin skunk (*Mephitis occidentalis major*) accounted for the largest measured losses of complete, unexposed pheasant nests, destroying 12 of the 22 nests on which records were obtained. Skunk predation was observed only at the nesting season.

Two well known native predators, the coyote (*Canis latrans lestes*) and the magpie (*Pica pica hudsonia*), are abundant in the intermountain region, often inhabit areas where pheasants are found, and are accused of making heavy inroads on pheasant numbers. Evidence in the field of either of these native species being a definite contributing cause to low pheasant populations, however, has not been established.

Throughout the West the magpie is commonly accused of being a serious enemy of the pheasant through destruction of eggs and young. Kalmbach (1927), on the basis of examination of 547 stomachs, reports the magpie food as about three-fifths of animal origin. The food of the young was 94 per cent animal matter. Stomachs of 234 nestling magpies showed 3.18 per cent of their food by bulk to be other wild birds and their eggs and 1.78 per cent to be domestic poultry and eggs. Farmers commonly complain of losses of both eggs and young domestic chicks through magpie predation. Similar losses to game birds are conceivable, particularly when local conditions favor, but no quantitative studies have proved them. On the Corinne tract, numerous magpies were seen eating pheasant eggs that had been uncovered and scattered about in the alfalfa fields by mowing operations. They had lively competition, however, from the California gulls (*Larus californicus*), which habitually follow the mowing of alfalfa in the Salt Lake Valley region. The gulls far outnumbered the magpies and hunted the eggs more persistently. The gulls also voraciously ate the young pheasant chicks exposed by mowing in these fields. These losses, however, cannot be charged directly to these two birds, but rather were due to the mowing. Of the 22 unexposed but rifled nests that were observed, 3 were destroyed by magpies and 2 by gulls or magpies.

Sperry (1941), in examining 8,339 coyote stomachs from 17 states, found only 11 stomachs from 5 western states that contained pheasant remains. These represented 7 months, none of them in the nesting season. It is logical to assume, however, that only a very small number of these coyotes were taken from pheasant ranges. Upland game birds as a group made up less than 1 per cent of the stomach contents and were found, on an average, in only one in every 36 stomachs. On the Corinne tract, one coyote was frequently seen and during 1940-1941, droppings collected at eight localities and in 7 different months all had pheasant remains in them.

During 1940-1941, the marsh hawk (*Circus hudsonius*), duck hawk (*Falco peregrinus*), and short-eared owl (*Asio flammeus flammeus*), were the only common raptors on the Corinne area. The two hawks both harassed pheasants occasionally but their depredations were not thought to be significant. During the summer and fall, adult pheasants commonly ignored the presence of hawks. In winter, however, when the duck hawk visits the area, the birds are more wary of all hawks.

Population Changes.—Kelker and McKean made an intensive

investigation of the year-long pheasant populations of the 640-acre Corinne tract in Box Elder County from November 1940 to November 1941. The results are believed to represent a fair sample of the annual changes in pheasant populations occurring in much of the intermountain region.

The number of birds on this tract, November 7, 1940, immediately following the hunting season, was approximately 96 birds, or 15 per 100 acres, as determined by a count made by two men using a dog. At this same time a count by 13 men of 81 birds flushed from the study tract and adjacent land revealed the sex ratio to be 1 cock to 4 hens.

The following spring a census of the crowing males showed 26 cocks (4.1 per 100 acres) to have established territories. In a count of the females at this same season, 64 were noted, the sex ratio then being 1 cock to 2.4 hens. However, during the early summer a nesting survey revealed that more than 64 hens were using the study area, hence it was believed the winter sex ratio gave better information on the numbers of hens than the actual spring count. The number of hens present on the area based on known numbers of cocks and ratio of 1 cock to 4 hens was determined to be 104, and the total population of hens and cocks 130. This indicates a movement of 34 birds into the area between the November and the spring counts.

A careful search for nests during the spring and summer revealed that approximately 154 nests, 24 per 100 acres, had been placed on this tract of land. Since only 104 hens had been estimated, it became apparent that considerable renesting was taking place. During the period from June 9 to June 19, at least 64 nests that had not yet been incubated were destroyed in hay mowing and the hens had escaped. It would have been necessary for approximately 50 of these 64 hens to renest to account for the 154 nests found.

The average complete clutch comprised 9.1 eggs. Therefore the reproductive potential of the 1941 spring stock of 130 birds may be expressed as 104 x 9.1 or 946 young birds, and the total potential fall population (disregarding losses) as 946 plus the 130 adults, or 1,076.

A census of the fall population on November 26, 1941, after the hunting season, showed that 105 birds (16.4 per 100 acres) remained on the area. Consequently the loss due to all factors is represented by the difference between 1,076 and 105 or 971 birds.

This loss could not be entirely itemized in the field but it was believed that the major causes were known. Six adult birds were known to have perished during the winter. Then followed the destruction of 91 nests principally by mowing and various predators. As the average completed clutch held 9.1 eggs, this loss was computed as 91 x 9.1 or 828 eggs. In the destruction of these nests, 26 hens were known to have been killed. Seven nests were deserted because of flooding, human interference, or predators, with a potential loss of 64 eggs. Only 3 eggs were found in hatched nests that were of proved infertility; however, it was not possible to determine the percentage of fertility for all of the eggs found.

Mowing operations, poaching, predators, and accidents were known to have killed 46 adults, 65 juveniles, and 4 pheasants of undetermined age during the summer.

The average size of 56 successful broods was 7.6 chicks. The size of 37 broods observed in mid-summer was 5.1 chicks per brood, indicating an average chick loss of 2.5 per brood.

The hunting removals were: Legal take 55 male birds; crippling loss, 9 known (18 estimated); and illegal kill, 6 known (12 estimated); plus 10 birds calculated to have been driven from the area by the hunting, or a total of 95. Counts showed 190 birds on the tract immediately preceding, and 105 following, the hunt.

MANAGEMENT

Pheasant management should be based on analysis of the factors that are locally known to affect pheasant numbers and distribution. At the present time, there have been no undertakings of a definitely, experimental nature conducted for a long enough time to demonstrate feasible programs. Scattered information on phases of the problem has been gained, as on controlled hunting areas and food patches in Utah, and on the trapping and transplanting of wild birds in Idaho. No critical appraisals, however, have been made of the effects of the propagating and transplanting programs that constitute the major efforts of all the western states in their work with pheasants.

There appears to be no fundamental difference in the problem of pheasant management on irrigated, and other cultivated, areas.

Any procedures designed to aid in improving hunting programs must deal with the same factors and these include not only the birds and their habitat but also the very important human element. Posting of land from the hunter and trespass troubles from the landowner are problems that are not limited to any particular region of the United States.

Hunting Control.—An attempt to control the human factor in pheasant management has been under way in Utah for the past three years, and indications are that the State-sponsored, but land-owner-operated, hunting areas will aid materially in that respect. Interviews with landowners reveal their general acceptance of the plan, as it provides control of the hunters and furnishes some revenue for certain common interests as churches, parent-teacher groups, and drainage districts. On the Corinne tract, 93 per cent of the hunters were in favor of the controlled hunting, 2 per cent had no opinion, and 5 per cent opposed and gave as a reason that it had not improved hunting conditions.

These Utah posted hunting areas consist of contiguous tracts of private lands of 1,000 acres or more that are posted with the co-operation of the State Fish and Game Department and operated by the landowners as a unit. Hunters obtain a permit by paying a nominal fee to the landowner. Ordinarily the areas are several times the minimum allowable size; their borders are dependent on natural boundaries rather than on property lines. The landowners promise cooperation in protection and propagation of pheasants and this offers one means of obtaining some management.

A review of seven areas in Utah having an average 4-day season in 1941 showed a total of 1,988 permits issued, an average take of 1.9 male birds per hunter per day, and of 9 birds per 100 acres. This kill was made on areas without habitat management.

The question of bag limits is of importance and while there is general acceptance of the idea of shooting only male pheasants, in certain western states, a limited number of hen birds are allowed to be taken. The experience of many states is that shooting of hens is definitely adverse to maintaining high pheasant populations. The practice is justifiable only where the object is to achieve reduction in the number of birds. Greater losses of hens than cocks caused by agricultural practices and predation in themselves are convincing reasons for protection of hens during the hunting season.

Short seasons appear to be a matter of habit or tradition in most states but the indications are that lengthened seasons would have little adverse effect on pheasant populations, and would have some favorable features in relation to controlled hunting areas.

Restocking.—On the basis of field observations in states of the intermountain region during the past five years, it appears very doubtful that the propagating of increased numbers of game farm pheasants is justified. The planting of artificially-propagated birds has been the means of trying the birds in a great variety of areas and of establishing them where conditions were favorable. Now almost all suitable areas have been colonized for many years and continued planting of birds in unsuitable areas is a waste of money. Live-trapping and moving of surplus birds is more often needed to curtail damage than to extend establishment of the species.

Trapping and transplanting of wild birds has been successfully conducted for nine years at the Lewiston orchards in western Idaho and for a shorter period on the Camas Refuge in the northeastern part of that State. This method is a much more economical way of providing birds for restocking than is the artificial rearing of birds. The costs of trapped wild birds have been only 15 to 45 per cent of that of propagated pheasants. Wild-trapped birds are definitely more capable of caring for themselves under field conditions.

Modifying Agricultural Practices.—Modification of agricultural programs, both as to land use and farm practices, to benefit pheasants appears in most respects impracticable. Agricultural operations are conducted and modified primarily through following habit, maintaining certain programs of work, or attempting to achieve better cash returns. Anything in the way of wildlife management must be secondary.

Heavy grazing destroys cover essential to the pheasant. Thus, moderating grazing and protecting certain areas for pheasants—steps that certainly are feasible—are modifications of agricultural practices that will increase pheasant numbers. Preserving from grazing-animals certain thickets and weed patches that will give pheasants good cover and food during periods of heavy snowfall and safe nesting cover to attract birds away from the hazardous alfalfa fields also appears to be practicable.

Pheasant nesting success can be definitely increased by delaying the first cutting of alfalfa. Hen and chick mortality possibly can be somewhat decreased by use of flushing bars, although it is very doubtful whether this practice would influence total nesting losses. The loss in alfalfa fields can perhaps best be lessened by increasing the extent of other desirable nesting cover.

Irrigation by use of furrows appears to have little effect on pheasant nesting, but the use of dikes to hold water at depths of several inches results in the destruction of nests. Burning of waste lands has a detrimental effect at every season. So far as practicable, these operations should be modified in favor of the pheasants.

Improving the Environment.—Irrigated lands were originally areas of restricted plant growth, mainly sagebrush and grass. Bringing it under cultivation has as a rule left no remnant stands of shrubs or woody cover beside that provided by willows and other growths along the stream bottoms. The only other important brushy cover available is that afforded by shrubs found on the unused areas of alkali soils. Such natural retreats are, therefore, restricted in this region just where there is a marked need for them.

Any management program for pheasants in irrigated districts must include consideration of cover and the birds' use of it. Observations show that areas "above the ditch," that is, higher than the irrigated fields, have little importance as year-long pheasant range. Winter movement of the birds is downward to the brushy stream beds and marshes, hence food, cover, and refuge areas should be provided there. Ditches, canals, and fencerows, if well vegetated, afford regular lanes of travel and can furnish leads into protected or developed areas thus making them more effective. Protection of shelter areas from excessive grazing will preserve both food and cover for pheasants.

Supplying food and grit in winter is often necessary. Improvement in winter feeding can best be attained by use of food patches (plate 19). Generally, standing corn has proved to be most satisfactory for this purpose. The use of cultivated sunflowers, kafir corn, and small grains has been nullified at times by the inroads of birds, particularly of large flocks of red-winged and Brewer's blackbirds in the fall. Flocks of waterfowl also have heavily utilized certain food patches. The use of pure stands of small grains is not entirely satisfactory as heavy snows may cover the plants at the time the feed is most urgently needed. Cutting of small grains and leaving it in the field in shocks has proved a good plan under certain conditions.

In one case, the combination of vigorous growth of Russian thistle and a thin stand of wheat proved to be very effective in providing both food and cover.

The use of winter food patches appears to be justified in many places and their trial in others can best determine how and where they will be most valuable. Their effectiveness is greatest when they are located near good cover. Cover can be improved by protection from excess grazing.

Russian olive (*Elaeagnus angustifolia*) in permanent plantings along fencerows, ditches, and in plantations is a good winter food plant, providing fruit that remains accessible in the deepest snow. This tree is adaptable to alkali soils. It furnishes both food and cover.

The Pheasant in the Pacific Northwest[1]

By ARTHUR S. EINARSEN

The Chinese ring-necked pheasant (*Phasianus colchicus torquatus*) was successfully transplanted to Oregon in 1881 through the gift of 28 birds by Judge Owen N. Denny, then United States Consul General at Shanghai, China. Judge Denny was accustomed to having these birds served on his table, as they were abundant generally in Chinese markets. Impressed by the similarity of the climate at Shanghai with that of Linn County, Oregon, where he lived before going to China, he conceived the idea of obtaining some of the birds from these markets and shipping them to his brother's farm in the Willamette Valley.

Available information indicates that several shipments left Shanghai. According to rumor, one lot was eaten by the ship's crew for a holiday dinner just before reaching the Pacific Coast of the United States. Another, however, arrived safely and the birds were taken to the old Denny homestead in the Willamette Valley, where they were liberated near Peterson's Butte (plate 20, upper), about 3 miles south of Lebanon and 18 miles east of Corvallis. This planting thrived and later provided stock that was transferred to other parts of the Northwest and even distant sections of the United States.

The pheasant proved well suited to conditions in the Willamette

[1]Acknowledgments:—The author is especially indebted to R. E. Dimick, Head of the Fish and Game Management Department of Oregon State College, for his careful analyses of data and helpful suggestions in the preparation of this chapter. Others of the College staff were fully cooperative. Credit is also due to the following graduate students, who worked on various phases of the investigation: Arthur K. Crews, Carl R. Eklund, Nils N. Nilsson, Eugene E. Crawford, Hugh Ross Newcomb, Frank Stanton, John Salls Morse, and Cecil Gubser.

Valley, where wild seeds, fruits, and small grains, as wheat, barley, and oats were plentiful. The high insect population of the valley undoubtedly favored growing chicks by supplying plenty of protein. The initial release was made in poor habitat, but near what is today considered excellent range. The birds soon moved to these better feeding areas.

Although there are many early newspaper accounts of poaching, and hotels were accused of serving the birds in lieu of chicken, for 10 years they spread and increased rapidly and at the end of that period were to be found throughout the entire Willamette Valley, 40 miles wide and 180 miles long.

This dispersal was astounding. The capacity of the bird for rapid spread, however, was substantiated during this study by data obtained from pheasant banding experiments. Records of recovered birds from game-farm stock indicate that it is not unusual for pheasants to migrate 30 miles in a year, although their average annual range is less than 3 miles in radius.

No accurate estimates of pheasant numbers in the Willamette Valley were recorded in 1891, when shooting them was first permitted, but published statements indicated they were very generally abundant, probably averaging 1 bird to each 5 acres. A resident near Peterson's Butte, who remembers the initial release and still hunts on the area, tells of one field of about 100 acres which he believes held 1 pheasant per acre in those early days.

As few restrictions on hunting were apparently thought necessary, pheasant abundance declined perceptibly after the first hunting seasons, continuing until in 1935, when only about 1.3 birds per 100 acres remained, despite the fact that from 1 to 15 thousand game-farm birds had been liberated annually for 25 years in the 10 Willamette Valley counties. Such was the situation in 1935 when the Oregon Cooperative Wildlife Research Unit was established at Oregon State College.

Investigation of the reasons for small game scarcity by the Research Unit was the first undertaken in Oregon. As the ring-necked pheasant was the principal game bird of the region, cooperators advised an immediate study to learn what factors limited its abundance. Study plots were selected, including a 5,200-acre experimental area on farmlands about 10 miles north of Corvallis. An ideal check plot was located on Protection Island, Washington, which was leased by the Unit. This 397-acre island, in the Straits of Juan de Fuca, was chosen because of the similarity of its climate to that of the Willamette Valley. Good control of conditions was possible because of its isolation by water.

GENERAL DESCRIPTION OF THE STUDY AREA

The Willamette Valley, in the Humid Temperate Zone, is the main river valley of western Oregon. There are 8,859,520 acres in the 10 counties, an area comparable to that of the States of New Hampshire and Connecticut combined. Throughout its length are many tributary streams, emptying into the Willamette River which discharges 13,740 second-feet during periods of normal water level and reaches the tremendous flow of 100,000 second-feet during flood stage. Twice in the past century, floods were recorded which nearly doubled even that high volume. There is sufficient elevated ground, however, to which the birds can move to escape inundation.

Cover

Cover for the ring-necked pheasant is very plentiful in the Willamette Valley, and the travelways from one area to another are amply sheltered (plate 20, lower). The native vegetation of the valley includes numerous deciduous trees and shrubs. Practically every swale has an abundance of ash (*Fraxinus oregona*), willows (*Salix*), and on the margins, oak (*Quercus garryanna*). On uncultivated fields, wild roses (*Rosa gymnocarpa*) spring up in profusion and are quickly followed by willows, alders (*Alnus*), and other deciduous trees, providing ample shelter for game birds. The introduced evergreen blackberry (*Rubus laciniatus*) provides escape cover for game birds that is impenetrable by man or dog. Fields left uncultivated for even a short time afford excellent cover, as tarweed (*Madia sativa*), which has considerable winter food value, and other weeds quickly overrun them.

Climate

The prevailing weather in our area certainly presents no hazard to adult pheasants. During the period of this study, however, there were three critical storm periods in the Willamette Valley. The first occurred October 31, 1935, when approximately 10 inches of snow fell, and on the next day with snow covering the ground and shrubbery, ring-necked pheasants were found moving about at daybreak as usual. While the snow remained in some places for several days, pheasants and other birds apparently were unharmed.

The second storm on January 31, 1937 was very exceptional in that about 3 feet of snow fell in the valley and remained for about 10 days. During that time no game birds other than two mourning doves (*Zenaidura macroura*) were found dead, either as a result of the storm or of malnutrition. However, there was ample evidence that flesh-eaters were taking daily toll. Numerous kills by hawks and other predators were found both in cover and in the open.

On January 6, 1942, a so-called silver thaw (the moisture freezing as rapidly as it fell) formed a sheath of ice over all of the grass blades and other vegetation (plate 21). The storm varied in intensity in different parts of the valley. By morning many of the cocks had heavily ice-coated tails, which had frozen to the similarly covered ground. The birds, finding themselves welded to the ground in this manner, became frantic and by great effort tried to wrench themselves free, often leaving all of their tail feathers.

Field work by six observers for a two-day period revealed no fatalities but in one or two areas where the ice storm was especially severe, about a third of the male birds had lost their tail feathers. On the whole, however, winter storms can scarcely be considered a serious mortality factor in this area.

Although the entire habitat was coated with ice, there were enough sheltered spots at the base of shrubbery or in clumps of vegetation to furnish green food, seeds, and insect larvae. Harding grass (*Phalaris tuberosa* var. *stenoptera*) and orchard grass (*Dactylis glomerata*) were partially available, but rose hips commonly considered winter food, were coated with ice.

Rain is usually heavy in the Willamette Valley during December, January, and February, although there are intermittent periods of cold weather. Regardless of the season, rains apparently have little effect upon adult ring-necked pheasants. During the winter the birds feed in grainfields, stands of clover or alfalfa, which are often green, and on newly-plowed ground. Despite the heavy downpours, specimens taken from time to time had full stomachs containing a wide representation of weeds, seeds, fruits, and other vegetable matter.

However, it is undesirable to take inventories during the first fall rains, as the pheasants then remain in seclusion for a week or 10 days. After that period of adjustment, they ignore the rain and carry on normally.

EFFECTS OF WEATHER UPON REPRODUCTION

While weather seems to have little effect on adult pheasants, it definitely affects survival of newly-hatched and immature birds. Birds hatched during periods of extremely wet or cold weather, do not survive. Survival records of immature pheasants, kept through six nesting seasons, indicate that wet, chilly weather during the hatching period is directly reflected in a lessened number reaching maturity.

NESTING

Theories as to rapid pheasant increase due to their rearing more than one brood a year are based on the common impression throughout western Oregon that the birds nest early in spring. Field observation, both on Protection Island and in the Willamette Valley, failed to substantiate this view. Nesting in Oregon begins early in April but does not reach its peak until the middle of June. In Benton County in 1937, 1938, and 1941, the average number of eggs per clutch varied from 10.02 to 11.68 and the fertility rate from 92.74 to 94.17 per cent.

Records for these 3 years show that more than 50 per cent of the nests were found in legume crops, including 36.74 per cent in vetch and 17.87 per cent in clover and alfalfa. Only 6.43 per cent were found in grainfields. As legume crops are cut in early or mid-summer, there is a heavy loss of nests. Flushing bars and other similar devices are not effective on high-speed harvesting machinery, because they do not flush the birds soon enough to protect them from injury; they are also a nuisance to the farmer in small fields. Regrettably, it seems that little can be done to encourage the pheasant to nest in safer cover.

Sixty-nine per cent of all the nests under observation were destroyed by farming practices. If this loss could be prevented, a much higher annual increase would result. On Protection Island under natural conditions, the 5-year increase was 277 per cent. In the Willamette Valley, production is only a fraction of that figure. Nevertheless, during the past few years, a remarkable increase has been attained through management practices which take into account prevailing limitations.

FOOD

The Willamette Valley has an abundant food supply, consisting of weed seeds, berries, and wild fruits, in addition to the grains and other cultivated crops. Perhaps in few parts of the United States can be found such quantities of wild fruits. Seedling apples grow throughout the valley, especially along fencerows and retain some fruit well after midwinter.

Counts on sample plots revealed an average of 30 edible seeds per square foot throughout the Willamette Valley in the fall when all weed seeds and grains had matured. This large supply, available throughout the winter, will carry a pheasant population far beyond the number that can be maintained in strictly agricultural areas.

During the period of this study, it has been obvious that greens made up much of the bulk of food taken by pheasants in the Willamette Valley. John Salls Morse, in an intensive study of the foods on Protection Island found that grass leaves and legumes contributed more than any other items to the volume of food as checked by pheasant droppings through January, February, and March. This bulk was supplemented by various weed seeds. For about a week in March and during the following period, extending well into June, the birds fed extensively on scouring rush (*Equisetum*), and showed a liking for chickweed (*Stellaria media*), apparently eaten entire, and seeds of brome grass (*Bromus marginatus*). When the fall-sown winter wheat had reached the dough stage, it began to show up predominantly in both stomach and fecal samples and so remained until the end of November. When fields were plowed to permit the reseeding of winter grain, a wide variety of foods appeared in the crop until the planted wheat had sprouted, after which it was found in stomach samples until January.

Field observations and the results of analysis of stomach and fecal samples, all offer conclusive proof that pheasants enjoy a wide variety of foods. While grain-eating birds, they take advantage of other available foods by seasons and according to weather conditions. In much of the humid Northwest, pheasants can maintain good flesh on a diet of green vegetation. On the Protection Island study plot, where the pheasant population in November 1941 was 1,540 on 397 acres, all of the unharvested grain crop had been eaten by the birds early in the winter. During banding work in January and February 1942, all the birds examined were in good condition, the cocks weighing as much as 4 pounds 1 ounce with an average weight of 3 pounds 8 ounces, and the hens averaging 2 pounds 3 ounces. As a rule, perhaps, in this region, pheasant foods are of no importance to man and therefore, heavy concentrations of the birds do not cause economic losses. Occasionally, however, damage to farm crops occurs.

Animal foods are apparently most important to the growing pheasant chicks. In much of the humid belt, insect populations vary with weather conditions and their abundance may not coincide with the period of greatest pheasant demand. Nevertheless, pheasant increases are satisfactory and the degree to which the scarcity of insects limits rearing success is problematic.

GRIT

Dearth of grit was one of the causes suggested for the decline of pheasants from 1891 to 1935. In the earlier years, there were only 11 per cent as many roads as at present and they were made without rock ballast. During the past 20 years, the availability of grit along roadsides has been greatly increased by the general use of crushed stone so that if there were no other source, roadsides today would furnish all of the grinding material needed.

The seeds of poison oak (*Rhus diversiloba*) also are hard enough to serve as grit and they are commonly found in pheasant gizzards. Poison oak is abundant throughout the entire area and with its seeds available on the plants for 5 months, and in ground litter the remainder of the year, they can be had as a substitute for, or a supplement to, grit at any time.

DISEASE

Diseases are commonly blamed for low game populations. The search for diseased pheasants claimed the attention of field workers throughout the full 6-year period of investigation, and in that time no evidence was found of sick or diseased birds. Except for mechanical injuries, no physical weaknesses of any kind were noted.

Dr. B. T. Sims, formerly head of the veterinary department, and the late Dr. W. T. Johnson, an outstanding poultry pathologist formerly in charge of poultry disease investigations, Oregon State College, gave careful attention to the search for pheasant diseases. Autopsies on more than 300 pheasants killed in the hunting seasons were performed by Dr. Sims and aside from those containing common parasites, no specimens yielded any indication of disease. In several instances early in the study, penned birds suffered from heavy parasitic infestations and aspergillosis, a fungus disease, but for the past several years this condition has not recurred.

Plate 21.—Grass covered with ice during silver thaw, Benton County, Oregon, January 8, 1942.

Plate 22.—Upper. Douglas's ground squirrel.
Lower. Pheasant eggs emptied by Douglas's ground squirrels.

Plate 23.—Group breeding pens for pheasants, Rogers's movable type, Sherburne Game Farm, N. Y. (By permission of New York State Conservation Department)

Incubator, 90 pheasant-egg capacity.

Plate 24.—Front view of a shelter in a winter holding enclosure.

Banner B. Morgan in his thesis "Parasites of Poultry and Game Birds in Oregon," submitted to Oregon State Agricultural College in 1939, prepared a list of the parasites found in some of the game birds of Oregon. Those found in pheasants included the threadworms, *Capillaria* sp., *Heterakis gallinae*, and *Syngamus trachea* (the common gapeworm in captive birds), and the tapeworms, *Hymenolepis carioca* and *H. cantaniana.* Parasitism in wild pheasants has not been found to be excessive.

The practice of liberating from ten to twenty-five thousand game farm pheasants each year might be thought to have an influence on abundance of parasites, as birds penned on game farms are more generally exposed to parasites than wild birds. However, field work did not prove this to be the case. There has been a gradual change at the two local game farms to a system of rearing ring-necks by the open-field method through which danger from disease is greatly minimized.

PREDATION

After several years of intensive field work, it is impossible to agree with the common belief that predation drastically curtails the natural reproduction of game birds in the Willamette Valley. Returns from a large enough number of banded birds to have significance, showed 4.5 per cent killed by hawks and owls, 5.5 per cent by unknown predators possibly hawks and owls, 3.5 per cent by cats and skunks, and 3.5 per cent by dogs.

The pheasant population increased from 1.3 birds per each 100 acres in 1936 to about 17 birds to each 100 acres in 1941 throughout the valley. In the light of this evidence, predatory control campaigns seem unnecessary.

In an intensive study at Protection Island, Washington, where causes for pheasant mortality could be more accurately determined, the yearly kill by predators amounted to about 9 per cent of the population. Of that take, hawks and owls were responsible for about 30 per cent, crows less than half of one per cent, and cats and dogs for 8.43 per cent each.

Although there has been a general tendency for sportsmen to encourage "varmint hunts" aimed at the extermination of feral house cats, this study showed that they were no more destructive than supposedly domestic dogs.

On Protection Island, the crow was found to be destructive to pheasant eggs. Of 634 pheasant eggs under observation in 1941, 83, or 12.3 per cent, were destroyed by crows and this caused an unknown number of nests to be abandoned. Only one record is available of an immature pheasant kill by crows. Despite predation, the population on the island increased from the original liberation of 2 cocks and 6 hens in 1937 to 1,540 pheasants in 1941.

Douglas's ground squirrel (*Citellus beecheyi douglasii*) (plate 22, upper), although not generally suspected of this activity, was found to be a predator upon the eggs of upland game birds. Its uncanny ability in locating nests results in a high rate of destruction. In studying this predator, 100 dummy nests were placed in an area commonly used by pheasants, quail, and ground squirrels; 80 per cent of these sets were disturbed. Definite evidence (plate 22, lower) of 43 sets being visited by 73 squirrels and of 20 others being molested was found. Forty-two per cent of the sets were raided more than once. It should be stated that results from man-made nests are likely to appear more damaging than those occurring in nature as man's trails to the nests apparently are followed by various animals.

During the period of the study, 4 out of every 5 predators caught were ground squirrels. In some localities, Douglas's ground squirrels proved to be destructive also to mountain quail eggs, and they may have been one factor responsible for the decrease of these birds in the past two decades.

About 25 years ago a campaign was organized to control the Douglas's ground squirrel in the Willamette Valley, but since that time little has been done, and it is now widely distributed in large numbers. Since it is destructive of forage and grain crops, there is ample reason for taking control measures which would benefit also both pheasants and quail.

In general, predators destroyed about 14 per cent of the pheasant nests. Skunks were found to be the most important, rifling about 4.5 per cent of the nests. Desertion for various causes, part of which might also have been due to skunks, accounted for a loss of 14 per cent.

In summing up the subject of predation, it is apparent that each predator group has some effect upon the pheasant population. Both at Protection Island, where predation is uncontrolled, and in the Willamette Valley, where it is occasionally checked, game populations have increased when man's destructive activities were curbed. Naturally, the increase would be more rapid if all losses to predators were eliminated, but this may be necessary only on such areas as game farms or refuge units, where maximum production is desired. It should be borne in mind that if there were no predators at all, the pheasant population would still be limited by the carrying capacity of the range.

HIGHWAY MORTALITY

Aside from mortality caused by farm machinery and hunting, the most important pheasant loss in Oregon is the highway kill by motor vehicles. This has grown in direct proportion to the development of high-speed highways and increase in the number of motor-driven vehicles. By 1939, mortality from this cause had become a menace to the at-that-time low pheasant population and losses grew rapidly with increase of the birds. Woven-wire fence, erected to protect domestic animals, added a new hazard. Fencing composed of graduated meshes, the smallest less than 1 inch at the bottom was used in many instances. These were not penetrable by pheasants and birds attempting to cross the road sometimes rushed back and forth across the highway between these fences, increasing the number struck down by traffic.

Game managers recommend that fencerows and ditch banks be allowed to grow up to brushy cover but this practice increases the danger to wildlife along high-speed roadways.

In one study area where a drainage ditch filled with cattails paralleled the highway, pheasants made much use of its cover. On a trip over this road, 28 dead pheasants were found on a mile of pavement. On the next mile, where there was no roadside or ditch cover, only 1 pheasant carcass was recovered. Obviously cover next to high-speed highways is undesirable and, where necessary to protect pheasants and other wildlife, it should be removed from the road shoulders for at least 50 feet on each side.

Total Mortality.—Excluding that due to mowing (see p. 258), pheasant mortality calculated from the returns from banded birds had the following causes and percentage rates: Legal and illegal hunting 58.0, automobiles 15.5, mechanical equipment 6.0, miscellaneous predators 5.5, hawks and owls 4.5, cats 3.5, dogs 3.5, and unknown 3.5

VERSATILITY OF THE PHEASANT

The ring-neck is adaptable to a wide range of habitat and climatic conditions. On the Pacific Coast, from British Columbia to central California, the pheasant lives in a humid zone, where grain and seed crops are often not abundant, but where green vegetation—grasses, legumes, and weeds—are available throughout the year. On this diet, it thrives. It has been assumed that in habitats without corn, millet, wheat, and other grain crops or seed-producing food plants, the birds can not survive rigorous winters. This is true, however, only where snow and ice cover the ground for long periods. Early experience with food patches in the Willamette Valley showed their value to be chiefly that of furnishing roosting cover.

Pheasants in our area occupy ranges where grainfields are limited as in the cut-over timber lands on Whidby and Camano Islands, in Puget Sound, Washington. In Chimicum Valley, Jefferson County, Washington, where little grain is produced, the birds live in hayfields and adjacent cut-over lands. In each of these instances, high populations have been noted periodically, reduction in which has usually been due to man.

Since 1933, the Territory of Alaska has experimented with ring-necked pheasants. Survival of plantings made near Petersburg and Wrangell, where the rainfall exceeds 100 inches per year, has been surprising. In this muskeg and deep spruce-hemlock timber habitat, precipitation in some form is heavy each month of the year. When snow reaches a depth of 5 feet, the pheasants, in desperation, resort even to dooryards of both cities.

From the dry, desert-like valleys of central Oregon, through all ranges of climate to the mild, humid Pacific Coast region, the pheasant makes a vigorous stand and fails to increase only under especially severe conditions or poor management. Its versatility is amazing.

HUNTING IN RELATION TO PHEASANT NUMBERS

The ring-necked pheasant was brought to Oregon at a time when game management, if it may be so called, consisted merely of stocking a species, giving it a period of protection, and then providing an open season. This practice continues today in altogether too many localities, there being no attempt to measure the population and set the season to correspond with the potential crop.

It is impossible to determine specifically what conditions prevailed in early pheasant history in the Willamette Valley, but it appears that after the liberation of the pheasants, the long period of protection from 1881 to 1891 gave the birds a degree of confidence which made them an easy prey for gunners. Hunters of that day report that most shots were fired at from 10 to 25 yards, and at least 75 per cent of the birds flushed were within range. Anyone with a keen desire to hunt and aided by a good dog could make great inroads on the pheasant population. Two market hunters, who operated near Albany and Corvallis, Oregon, stated that it was not unusual for them to shoot 100 birds, although the average would run closer to 75, per day. Another told of shooting 30 birds on one farm on a Saturday forenoon. Informed that the owner of the farm would like to have an equal number to present to friends, he returned in the afternoon and obtained 75 (a buggy load) without undue trouble. He stated that the ground had not been shot over for several days and was abundantly stocked, the birds lying well to the dogs.

With no attempt at measuring abundance, and with liberal provisions favoring the hunter, it seems almost miraculous that pheasants survived the first few open seasons in the Willamette Valley. High prices were paid and market hunting was a definite factor in reducing the number of pheasants. In one year express receipts showed that 1,400 dozen pheasants were shipped from Oregon to the San Francisco market alone. Poultry dealers in Portland, Oregon, accepted as many pheasants, quail, snipe, or waterfowl as were brought to them. In fact, it was not until 1905 that the sale of upland game was prohibited by law. Even this restriction was not effective until many years later, when the Migratory Bird Treaty Act of 1916 served to strengthen enforcement of game protective regulations.

In 1891 the total human population in Oregon was about 300,-000 but it had increased to more than 1,100,000 in 1940. There were no automobiles in Oregon in 1891, but shortly after 1900 they began to put in their appearance, increasing to 83,332 in 1919. By 1935 they numbered 270,464, and at present more than 382,000. The general use of the automobile assured an almost universal distribution of hunters over all pheasant range in the Willamette Valley, as these 10 counties contain 60 per cent of the population of the State. Hunters numbering approximately 30,000 requested annually a 15-day season with a 16-bird bag limit. The threat of complete extirpation of the pheasant was imminent, with a total take of over 400,000 possible under the law, not including the usual crippling loss of from 30 to 50 per cent. Yet at that time the total pheasant population of both sexes was undoubtedly less than 100,000 birds.

Thus hunting pressure was increasing and the pheasants decreasing; something had to be done. After a survey of conditions, recommendation was made in 1939 for greater reliance on natural reproduction than on restocking, with suitable protection and management. The suggestions were accepted by the Oregon Game Commission, and after three nesting seasons, relative abundance prevailed. By measuring the crop and making regulations in accordance with the findings, the 1941 hunting season not only was a real success but left abundant brood stock to assure future harvests.

INVENTORIES AS THE BASIS FOR MANAGEMENT

There is often little correlation between popular estimates and actual game numbers. Hence early in this study, we sought to establish an index for measuring population trends. After considerable experimentation, a plot sampling method was adopted.

Through availability of as many students of the Agricultural College as were needed, the drive method of counting was employed. Enough counters were used to flush all of the birds on the sample tracts, which averaged 60 acres in size. The method was tested on Protection Island where the number of pheasants was definitely known and found to have an error of less than 20 per cent, usually in the direction of an under- rather than an over-count. One hundred and fifty areas in 10 counties (1/300 of the total acreage) were driven twice each year for three years. In this territory in which the pheasant population averaged only 1.3 birds per 100 acres in 1936, the numbers rose to 11.9 in 1939, 14.5 in 1940, and 16.4 in 1941.

The sample plot inventory method has proved its value in several different ways: (1) It furnishes definite information as to increase or decrease of birds by districts and seasons; (2) measures the hunting kill; (3) shows areas of low and high populations, calling attention to units needing special attention, as to management practices; (4) gives an index of sex ratios and reproduction; and (5) can be applied at a cost of approximately $55 per million acres of habitat.

Conservative estimates obtained by this method aid by permitting management practices to be based on sound information, rather than on casual and usually optimistic observations resulting in too liberal hunting privileges. Lack of definite information on seasonal populations and unsound regulatory methods have probably been the causes for more disappointments in game management programs than has failure of the game birds to reproduce satisfactorily.

ROTATING REFUGE SYSTEM

In parts of the Willamette Valley most accessible to hunters, areas were so combed for the last pheasant that only the great wariness of some of the birds enabled any seed stock to survive. Thus it appeared desirable to determine if sections of the valley, suitably distributed, could be set aside as "refuge islands" upon which hunting would be prohibited for a period of years until pheasants reached satisfactory numbers. Then new areas could be selected upon which to repeat the process.

Because of the rather extensive daily range of the pheasants, it was found that to be effective in protecting them, the refuge areas must be large—at least 500 acres, and preferably from 1,000 to 3,000 acres each. It is desirable to set aside as much as 20 per cent of the range as refuges, if it can be procured by easements. No such proportion could be included if cash outlays were required.

It was found, however, that game management rights on farms could be obtained through easements, without fees. The best general approach seemed to be to offer the farmer help in orderly economic management of his lands. In Benton County, interviews with 292 individual farmers in suitable pheasant range revealed that 30 per cent of their land could be put under contract for this purpose, without charge.

A detailed survey of the cooperative management possibilities assured the practicability of a program, to be managed by the Oregon State Game Department. It was undertaken on some 150,000 acres of the Willamette Valley, set aside as "rotating refuges." Each refuge was inventoried for game, given attention by the management personnel, the farmer, and the game officials, and finally opened to hunting when the game population warranted.

The program was initiated under provisions for Federal aid to the states in wildlife restoration, and has been administered by the State of Oregon as part of its plan for perpetuating upland game.

The arrangement has already shown its usefulness by: (1) Providing refuge "retreats" for the heavily hunted birds; (2) encouraging natural pheasant production; (3) cultivating a broader interest by hunters in natural restoration as contrasted to reliance upon artificial means of keeping up game bird populations; (4) maintaining centers of game production over the entire habitat; and (5) assuring a high survival of game under protection by field workers of the State.

Since there is little cost connected with the acquisition of leases, allotted funds can be applied directly to game management practices. These and labor have cost less than 4 cents per acre per year. Even that low cost can be materially reduced when all organizing is completed and refuges are alternately used. The program is cheaper than liberating artificially-reared birds, whose direct cost is rarely less than $1.00 each. Annual planting of large numbers of pheasants without improvement of habitat has usually proved unproductive except in unusually good areas. Natural reproduction is the real foundation for an optimum pheasant population, and a bird to the acre can eventually be obtained in the Willamette Valley, where not detrimental to farm crops. In Linn County, the present management plan has already resulted in a population of 50 pheasants per 100 acres without serious damage.

LIBERATION OF GAME FARM BIRDS

Many upland game programs involving the annual stocking of artificially-reared birds have been carried on to please sportsmen. While this procedure usually results in the waste of most of the game birds involved, it has the merit from the game department point of view of satisfying public opinion.

Practice in Oregon had not differed from that of other states in this respect, but investigation of the results obtained from a few liberations quickly convinced the Game Commission that the plan was inefficient. In one area of Yamhill County, game farm pheasants had been released for six consecutive years without producing a measurable increase. In fact some tracts were stocked again and again, and after 10 years of trial did not yield increasing returns.

One reason for failure was delay in making arrangements with sportsmen's organization, which kept the birds for long periods in holding crates. The further practice of planting pheasants in counties in proportion to their hunting license sales without proper consideration of suitable habitat and survival conditions inevitably resulted in many failures.

Results from restocking operations in ten counties are indicated in the following tabulation:

County	Number of pheasants liberated, 1935-1939, inclusive	Acres of habitat per pheasant liberated	Pheasant density per 100 acres 1939	1941
Linn	7,775	105	23.2	45.4
Lane	7,811	38	23.2	43.5
Benton	7,328	30	15.2	20.7
Polk	5,365	41	20.7	17.2
Marion	9,897	45	14.2	10.3
Yamhill	6,961	42	5.7	7.7
Columbia	3,773	22	11.1	6.8
Multnomah	4,145	26	3.2	4.7
Clackamas	6,667	80	4.7	4.5
Washington	7,065	26	4.0	2.7

Conducted over a period of years, sample plot surveys reveal general trends. They indicate the effectiveness of artificial liberation in certain counties and also show that stocking can be discontinued in several counties without affecting pheasant abundance. Other management practices may be of more value in these areas. They show the need for special work in areas of low production to determine causes and whether improvement is possible. For example, the last three counties in the preceding list are areas of high human population density. Clackamas County is suburban, and has most of its area cut up into farms averaging 6 acres each, largely in berries and small fruits. Most of Columbia County is in pasture or cutover lands. Washington County has had a sudden boom resulting from an influx of home builders. Pheasant releases in these areas have been sheer waste.

After consideration of the history of pheasant distribution, it became evident that all areas supposedly eligible for stocking should be carefully scrutinized by regular game department personnel. Since 1938, therefore, this has been a regular procedure of the Oregon Game Department, and a comprehensive set of records has been compiled so that vital data on plantings, survival, and population trends are available.

Plantings are made entirely upon the basis of need, and then only when the areas concerned are deemed suitable. Results from this system of inspection before planting have been so satisfactory that the Game Department has employed two trained game managers to carry on the work, with additional help as needed. For this purpose, the State has been divided into two regions, west and east, respectively, of the Cascade Mountains.

All liberations of immature pheasants are made in late summer or early fall after thorough investigation has demonstrated that supplies of food, grit, water, and cover on the planting area are ample; that the site is remote from high-speed highways; and promises to be free from human interference. Except on seed-stock refuges established to accomplish restoration, for economy, liberations should not exceed two ring-necks per 100 acres. Following these provisions has prevented waste of birds and has bolstered the ring-necked pheasant population where most needed.

LACK OF REGULATORY AUTHORITY AS A HANDICAP TO MANAGEMENT

Although Oregon has a most practical and scientifically-minded Game Commission, it was early found that, despite its keenness to undertake sound management practices, the necessary legal machinery, was lacking, as the State legislature reserved to itself most of the regulatory powers. This was a serious handicap to sound game management as it prevented flexibility in procedure. Furthermore, game law enforcement rests with the State Police, through funds provided in part by the game department, but the State patrolmen cannot be utilized in game management procedures, as taking inventories, making stream surveys, carrying on banding programs, and attending to the many duties of a wildlife manager. Fortunately, the legislature in 1940, at the request of Oregon citizens interested in conservation, corrected this weakness by granting the Game Commission discretionary powers within certain limits. However, the divided authority as to law enforcement and field game management still continues. Under the present system, manpower cannot be drawn upon quickly for vital duties not covered by the term "law enforcement."

Pheasant Propagation

By WOODROW W. BAILEY[1] and RALPH B. NESTLER

There are more breeders of the ring-necked pheasant than of any other species of game bird. According to a survey made by the Fish and Wildlife Service, in 1940 there were at least 2,029 licensed breeders of ring-necked or Chinese pheasants in North America, as compared with 711 of the bobwhite, the next most popular game bird.

Although pheasants can be raised in captivity in nearly every section of the United States, it is generally recognized that the region (figure 1) where they can be successfully liberated is restricted. East of the Mississippi River, latitude 38° marks the approximate southern boundary, whereas west of the Mississippi River, latitude about 36° is the limit. A few pheasants are localized in the valleys of the Gila and Salt Rivers and in similar areas in southern California, but their ability to survive long in those regions is problematical. The northern limits of the range coincide more or less with those of the lower Great Lakes, and the northern wheat, regions. It is desirable that the prospective propagator of pheasants consider carefully the above-mentioned limitations of pheasant range before investing in pheasants for the purpose of liberation.

As most states require a license for the propagation of game birds and have regulations regarding their disposal, persons desiring to propagate pheasants should first consult the state game department or conservation commission.

---

[1]Col. Bailey died August 21, 1944 from wounds received on duty in France. Awarded posthumously the DSC and the Purple Heart.

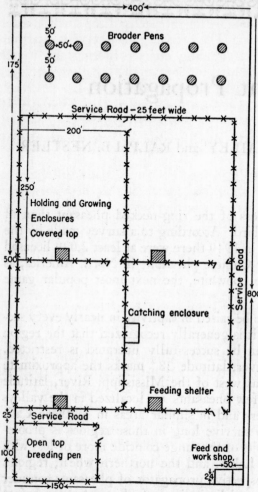

Because of the danger of contracting diseases of domestic fowls, pheasants should not be raised near poultry farms. Likewise, the vicinity of the pens must be kept free of manure piles, garbage heaps, and other sources of contamination. If the pens are more than 500 feet from sources of infection that might be transmitted by flies, the danger of disease will be lessened.

Figure 10 shows a plan for a pheasant farm that would cover approximately 7½ acres. It is designed for 200 pheasant hens and 40 cocks, allowing 60 square feet for each bird. Each brooder pen would accommodate about 200 chicks. The holding and growing enclosures require 4.7 acres and have a total capacity of 5,000 mature birds.

Figure 10.—Layout of pheasant propagation plant on seven and one-half acres, with a capacity of 5,000 mature birds.

HOUSING AND EQUIPMENT

There are two methods commonly used by propagators in mating ring-necked pheasants, namely, group or "harem" mating, and community mating. In group mating, five or six hens and a single cock are confined in a small pen throughout the egg-laying period; whereas, in community mating all the breeders are kept together, in a ratio of five or six hens for each cock bird, in a large open-top enclosure.

Group mating is most suitable for the needs of the small breeder, as it requires less equipment. The breeding pens serve a dual purpose through being used as holding quarters during the winter. Likewise, these pens may be used for bantam hens that are employed for incubating and brooding the pheasant chicks.

Community mating, however, is more practical and efficient for the large-scale producer. Whereas the initial cost of equipment is greater, the expense per bird is much less than it is in the group mating system.

Group Laying Pens.—There are almost as many different designs for pheasant group-laying pens (plate 23) as there are propagators and all apparently give satisfactory service. In general, a pen constructed of light-weight material so as to be easily movable and providing not less than 20 square feet of ground space for each breeding bird, meets most requirements. An enclosure 10 feet by 12 feet by 4 feet is very satisfactory for six or seven breeders.

One should place the pens on a heavily-sodded and well-drained area (preferably sloping toward the east) that has not at least for two years been used as poultry range. Pens in rows 100 feet apart with a space of 14 feet between the pens make the most economical use of the space. This arrangement permits of their being moved to clean ground without the same plot being used twice. Shifting the pens to clean soil three or four times a season is usually sufficient.

Community Laying Pens.—This type of breeding pen is an enclosure fenced with hexagonal poultry netting and having an open top. The size of the pen depends on the number of birds to be confined and should provide not less than 35 square feet of space per bird. A 6-foot fence, constructed around the enclosure with 5½ feet above ground and the other half foot buried in the ground, usually prevents predators from digging under the fence. The corner posts and braces should be placed on the inside of the enclosure to keep cats or other animals from entering the pen by climbing the braces.

A solid border 2 feet high at the bottom of the fence will usually prevent the birds from trying to escape and will also make them more contented, as they cannot see what is happening on the outside. The use of second-hand burlap bags is the simplest and least expensive as well as a very effective way to provide the border. Boards or building paper also may be used. Tree branches piled in the center and along the edges of the breeding pens provide shelter for the birds as well as choice nesting sites. Also the more timid birds may escape attacks from hostile penmates by hiding in the brush.

BREEDING STOCK AND ITS CARE

Selection of Breeders.—The quality and care of breeding birds are primary considerations in successful game farming. The importance of selecting large, healthy, vigorous, and early-maturing birds cannot be overemphasized. Early maturing females can be selected in September and October; whereas cock birds are more profitably chosen later in the season. The offspring of birds that produce more than the average number of eggs of good fertility and hatchability usually turn out to be good producers themselves. It works very satisfactorily to hold the best yearling breeders for the second year and replace the inferior stock with offspring from the former good producers. Two-year-old birds produce as well as yearlings, whereas older birds are not always reliable breeders. Some propagators prefer to keep all young birds for breeders, but good results are obtained when yearling cocks are mated to 2-year-old females or when 2-year-old cocks are mated to yearling females. The "egg-eating" habit in pheasants is believed to be more prevalent among birds that are 2 years old or older than in yearlings; for this reason alone, some propagators prefer yearling breeders.

Care of Breeders in Winter.—Birds selected as breeders should be isolated from the rest of the flock. This precaution tends to prevent an outbreak of disease that might wipe out the entire flock. It is wise to reserve a few more birds for breeders than are needed, in order to allow for winter mortality.

It is important that these selected birds receive the best of care. The winter holding enclosure should be provided with shelters (plate 24, left) and windbreaks where the pheasants can seek protection from snow, wind, and rain. An ample supply of feed and water should be kept in a dry place under the shelter where the birds can have free access to it during all kinds of weather.

Breeding Principles.—Excessive inbreeding on the game farm, especially of closely related individuals, as brother and sister, mother and son, without the strictest selection, tends to reduce the production and hatchability of eggs and lowers the constitutional vigor and growth rate of the resulting progeny.

Line breeding is systematic inbreeding, by which relatives are mated in such a manner that a given ancestor will appear in the pedigree of the progeny more often than any other. It is designed to avoid the possible dangers arising from the miscellaneous mating of individuals that are too closely related. In order to practice line breeding successfully, however, a breeder must have a good understanding of the principles of selection. When line breeding is correctly used among several hundred breeding birds, outcrossing will not be necessary for many years.

Outcrossing is the introduction of new blood from birds of the same variety but of different strains. When inbreeding has been accompanied by a decline in vigor, outcrossing usually results in the full recovery of vigor in the next generation. This is true even though the relatively unrelated birds are themselves closely inbred.

New blood can be satisfactorily brought into the pheasant flock through the purchase of cock birds from, or exchange of birds with, another propagator who has an unrelated flock. Such new birds should be quarantined for a period of 3 weeks before being mixed with the flock. This period will usually suffice for the detection of any ailing birds and tends to prevent the spread of disease.

There is some difference of opinion among game propagators and geneticists regarding the desirability of introducing wild male birds into a game-farm flock in order to maintain wildness. One state conservation official points out that "most of the original pheasant stocking in this country was made with birds which had been reared on game farms." Again, much of the game farm stock came originally from England where the birds had been artificially propagated for years. "In these cases, it is evident that the birds retained enough of the wild characteristics to enable a fairly large proportion of them to adapt themselves to the wild environment." He points out that "unless the pedigree of the birds introduced was well known and satisfactory, a great deal of harm genetically, might come from such an introduction."

An official of another state commission, on the other hand, believes that "the introduction of wild trapped stock at various intervals is absolutely essential to the continued production of game of high quality for restocking purposes." Work with turkeys has convinced him that "in turkeys, 'wildness' is not only the result of parental education, association with other individuals, and reactions to environmental stimuli, but also of hereditary factors." A prominent poultry geneticist concurs in the latter belief.

Mating.—Ring-necked pheasants are polygamous and are successfully mated in ratios of one cock bird to five or six hens. Breeding usually begins near the first of April and continues through June. Mating groups are picked arbitrarily from the flock of selected breeders. These birds generally are moved from the winter holding quarters to the breeding pens sometime during the last 2 weeks of March. This move gives the birds a chance to become accustomed to the new enclosure before egg laying begins. When community mating is practiced, new blood should be introduced to the flock before the birds leave their winter quarters. This practice will often prevent fighting among the strange cocks at breeding time. However, when group matings are practiced with only five or six hens confined to each enclosure, this precaution is not necessary. The strange cocks can be put directly into the breeding pens from the quarantine enclosure.

Wing Clipping.—It is necessary to clip the flight feathers of the breeding birds that are confined to open-top enclosures. This is most satisfactorily done by cutting the primary feathers of one wing close enough to prevent the birds from flying, but not so close as to draw blood. If care is used not to pull any feathers, new ones will quickly grow and enable the bird to fly again.

Preventing Disturbances.—Naturally wild and flighty, the pheasant is easily disturbed in captivity. Minor commotions often cause breeding birds to go out of production for several days. Therefore, it is undesirable to permit dogs, cats, and other domestic animals near the breeding pens. Frequent visits by strangers also should be avoided. Handling the birds or introducing new ones into the flock after breeding starts is disturbing.

Sanitation.—Breeding pens, as previously stated, should be located on well-drained areas. The 10- by 12- by 4-foot group-type laying pens should be moved several times during the breeding season. With the community-type laying pen, it is an excellent practice to plow and lime the ground at the end of each breeding season and to sod it with a mixture of red clover, alfalfa, and timothy, or other locally suitable combination of plants.

Keeping clean the receptacles for feed and water, removing waste feed from around the hoppers regularly in order to avoid attracting flies, removing sick or dead birds from the pens as soon as they are noticed, and burning the carcasses of the dead, all are important sanitary measures.

Care of Eggs.—In confinement a single nest is often used by several layers. Regardless of the presence of nests, many of the eggs are scattered about the yard. This often encourages birds to begin eating eggs. Therefore, where a large number of breeders are confined to the same enclosure, it is desirable to collect the eggs twice daily. The habit of "egg eating" among confined pheasants is sometimes corrected by clipping the beak of the offender. If this measure fails to break the habit, remove the guilty birds from the breeding pen. The vice of "egg eating" should be checked as soon as discovered, so that other birds will not learn it.

It is not desirable to keep pheasant eggs more than 7 days before starting incubation. Eggs placed with the large end up in racks, stored in a moist, cool place at a temperature of from 50° to 55° F., as soon as they have been collected from the breeding pen, and turned twice daily until time of incubation, will give the best results.

FEEDING

Water.—It is very important to have a constant supply of clean, fresh water before the birds at all times. In the domestic fowl, water is approixmately 56 per cent of a bird's body and 72.5 per cent of the egg content—figures that undoubtedly approximate those for pheasants. Water ranks far above any other substance in rate of turnover in the body. Laying birds can go 24 hours without food and not suffer an appreciable check to reproduction; but if they are deprived of water for the same period of time, complete cessation of egg-laying may result. Readily cleaned fountains should be used.

Grit.—When grit is present, there is a more efficient utilization of feed and less energy is required by the gizzard for grinding feed.

It is well to keep a supply of insoluble, nonfriable grit before the pheasants, therefore, although gallinaceous birds can live without grit and even digest whole grain without its aid.

Greens.—Green leaves are a good source of a number of valuable dietary ingredients. If the bird receives a diet that contains optimum levels of the essential vitamins, minerals, and amino acids, however, greens are not necessary. Under such conditions they would serve as a relish more than anything else. Lawn clippings, freshly-cut alfalfa, or bits of lettuce may be given twice a week or oftener if available.

Mashes.—So far as is known, no specific research has been reported on the nutritional requirements of the breeding pheasant. Several commercial feed manufacturers have put on the market, however, breeding diets for game birds that are recommended for both quail and pheasants. Several of these feeds are being used by pheasant propagators with excellent results. Until more information is available on the nutritional requirements of the breeding pheasant, however, it is recommended that the propagator use a well-balanced diet containing not less than 25 per cent protein.

Table 19 names the ingredients of an all-mash breeding diet that was formulated at the Patuxent Research Refuge for bobwhite quail. It has not been tried with pheasants, but in the light of the above statements, it should be satisfactory. No grain mixture is to be fed as a supplement to this mash. Breeding birds are placed on this diet about a month before egg-laying begins. A gradual change from the maintenance ration, made over a period of at least 4 or 5 days by blending the two, is recommended.

Weatherproof feed hoppers have been used with satisfactory results. To prevent waste of feeds, the hopper is kept no more than three-fourths full, though never permitted to become empty. Feed and water containers should be well distributed over the entire enclosure. The "egg eating" vice is less apt to occur among pheasants when a plentiful supply of feed is made available in all parts of the breeding enclosure.

INCUBATION

For commercial pheasant production, artificial incubation is the most practical way to hatch the birds.

Types of Incubators.—Almost any of the commercial incubators designed for use with domestic poultry will satisfactorily hatch pheasant eggs. The pheasant-egg capacity of an incubator will be approximately 1½ times that for chicken eggs. Most box-type incubator trays are satisfactory for pheasant eggs. However, some that have trough-like egg-holders designed for chicken eggs, will have to be modified before they will accommodate pheasant eggs. This can be accomplished by folding strips of hardware cloth (3 meshes to the inch) into trough-like egg-holders that will fit the pheasant eggs. These can then be fastened inside the regular holders.

TABLE 19.—Diets for ring-necked pheasants

All-Mash Breeding Diet (26 per cent protein)
(Start 1 month before breeding season)

	Pounds
Ground yellow corn	32.7
Standard wheat middlings	10.0
Dehydrated alfalfa leaf meal	10.0
Dried buttermilk (or skim milk)	5.0
Sardine fish meal	5.0
Soybean meal (high temperature processed)	30.0
Special steamed bonemeal	3.1
Pulverized high grade limestone	2.7
Salt mixture	1.0
Vitamin A and D feeding oil fortified	0.5
Total	100.0

Growing Diet

Ground yellow corn	11.2
Wheat bran	15.0
Flour wheat middlings	12.5
Ground oats	10.0
Dried skim milk	12.5
Alfalfa leaf meal	5.0
50 per cent protein meal scraps	11.0
White fish meal	2.75
Soybean meal	19.5
Salt	0.5
Vitamin A and D feeding oil fortified	0.25
Total	100.20

Maintenance Diet

Coarse-cracked yellow corn		100
Wheat		100
Oats		50
Buckwheat	or 100 lbs.	50
Barley	of one	50
Total		350

According to research in New York State on incubation of the eggs of upland game birds, pheasant eggs hatch best when incubated in an agitated-air type machine for the first 20 days and then transferred to a still-air machine for hatching. Although this successive use of the machines is preferred, nevertheless, with proper adjustments the agitated-air type machine will both incubate and hatch pheasant eggs satisfactorily. In order that the proper temperature and humidity may be maintained throughout incubation, however, a separate machine for hatching, with either still or agitated air, is desirable. In a small machine the temperature and humidity can be more accurately controlled than in a larger one.

Operation of Incubators.—Before setting any eggs, it is desirable to operate the incubator 24 to 48 hours in order that proper adjustments can be made in temperature, humidity, and ventilation. The machine must be level, especially if it is of the still-air type, so that an even temperature will be maintained throughout; and space 2 to 4 inches must be allowed underneath for free circulation of air. The incubator room should have a temperature of about 70° F., and be properly ventilated without drafts. Distilled water and a clean wick insure proper reading of the hygrometer.

Game-birds eggs hatch best when set in a vertical position with the large end up. In order to prevent shifting or turning from the vertical position in the incubating tray, place the eggs firmly against each other and fill the space at the end of each row with crumpled pieces of paper. Loosely packed eggs may be broken by rolling against each other during the process of turning. Pheasant eggs hatch best when turned three to four times daily up to the 20th day. After being transferred from the incubator to the hatcher on the 20th day, the eggs should not again be turned or disturbed. For the first 20 days of incubation, the dry bulb on the thermometer in a force-draft or agitated-air machine should read 99.5° F., and the wet bulb 88° to 89° F. In still-air machines, heated with either water or air, the dry-bulb thermometer should read 102.5° F., when the bulb of the thermometer is level with the top of the eggs, and the wet-bulb thermometer should read 89° to 92° F.

In order to obtain the most efficient use of space in the incubator, all eggs with soft or cracked shells should be rejected. Infertile eggs or those with dead embryos may be removed at the end of a week. These are best detected by candling with a spotlight tester. When light is passed through an infertile egg, no sign of embryonic growth is seen and the egg has a clear appearance. A dead embryo appears as a floating dark spot surrounded by a faint blood ring. A live embryo a week old fills about one-third of the egg and shows definite signs of life even after only 1 week of incubation. A second candling may be made on the 14th day of incubation to reveal additional dead embryos. By this time the living embryo fills about two-thirds of the egg, whereas the dead embryo occupies less space and shows a definite blood ring. Candling can best be done in a dark room or at night. Care should be exercised not to jar the eggs nor to allow them to remain out of the incubator very long.

On the 20th day of incubation, when the eggs are transferred from the incubator to the hatcher, a cover is placed on the trays. This prevents the newly-hatched chicks from escaping and falling to the bottom of the machine. The temperature of the hatcher in an agitated-air machine should be 99° F., and the wet-bulb reading should be from 87° to 88° F. In the still-air machine the temperature should read from 101.5° to 102° F., and the wet-bulb thermometer from 88° to 91° F.

As the rate of exchange of oxygen and carbon dioxide is in proportion to the size of the embryo, the amount of fresh air entering the machine needs to be increased as the embryo develops. As the adjustment of the ventilators on one make or type of machine does not necessarily apply to those of another make or type, it is advisable that the operator follow very closely the instructions of the manufacturer. In general, the following rule may be observed: adjust the intake and exhaust vents so that they are about one-fourth open during the first week, one-half open during the second week, three-fourths open through to the 20th day, and completely open thenceforth.

Not all machines of the same make and model incubate and hatch equally well. Such differences may require special adjustment of the incubator as to temperature, humidity, ventilation, and air movement in order to obtain normal hatches. It is advisable for the operator to determine the necessary combination of adjustments by varying only one factor at a time.

The best results come from leaving the chicks in the incubator 24 to 36 hours after hatching in order that they may dry without becoming chilled. During this period the ventilation is increased and

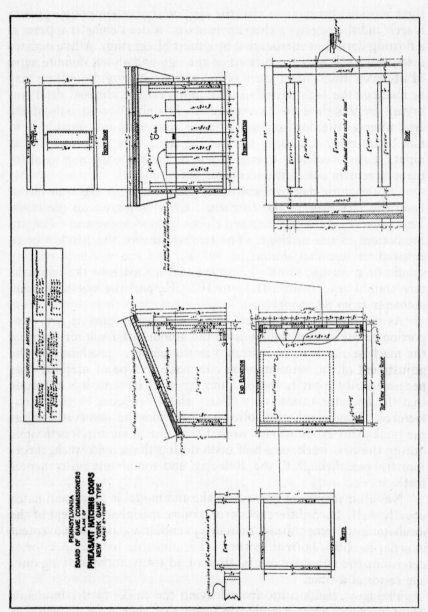

Figure 11.—Plan of hatching coop used for brooding pheasant chicks with a bantam hen. (Permission of the Pennsylvania Game Commission)

the humidity decreased so that the birds will dry as quickly as possible. It is not necessary to supply food and water during this time, as nature has provided a storage of food in the egg yolk which is gradually absorbed by the chicks through from 24 to 48 hours after hatching.

Small-scale Operations.—When operating on a small scale it is not advisable to go to the expense of obtaining special equipment. Midget incubators or bantam hens may be satisfactorily used by 4-H Club members, farm boys, sportsmen's clubs, and others for hatching only a small number of eggs. Several manufacturers of poultry equipment make electric and oil-heated incubators of small capacity that are efficient, yet inexpensive. An electric midget incubator (plate 24, right) has a capacity of about 90 pheasant eggs. As in the larger machines, the temperature controls are automatic. For approximately the same price, an oil-heated incubator of 150 pheasant-egg capacity can be obtained.

Bantam or medium-weight domestic, broody hens with healthy appearance and gentle temperament are likewise satisfactory to incubate pheasant eggs on a small scale. Breeds with featherless legs are to be preferred, as mites, lice, and similar parasites are often harbored in the leg feathers. Furthermore, these feathers increase the trampling hazard and when wet or muddy, present an undesirable hover to the pheasant chicks. For both incubation and brooding purposes, the Seabright bantam and Rhode Island Red breeds have been found satisfactory.

The hatching coop (plate 25 and figure 11) is used extensively on game farms in Pennsylvania and New York. The nest is built on the ground, as the coop has no bottom. It will be noted in figure 11 that the recommended coop of the Pennsylvania Game Commission has one removable slat in order that the hen may be taken out and placed in an exercising pen. The top is hinged at the front of the coop and hooked with a fastener at the rear to prevent storms from dislodging it. After the chicks are hatched, the coop is used to confine the hen on the rearing area.

Lice and mite infestations can be effectively controlled by dusting the broody hen with a standard brand of insect powder at the beginning of the incubation and again about 10 days later. Lice alone can be effectively eliminated by use of sodium fluoride applied in pinches at the vent, breast, inside each leg and wing, on the back near the tail, and on the neck. The brood hen is confined in the nest box or hatching coop, except for a 20-minute period each morning during which she is released to feed, drink, and exercise. In inclement weather the hen is returned to the nest as soon as possible in order to prevent the eggs from becoming chilled. It is important to remove the hen regularly, if only for a short time. When not released at the usual time, she is likely to become restless and try to free herself. As a consequence, she may break some of the eggs or defecate in the nest.

BROODING

There are in general two types of houses used by commercial breeders for rearing pheasants—the colony and nursery houses; both have proved satisfactory.

Colony House and Its Equipment.—Various styles of colony brooders have been in use on the larger pheasant farms for many years. The round-type house is a favorite with most pheasant breeders. In this form the chicks are not so apt to crowd in large groups as in one having corners. Nevertheless, the hexagonal and rectangular styles of brooder houses also are in wide use. The colony-house brooder is mounted on skids so that it can be moved easily from place to place by use of a horse or tractor.

The house illustrated in plate 26 is 6 feet high and has a floor space of 112 square feet. It will accommodate from 225 to 250 pheasant chicks up to 6 weeks of age. The sides and top are constructed of a composition insulating material fastened to a framework of wood. The material itself is a good nonconductor of heat and will stand exposure to weather well if painted. The floor is made of wood, closely fitted so as to eliminate cracks or crevices where filth or harmful organisms might collect.

Each house is provided with a movable outside run. This enclosure is fenced with 1-inch mesh poultry wire 4 feet high, firmly pegged to the ground. The outside run should provide 5 to 7 square feet for each bird; thus a 40 by 40-foot enclosure will accommodate about 250 pheasant chicks. When the yard becomes bare or contaminated, the run should be moved to clean soil.

There are several types of brooder heaters that will operate successfully in the colony brooder house. The coal brooder stove, oil-burning stove, and electric brooders are successfully used, but the last named (plate 27) is the most efficient and reliable. For a house having a floor 12 feet across, the hover should be about 56 inches in diameter. An electric brooder of this size should be equipped with a 440-watt heating element. The hover is hung from the center of the ceiling by a rope and pulley attachment, so that it can be raised or adjusted to any desired height to facilitate the cleaning of the brooder room and to regulate the heat given the chicks. A guard is useful for the first 3 or 4 days of brooding. It may be made of galvanized roofing, 1 foot high, and of sufficient length so that when the ends are joined it will enclose a circular area about 2 feet greater in diameter than that under the hover.

Ventilation for the colony brooder house is provided by adjustable windows and a roof ventilator. It is important that the birds be provided with a supply of fresh air at all times but that direct drafts be avoided. If moisture gathers in the litter and on the walls, the ventilation is insufficient. Bad ventilation is often responsible for the development of colds and roup among pheasants.

Nursery House.—The nursery type of brooder has been in use by pheasant propagators only a few years. It is becoming popular as it has been found very efficient in mass production. Some nursery houses are 28 by 54 feet, have two stories, and will accommodate approximately 3,200 pheasant chicks. Each floor is divided into eight pens, 10 by 11 feet each, with a feed room at the end. The pens are constructed of 1-inch mesh poultry wire along each side of the building, which has an 8-foot aisle down the middle to facilitate cleaning and servicing the units. The walls and ceiling are covered with insulating board. The interior of a typical nursery house is shown in plate 28.

No special equipment is needed, as that used for poultry will answer. For the first 4 or 5 days of brooding, the feed may be given on pie pans or similar flat receptacles. Earthenware waterers are excellent because filth shows up readily and may be removed easily. Small chick feeders may be used after the first few days. Later, when the birds are 3 to 4 weeks old, larger containers may be used. For the feeding of greens, a white-enameled pan is desirable.

Methods for the Small-scale Breeder.—The simplest and most inexpensive method is use of the bantam that hatched the pheasants to brood them. Feeding and watering equipment may be the same as that used by the large-scale breeder. A simple yet effective kerosene heater that can be used in place of a bantam in small-scale operations is shown in plate 29. The heater is placed in a small enclosure—about 42 inches long, 16 inches wide, and 10 inches deep (all inside dimensions) that is made from one board, 10 inches wide and 10 feet long. This brooder is kept indoors and will accommodate 35 to 60 chicks.

Chick Mortality.—The greatest mortality among captivity-reared pheasants occurs during the first 4 weeks after hatching. Most of the early mortality is among weak or abnormal chicks, which are the result of poor breeding, bad management of breeders, improper care of eggs, and faulty incubation. Other common causes of early mortality are incorrect brooding temperature and ventilation, cannibalism and feather pulling, disease, and mechanical injuries. With proper management, however, these early losses can be greatly reduced. For information on diseases and their control, see the publications named in the list of literature cited under the entries: Buckley, Bunyea, and Cram (1936), and Shillinger and Morley (1942).

Cannibalism.—Cannibalism is a vice that is sporadic among most game birds in capivity. It may occur from several days of age to maturity, but the greatest loss from it among pheasants comes during the first 6 weeks. The most common manifestations of the vice are toe-picking, beak-picking, and feather pulling. Of these, toe- and beak-picking are the most disastrous. In the case of toe-picking, the injury is on the upper surface of the foot and is at times so severe as to expose the tendons. Besides losing blood, affected birds are often so severely wounded that they are unable to reach feed and water and die of starvation. The vice often begins as the result of one bird picking at a particle of food clinging to the foot or beak of another. If the skin is broken in the attempt to obtain the food, and blood appears, the picking continues. Feather pulling in pheasants occurs most frequently while the feathers are in the blood stage.

Cannibalism appears to be the result of a combination of factors which, however, can be controlled largely by proper management. For instance, there seems to be a marked relationship between cannibalism and the intensity of light in the brooder pens. The brighter the pens, the greater is the opportunity for pecking. Hence many of the larger producers keep the chicks in semidarkness during the brooding period. This has been largely responsible for the development of the nursery-type brooder house.

Overcrowding, overheating, chilling, and poor ventilation also may contribute toward cannibalism. Likewise, improper feeding practices—as failure of the feed and water supply for several hours, lack of sufficient feeding space, or use of an unpalatable feed may cause an outbreak of picking. The addition of common salt to the diet at the beginning of an outbreak is claimed by many propagators to be an effective curative for the vice. Working with quail, the authors found that salt will effectively check picking in many birds if sprinkled on the feed in the hopper in a thin, visible layer as soon as the vice is noticed. One or two "saltings" are usually sufficient. If the vice continues despite every precaution, as a last resort the upper mandible of all the birds may be clipped or pared back to the quick with sharp shears or a knife.

CARE OF THE YOUNG

By the Commercial Breeder.—Before the pheasant chicks are moved from the incubator to the brooder house, it is necessary that the pen and its equipment be thoroughly cleaned, disinfected, and dried. Fresh litter, as shredded cane or soft wood shavings, should be placed on the floor, and feed and water should be made available.

Avoid cool atmosphere or drafts in the room when the chicks are removed from the incubator. Place suitable containers close at hand for holding and conveying chicks to the brooder house (plate 29, lower). Cardboard "pullmans," manufactured for domestic chicks, with a thin layer of excelsior or pine needles on the bottom, are satisfactory.

The temperature on the floor under the hover should be kept from 96° to 98° F., at the start of brooding and reduced to 90° F., by the end of the first week. After the first week, lower the temperature 5° F., each week for four and a half weeks and discontinue artificial heat thereafter. Some propagators prefer reducing the temperature by changing the thermostatic controls; others obtain the same result by gradually raising the hover.

Confine the birds near the heat for the first few days by using a guard encircling the brooder about 6 inches from the edge of the hover. Enlarge the circle a little each day, and remove the guard after the fourth day. The hover guard keeps the young birds near the source of warmth and prevents them from crowding, or getting lost, in cool corners.

Beginning the second week, weather permitting, birds may freely use the outside yard during the day. At the end of the fifth week, they should be moved into the holding pens. Heavy losses are likely to occur if they are moved during rainy or extremely cool weather, especially to holding pens not provided with shelters.

Birds in a nursery brooder house are managed very much as are those in a colony house, except that they have no access to outside runs and are kept under controlled light.

By the Small-scale Breeder.—In brooding chicks with a foster mother, the hen is confined to the coop by means of vertical slats (plate 30, upper) so spaced as to hold her in confinement yet permit the chicks to pass freely. Though the chicks are always confined to the coop for the first day, on the second day, if the weather permits, they are allowed to use a small nursery run attached to the coop.

The nursery run is removed after the third day, permitting the young birds to range freely and to return to the broody hen at will. During the first two weeks, the birds are not released in the mornings until the grass is dry.

The mother hen and chicks are fed together during the first week, but thereafter the chicks' feed is placed outside on a clean board or in feed containers. The regular removal of waste feed is necessary.

Birds should be trapped during the eighth and ninth weeks and shipped for liberation, or confined in covered pens. When they are left on free range for longer periods, many escape.

The simplest, yet most effective, way to catch range-reared pheasants is to trap them at their feeding station by use of a wire-covered enclosure (6 feet by 10 feet by 10 feet) similar to that used for trapping pheasants in the holding pen (plate 30, lower). After the habit of feeding at a definite place has been formed, the trap is placed there until the birds become accustomed to it. The doors are left open to allow birds to pass in and out freely, and the trap is baited with the regular feed, some of this being scattered outside. After the birds have become accustomed to the trap, all of the feed is placed inside. The operator of the trap then conceals himself in a nearby blind and drops the door by means of a single cord or wire. Trapping not oftener than twice a week is less likely to cause the birds to become wild and attempt to escape or avoid the trap.

Sanitation.—Strict sanitation at all times for stock of all ages, but especially for the very young, cannot be overemphasized. Although disease can and does appear when apparently all precautions have been taken, the operator should not be discouraged, but should remember that it can be combatted successfully only where cleanliness is scrupulously maintained. The following simple rules can save the breeder many dollars and much worry:

(1) Thoroughly wash and disinfect the brooder room and equipment between broods. Disinfectant does not take the place of good scrubbing with soap and water. Treatment with creosol or some similar germicide, is beneficial only after coatings of filth have been removed.

(2) Keep waterers clean and filled with fresh water.

(3) Do not leave uncovered garbage cans, manure piles, or refuse heaps near the brooder pens. Such objects are attractive to flies and become focal points for the spread of disease.

(4) Do not leave dead birds lying in the brooder pens. Remove the carcasses promptly and burn them.

(5) Renew litter frequently. Wet, musty, or caked litter is dangerous.

(6) Do not allow birds to run on sour, bare yards or where water stands after each rain. Sweeten the soil with a light coating of lime spaded in and keep it in good sod. An excellent practice is to shift the colony type of brooder house frequently to fresh ground.

(7) Wash the hands thoroughly after cleaning out filth or handling sick or dead birds, especially before watering and feeding stock.

Feeding.—According to research at Cornell University and at the Pennsylvania State College, optimum growth of pheasant chicks during the first 8 weeks was obtained with a starting mash containing 28 per cent protein. The formula presented in table 1 is recommended by the Cooperative Unit at the Pennsylvania State College as giving "excellent results as measured by growth, efficiency of feed consumption, mortality, cannibalism, and occurrence of perosis." No grain is used with this diet.

Pheasant chicks should be supplied with feed and fresh water at at all times, and grit should be furnished after the birds learn to eat. The sprinkling of finely-cut green alfalfa, clover, or lawn clippings over the feed will encourage young pheasants to eat. As the birds pick at the colored particles, some of the feed also will be taken. Likewise, greens floating in the drinking water will attract attention.

It is important, however, that such material should not be permitted to spoil in the feed and water containers.

It is desirable that the birds have ample feeding space so that crowding will not occur. When there is insufficient room, the smaller birds of the group are unable to compete with the more vigorous ones. When a commercial domestic-chick-size feeder is used for pheasant chicks, about 1 to 1½ inches of feeding space should be provided for each bird. Feed containers should be well distributed over the brooder floor so as to be readily accessible to all of the chicks. During the first few days of brooding, it is necessary that feed containers be kept filled to the top in order to make the feed easily available to the small birds. To prevent waste of feed, however, after the chicks have learned to eat, the hoppers need be kept only two-thirds full, larger feeders being substituted when necessary.

Correcting Deficiencies in the Diet.—When considering the breeding and growing diets given in table 19, the propagator must remember that the soil in certain sections (and consequently the grains and other crops thereon) may be deficient in iron, iodine, or copper, all of which are important in pheasant nutrition. Where these deficiencies are suspected, the use of one of the following salt mixtures is suggested to supplement the diet:

Salt Mixture No. 1
(Without iodine)

	Pounds
Common salt (NaCl)	50.000
Anhydrous manganous sulfate ($MnSO_4$)	0.850
Anhydrous ferrous sulfate ($FeSO_4$)	0.550
Anhydrous copper sulfate ($CuSO_4$)	0.020
	51.420

Salt Mixture No. 2
(With iodine)

Mixture No. 1	51.420
Potassium iodide (KI)	0.035
Anhydrous sodium thiosulfate ($Na_2S_2O_3$)	0.032
Calcium carbonate ($CaCO_3$)	0.035
	51.522

It is especially important that the supplements for either mixture be weighed accurately and thoroughly pulverized by a druggist or chemist and then carefully mixed with the common salt. As many druggists probably do not keep certain of these ingredients on hand, it would be desirable to purchase 1 or 2 pounds of each wholesale. Substitutes for the exact chemicals recommended are not acceptable.

Manganese is necessary for the prevention of perosis, or slipped tendon, a leg deformity resulting from a nutritional deficiency. One simple method of preparing a 50-pound lot of the manganese-salt combination is to spread about 10 pounds of common salt on the bottom of a clean, dry washtub, sprinkle 0.85 pound of powdered anhydrous manganous sulfate evenly over the surface, and mix thoroughly. To this the remaining 40 pounds of salt are added and again mixed thoroughly, with either the hands or a paddle. Stored in a dry place, this mixture will keep indefinitely, though high humidity may cause lumps which need to be broken down by forcing them through a sieve.

The sodium and calcium compounds used in Mixture No. 2 to stabilize the iodine should be mixed with the potassium iodide before the latter is combined with the other chemicals.

Two of these diets (table 19) call for feeding-oil fortified with vitamins A and D, which is at least four times as potent in these vitamins as is ordinary cod-liver oil. It should meet all the specifications for U. S. P. cod-liver oil, except that each gram should contain not fewer than 400 international units of vitamin D and 3,000 international units of Vitamin A. To have the oil evenly distributed throughout the feed, it is first mixed with a part of the ground corn or with about 5 per cent of the entire ration. After removing all lumps, the mixture is combined with the bulk of the ingredients.

Recently, D-activated animal sterol has received considerable publicity as an excellent substitute for feeding-oil, as a source of vitamin D. If difficulty is experienced in obtaining the vitamin A and D feeding-oil, or if the price is prohibitive, the D-activated sterol may be substituted for a part or all of the oil. It is suggested that 1.2 parts of the sterol (450,000 i.u. units per pound) be mixed thoroughly with 8.8 parts of finely-ground yellow corn. This mixture is then fed as 0.333 per cent of the diet for each 0.1 per cent of the vitamin A and D feeding-oil fortified that it replaces (table 19).

One must realize that the D-activated sterol does not furnish vitamin A, as does the feeding-oil. When the oil is omitted, alfalfa leaf meal and, to a lesser extent, yellow corn may be used to supply the necessary quantity of vitamin A. Therefore, it is essential that the alfalfa leaf meal meet the requirements given. Five per cent of dehydrated alfalfa leaf meal from the previous harvest that has been properly stored, should supply sufficient vitamin A. However, 7.5 per cent of the meal would give a better margin of safety.

The dehydrated alfalfa leaf meal should be "U. S. extra-green medium," containing not more than 18 per cent of crude fiber and not less than 19 per cent of crude protein. It should have 85 per cent or more of leaf particles.

Oats used in the growing diet should weigh approximately 38 pounds to the bushel.

The soybean oil meal is best if it has been processed at a high temperature or toasted, but not scorched.

If dried skim milk or dried buttermilk is difficult to obtain or the cost is prohibitive, a mixture of 63 parts by weight of fish (preferably sardine) meal and 37 parts of dried whey or a fermentation by-product may be substituted. There are several of these on the market, among which are B-y Feed, Paco, Produloc, and Curbay. This list is by no means complete, and the inclusion or omission of any names is not to be considered as implying endorsement or discrimination.

All or part of the fish meal can be replaced by soybean oil meal. Such a modification of the diets should not be attempted, however, except in an emergency.

Determining the Sex of Day-old Chicks.—A simple but effective method of sexing day-old pheasant chicks was discovered by Latham of the Pennsylvania Game Commission. This method, based on the feather development on the side of the head, can be applied by game-bird propagators and research workers with an accuracy of 90 per cent or more. See Figure 12.

As pointed out by Latham (1942) as pheasants are polygamous birds, there are many practical uses of such a technique.

For example, in Pennsylvania, where the shooting of only male ringnecks has been permitted for almost 20 years, the State Game Commission requires for its spring stocking program far more male than female pheasants. To date, however, the production of one thousand cock birds has necessitated the rearing of approximately two thousand individuals of unknown sexes to six to eight weeks of age, when the

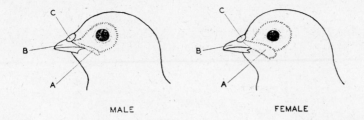

MALE   FEMALE

OUTLINE DRAWING DAY-OLD PHEASANT CHICKS
SHOWING MALE AND FEMALE CHARACTERISTICS
LEGEND: "A"-STRIP OF LONG DOWN. "B"-UPPER MANDIBLE. "C"-CERE.

MALE   INTERMEDIATE   FEMALE

TYPICAL RINGNECK PHEASANT CHICKS

Figure 12.—Cheek patches of day-old pheasant chicks. (Courtesy of Pennsylvania Game Commission.)

Plate 25.—Interior of hatching coop showing newly-hatched pheasants. (By permission of the New York State Conservation Department)

Plate 26.—Upper. Brooder house, colony-type; exterior.
Lower. Partial view of interior. (Courtesy of the Pennsylvania State Game Farm, Loyalsock, Pa.)

Plate 27.—Electric brooder in a nursery house. (By permission of the New York State Conservation Department)

Plate 28.—Interior of a nursery house for pheasants. (By permission of the New York State Conservation Department)

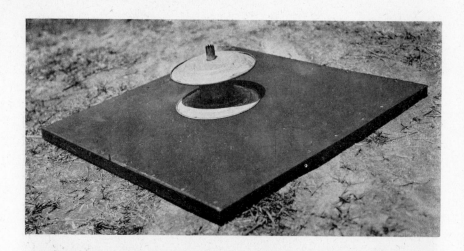

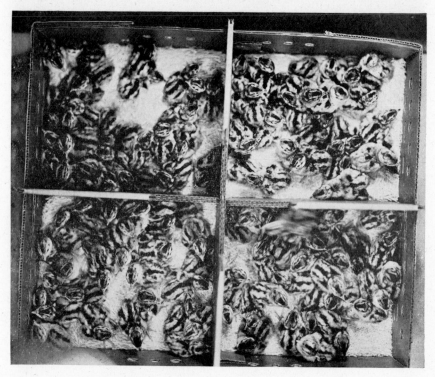

Plate 29.—Upper. A kerosene hover.
Lower. Day-old pheasants in shipping carton. (By permission of the New York
Conservation Department)

Plate 30.—Upper. Brooding coop in rearing field.
Lower. Catching pen in corner of the holding pen at Pennsylvania State Game
Farm, Loyalsock, Pa.

Plate 31.—Upper. Capturing pheasants inside the catching pen for crating.
Lower. Shipping crate for pheasants. The trough in
front is for feed. (Courtesy of Pennsylvania State Game
Farm, Schwenksville, Pa.)

characteristic plumage differences are first discernible. The practical advantages of being able to rear birds in any desired proportion of sexes are, therefore, obvious.

In ring-neck chicks, the shape and extent of the cheek patch, or eye field, is used as the sex indicator. (The variations in color and markings of the down are completely disregarded.) . . . In the day-old chick, the cheek patch of both sexes is entirely covered with natal down. This is shorter than that covering the surrounding areas, thus producing a definite outline surrounding the eye field.

The down-covered field of the typical female chick is more nearly round than that of the male and in some instances forms an almost perfect circle. Extending from the nasal opening posteriorly downward along approximately one quarter of the circumference of cheek patch, runs an unbroken, comparatively wide strip of longer down [figure 12, right column]. This varies from about one-sixteenth to three-thirty-seconds of an inch in width.

In the male, the eye field is rounded at the back . . . but is definitely angular on the side extending forward toward the bill. This pointed section protrudes far into the "V" formed by the upper mandible [figure 12, left column] and the cere, thus greatly reducing the width of that strip of long down so characteristic of the female chick.

Though not a positive indicator of sex, it may be helpful to know that in profile the line formed by the forehead and the upper mandible is usually more nearly straight in the case of males than among females. In other words, as a rule, the foreheads of the females rise more abruptly from the beaks than do those of the males.

It was discovered in developing the technique that in addition to those individuals exhibiting either typical male or female eye patches, a small percentage of the chicks were of an intermediate type, showing both male and female characteristics. In this group, a portion of the eye field enters the "V" posterior to the upper mandible as in typical males, yet the strip of down immediately below is of sufficient width to be characteristic of females. It has so far been impossible accurately to sex individuals of this type. It is, however, not unlikely that further use of the method and continued experimentation will make possible a reduced percentage of birds which must be so classified, or perhaps eliminate them entirely.

HOLDING PHEASANTS OVER WINTER

Housing and Equipment.—The holding pen is simply a netting enclosure. Many such pens do not have poultry netting overhead, but the superintendents of several state farms consider it worth the extra cost, as it prevents the birds from escaping and keeps out predators. Two-inch mesh netting is used on the top and upper part of the sides, whereas 1-inch netting is best next to the ground. Allowing 12 square feet of space per bird, 500 pheasants can be kept in an enclosure of approximately 6,000 square feet (a square area having 77 feet to each side). Each spring this plot should be plowed, harrowed, and planted to a fall cover crop. Feeding equipment for the holding pens may be the same as that used in the breeding enclosure.

Danger at Time of Changing Pens.—A sudden change of temperature is dangerous and often disastrous to young pheasants, especially at the time when they are being moved from the brooder house to the holding pen. It may sometimes be advisable to keep the birds in the brooder house longer than 6 weeks when there is inclement weather, as heavy losses are often caused by rainy and cool weather during the first few days after the birds have been moved. Shelters (plate 24, left) provided in the holding pens help to prevent such losses and they also provide a place where the feed hoppers may be kept dry.

Care of Stock.—Winter management of captive pheasants consists chiefly of keeping a supply of wholesome feed and water before the birds at all times. A constant supply of water may be maintained during freezing weather by use of an oil-burning heater which is sheltered from drafts by a wooden box. Where no heater is provided to prevent the supply from freezing, it should be renewed twice a day. In regions where the winters become very severe, it is desirable to provide windbreaks in the lee of which the birds may seek protection.

Feeding.—Very little information is available on the nutritional requirements of captive pheasants during the winter season. For a maintenance diet, most propagators feed cracked corn and whole wheat in equal proportions, supplemented with lettuce, cabbage, or alfalfa hay two or three times a week. According to reports from the Pennsylvania State College, the formula for a maintenance diet presented in table 19 has given good results with the pheasants and it is suggested as a winter ration, to be supplemented with greens several times weekly. A feed containing at least 25 per cent protein is a necessary substitute for the grain mixture one month prior to the breeding season.

DISPOSAL OF BIRDS

For Restocking and Hunting.—Captive pheasants are produced primarily for the purpose of restocking depleted coverts or establishing the birds in new areas. The pheasant farmer may release the birds on his own land or sell his stock to sportsmen, state game commissions, or to private breeders.

The propagator has a choice of selling his birds for either fall or spring liberation. For fall liberation, the birds are released as soon as they reach 10 to 12 weeks of age. Prior to the release, sites with adequate food and cover to support the birds throughout fall and winter should be selected.

Spring liberation should be made in March, so that the birds will have an opportunity to become adjusted to their new environment before egg-production begins. When pheasants are liberated for reproduction in the wild, it is important that they be assured of adequate food, cover, and legal protection throughout the breeding season. Liberations usually include three or four hens and a cock at one place, but can profitably be made in larger numbers.

For catching pheasants, one corner of the holding pen is partioned off to make a very small enclosure (plate 30, lower). The pheasants are driven into this enclosure through a long, narrow trapdoor at the bottom of the front end. As soon as the catching pen is filled with birds, the door is dropped.

A large bird-net, such as that illustrated in plate 31, upper, is useful for capturing the pheasants after they have been driven into the catching pen.

For shipping, it is important to have pheasants properly crated. A cardboard crate, 2 feet by 3 feet by 10 inches high, will satisfactorily accommodate 10 to 14 birds. This type of crate is suitable only for short shipments where the birds will be in transit 24 hours or less. For longer periods, a more substantial crate (plate 31) provided with feed and water containers should be used.

Pheasants should be taken to the point of liberation in the shipping crates. The best method of turning them loose is to place the crate on the ground near a thicket, scatter some cracked corn and wheat in the cover nearby, open the door, and then depart until the birds leave the crate. Thus the pheasants will have the opportunity, without excitement, to leave the crate and become adjusted to their new surroundings. It is good practice not to remove the crate until the following day.

For Food.—For many years the propagation of captivity-reared game for food has received very little recognition by the American public, undoubtedly for three reasons: (1) Such sales are believed generally to be illegal; (2) there is a fear that game-bird flesh will not receive a ready sale at a price that will give a fair profit to the producer; and (3) official encouragement has been limited.

According to questionnaires on this subject, returned by 45 states, 37 permit the sale of captivity-reared game birds for meat. In most most of these states the game propagator's license covers the marketing of game as meat. Five states, however, require a special permit in addition. Three states require purchasers of game-bird meat to have a game-food dealer's permit.

The majority of the pheasants sold as food are marketed to special trade, as hotels, restaurants, and clubs. In 11 states, however, it is definitely known that captivity-reared game birds are sold in public markets.

During 1941 at least 35,000 game birds, mostly pheasants, were sold as food in the 22 states that hazarded even a guess as to the number involved. In Washington, more than 3,000 pheasants were canned during the same year for public consumption, and in Pennsylvania, one large propagator planned an enterprise for the quick freezing of pheasants. The introduction of such methods of processing indicates growth of the game-bird industry in a new direction.

Breeders who are interested in the marketing of their birds as meat should inquire of their state game or conservation departments regarding regulations.

LITERATURE CITED[1]

Allee, W. C.
 1931. Animal aggregations. University of Chicago Press (Chicago, Ill.), ix+ 531 pp., illus.
 1938. The social life of animals. W. W. Norton and Co. (New York, N. Y.), 293 pp., illus.

Barske, Philip
 1940. The relative values of Japanese barberry (*Berberis thunbergii*) and bayberry (*Myrica carolinensis*) as winter pheasant foods. Department of Forestry and Wild Life Management, University of Connecticut (Storrs). Unpublished thesis.
 ? Experimental evaluation of *Berberis thunbergii* and *Rosa multiflora* as foods for pheasants during critical winter periods. Department of Forestry and Wild Life Management, University of Connecticut (Storrs). Manuscript.

Baskett, Thomas S.
 1941. Production of pheasants in North-central Iowa in 1939. Journal of Wildlife Management (Secretary, Wildlife Society, State College, Pa.), 5(2), pp. 168-174, 4 tables.
 1942. Production of the ring-necked pheasant (*Phasianus colchicus torquatus* Gmelin) in North-central Iowa. Iowa State College Library (Ames). Unpublished thesis.

Bates, Carlos G.
 1936. The wind break as a farm asset. U. S. Dept. Agriculture (Washington, D. C.), Farmers' Bulletin 1405, 19 pp., 6 figs., 1 table.

Baumgras, Philip S.
 1943. Winter food productivity of agricultural land for seed-eating birds and mammals. Journal of Wildlife Management (Secretary, Wildlife Society, State College, Pa.), 7(1), pp. 13-18, 2 figs., 2 tables.

Beebe, William
 1936. Pheasants. Their lives and homes. Doubleday, Doran & Co., Inc. (Garden City, Long Island, N. Y.), 2 vols. in one, xxviii+257+309 pp., 69 pls. (32 col.). Abbreviated from his monumental Monograph of the Pheasants (4 vols., 1918-1922).

---

[1]This is not intended as a general bibliography of works on the ring-necked pheasant. It includes only references the authors found it desirable to make in the various chapters.

Beed, W. E.
1938. Do fur-bearers affect upland game birds in winter? North American Wildlife Conference (American Wildlife Institute, Investment Building, Washington, D. C.), Transactions, Third, pp. 508-510.

Beer, James R., and Wayne Tidyman
1942. The substitution of hard seeds for fruit. Journal of Wildlife Management (Secretary, Wildlife Society, State College, Pa.), 6(1), pp. 70-82, 6 figs., 8 tables.

Benjamin, Joel R.
1941. State supervised hunting in Ohio in 1940. Ohio Division of Conservation and Natural Resources (Columbus, Ohio), Bulletin 206, 32 pp.

Bennitt, Rudolf, and Werner O. Nagel
1937. A survey of the resident game and fur-bearers of Missouri. University of Missouri Studies (Columbia), 12(2), 215 pp., 8 figs.

Bent, Arthur C.
1932. Life histories of North American gallinaceous birds. U. S. National Museum (Washington, D. C.), Bulletin 162. Ring-necked pheasant, pp. 310-322, pls. 70-73.

Buckley, John S., Hubert Bunyea, and Eloise B. Cram
1936. Diseases and parasites of poultry. U. S. Dept. of Agriculture (Washington, D. C.), Farmers' Bulletin 1652, 69 pp., 28 figs.

Bump, Gardiner, and Ben Bradley
1940. Some effects of winter conditions on pheasants in New York. Wildlife Society, New England Section (Massachusetts Fish and Game Association, 20 Spruce St., Boston), Proceedings, April 13, pp. 5-12 (mimeographed).

Clark, Arthur L.
1936. The liberation of pheasants in relation to reports of pheasants killed in Connecticut. Connecticut State Board of Fisheries and Game (Hartford), Game Management Circular 5, 12 pp.

Dalke, Paul D.
1938. Amount of grit taken by pheasants in southern Michigan. Journal of Wildlife Management (Secretary, Wildlife Society, State College, Pa.), 2(2), pp. 53-54, 2 tables.

Davison, Verne E.
1939. Protecting field borders. U. S. Dept. of Agriculture (Washington, D. C.) Leaflet 188, 8 pp., 13 figs.

Edminster, Frank C.
1938. The farm fence in wildlife. American Wildlife (American Wildlife Institute, Washington, D. C.), 27(2), pp. 38-39, 45-46, 1 map, 3 tables.

1942. Wildlife management through soil conservation on farms in the Northeast. U. S. Dept. of Agriculture (Washington, D. C.), Farmers' Bulletin 1868, revised, 52 pp., 25 figs., 3 tables.

English, P. F.
    1933. Causes of pheasant mortality in Michigan. University of Michigan
        (Ann Arbor). Unpublished thesis.
    1934. Game bird flushing apparatus. Michigan Department of Conservation
        (Lansing), Game Division Bulletin 2, 8 pp., 5 figs., 1 table.
English, P. F., and Logan J. Bennett
    1940. November foods of ringneck pheasants and bobwhites. Pennsylvania
        Game News (Pennsylvania Game Commission, Harrisburg), 11(6), pp.
        8-9, 31, 2 figs., 5 tables.
Errington, Paul L.
    1937. Emergency values of some winter pheasant foods. Wisconsin Academy
        of Sciences, Arts, and Letters (Madison), Transactions 30, pp. 57-68.
    1937. Food habits of Iowa red foxes during a drought summer. Ecology
        (Prince and Lemon Sts., Lancaster, Pa.), 18, pp. 53-61.
    1938. The great horned owl as an indicator of vulnerability in prey popula-
        tions. Journal of Wildlife Management (Secretary, Wildlife Society,
        State College, Pa.), 2(4), pp. 190-205, 4 pls.
    1939. The comparative ability of the bob-white and the ring-necked pheasant
        to withstand cold and hunger. Wilson Bulletin (University of Michi-
        gan, Ann Arbor), 51, pp. 22-37, 7 tables.
    1941. An eight-winter study of Central Iowa bobwhites. Wilson Bulletin
        (University of Michigan, Ann Arbor), 53, pp. 85-102, 4 tables.
Errington, Paul L., and Logan J. Bennett
    1933. Lost legions. Outdoor Life (Popular Science Publishing Co., New
        York), 72(3), pp. 18-19, 56.
Errington, Paul L., and W. J. Breckenridge
    1936. Food habits of marsh hawks in the glaciated prairie region of north-
        central United States. American Midland Naturalist (Notre Dame,
        Ind.), 17(5), pp. 831-848, 4 tables.
Errington, Paul L., and Francis N. Hamerstrom, Jr.
    1937. The evaluation of nesting losses and juvenile mortality of the ring-
        necked pheasant. Journal of Wildlife Management (Secretary, Wildlife
        Society, State College, Pa.), 1(1-2), pp. 3-20, 1 fig., 8 tables.
Errington, Paul L., Francis Hamerstrom, and F. N. Hamerstrom, Jr.
    1940. The great horned owl and its prey in north-central United States.
        Iowa Agricultural Experiment Station (Ames), Research Bulletin 277,
        pp. 758-850, 4 figs., 12 tables.
Foote, Leonard
    1942. Vermont pheasant investigation. Vermont Fish and Game Service
        (Montpelier), State Bulletin 8, 64 pp., 11 figs., 23 tables (processed).
Gerstell, Richard
    1937. The status of the ringneck pheasant in Pennsylvania. North American
        Wildlife Conference (American Wildlife Institute, Investment Build-
        ing, Washington, D. C.), Transactions, Second, pp. 505-511.

Gould, Ernest W.

1939. Progress report of the southern New Hampshire pheasant demonstration and research project. New Hampshire Fish and Game Department (Concord), Technical Circular 5, 10 pp., tables (mimeographed).

1939. A study of the pheasant in New Hampshire during the spring and early summer. New Hampshire Fish and Game Department (Concord), 10 pp., 1 fig., 2 tables (mimeographed).

Grange, Wallace, and W. L. McAtee

1934. Improving the farm environment for wild life. U. S. Dept. of Agriculture (Washington, D. C.), Farmers' Bulletin 1719, 61 pp., 20 figs., 3 tables.

Green, W. E.

1938. The food and cover relationship in the winter survival of the ring-necked pheasant, *Phasianus colchicus torquatus* Gmelin, in northeastern Iowa. Iowa State College Journal of Science (Collegiate Press, Ames), 12, pp. 285-314.

Hachisuka, ————

1937. Description d'une nouvelle race de faisan des Balkans. L'Oiseau et la Revue Francaise d'Ornithologie, N. S. 7, pp. 3-6, 1 map.

Hamerstrom, Francis N., Jr.

1936. A study of the nesting habits of the ring-necked pheasant in Northwest Iowa. Iowa State College Journal of Science (Collegiate Press, Ames), 10, pp. 173-203, 4 figs., 8 tables.

Hoover, Earl E.

1936. The pheasant in New Hampshire. Game Breeder and Sportsman (110 Grand St., New York, N. Y.), 40(9), Sept., pp. 190, 203.

Hosley, Neil W.

1938. Woody plants used by wildlife in the northeastern United States. University of Michigan (Ann Arbor). Unpublished thesis.

1940. Pheasant cover evaluation. New Hampshire Fish and Game Department (Concord), 8 pp. (mimeographed).

Kalmbach, Edwin R.

1920. The crow in its relation to agriculture. U. S. Dept. of Agriculture (Washington, D. C.), Farmers' Bulletin 1102, 20 pp., 6 figs., 2 tables.

1927. The magpie in relation to agriculture. U. S. Dept. of Agriculture (Washington, D. C.), Technical Bulletin 24, 29 pp., 11 figs., 2 tables.

1937. Crow-waterfowl relationships in the prairie provinces. North American Wildlife Conference (American Wildlife Institute, Investment Building, Washington, D. C.), Transactions, Second, pp. 380-392, 1 table.

Langenbach, John R.

1940. Crop damage by ringneck pheasants. Pennsylvania Game News (Pennsylvania Game Commission, Harrisburg), 10(12), pp. 10-11, 2 photos, 2 tables.

Latham, Roger M.
1942. A simple method of sexing day-old ringneck pheasant chicks. Pennsylvania Game News (Pennsylvania Game Commission, Harrisburg), 13(1), pp. 6-7, 3 figs., 2 tables. Also issued as Research Circular 2 of the Commission.

Leffingwell, Dana J.
1928. The ring-neck pheasant—its history and habits. Charles R. Conner Museum, State College of Washington (Pullman), Occasional Papers 1, 35 pp., 6 figs.

Leopold, Aldo
1931. Report on a game survey of the North Central States. Sporting Arms and Ammunition Manufacturers' Institute (Madison, Wisc.), 299 pp., 21 maps, 15 charts, 4 photos, 58 tables.
1933. Game management. Charles Scribner's Sons (New York, N. Y.), xxi+ 481 pp., 35 figs.

Leopold, Aldo, and P. L. Errington
1942. A summary of studies of animal populations, Prairie du Sac, Wisconsin, 1929-41. University of Wisconsin (Madison). Manuscript.

Leopold, Aldo, Orville S. Lee, and Harry G. Anderson
1938. Wisconsin pheasant movement study, 1936-37. Journal of Wildlife Management (Secretary, Wildlife Society, State College, Pa.), 2(1), pp. 3-12, 1 fig.

Lutz, H. J.
1930. Effect of cattle grazing on vegetation of a virgin forest in North Western Pennsylvania. Journal of Agricultural Research (U. S. Dept. of Agriculture, Washington, D. C.), 41(7), pp. 561-570, 3 figs., 3 tables.

McAtee, W. L.
1932. Effectiveness in nature of the so-called protective adaptations in the animal kingdom, chiefly as illustrated by the food habits of nearctic birds. Smithsonian Miscellaneous Collections (Smithsonian Institution, Washington, D. C.), 85(7), 201 pp., tables.

McCann, Lester J.
1939. Studies of the grit requirements of certain upland game birds. Journal of Wildlife Management (Secretary, Wildlife Society, State College, Pa.), 3(1), pp. 31-41, 3 figs.

McLaughlin, Charles L.
1942. Food habits of the ring-necked pheasant in the Connecticut River Valley, Massachusetts. Massachusetts Department of Conservation (Boston), Research Bulletin 1, 56 pp., 9 figs., 28 tables (processed).

Moss, A. E.
1939. Relation between take of upland game and agricultural land use in Connecticut. Journal of Wildlife Management (Secretary, Wildlife Society, State College, Pa.), 3(3), pp. 269-278, 10 figs., 1 table.

Newton, Alfred, and Hans Gadow
    1896. A dictionary of birds. (Adam and Charles Black, London, England),
        x+1088 pp., illus.

Ord, H. J.
    1937. Game statistics for Connecticut. Connecticut Cooperative Wildlife Re-
        search Unit (Storrs). Manuscript.

Phillips, John C.
    1928. Wild birds introduced or transplanted in North America. U. S. Dept.
        of Agriculture (Washington, D. C.), Technical Bulletin 61, 63 pp.

Randall, Pierce E.
    1940a. The life equation of the ringneck pheasant in Pennsylvania. North
        American Wildlife Conference (American Wildlife Institute, Invest-
        ment Building, Washington, D. C.), Transactions, Fifth, pp. 300-320,
        9 figs., 12 tables.

    1940b. The ecology and management of the ring-necked pheasant in Penn-
        sylvania. Library, The Pennsylvania State College (State College, Pa.).
        Unpublished thesis.

Rood, Ronald W.
    1941. Pheasant feeding experiments. Department of Forestry and Wildlife
        Management, University of Connecticut (Storrs). Manuscript.

Scott, T. G., and T. S. Baskett
    1941. Some effects of the 1940 Armistice Day storm on Iowa's wildlife. Iowa
        Bird Life (Winthrop, Iowa), 11(2), pp. 21-29, 3 pls.

Shaw, C. F.
    1914. The soils of Pennsylvania. State College Agricultural Experiment Sta-
        tion (State College, Pa.), Bulletin 132, pp. 210-242, 1 table, 1 map.

Shillinger, J. E., and L. C. Morley
    1942. Diseases of upland game birds. U. S. Dept. of the Interior (Washing-
        ton, D. C.), Conservation Bulletin 21, 32 pp., 8 figs.

Short, Alexander W.
    1939. Improvement in farmer-hunter relations in Ohio. North American
        Wildlife Conference (American Wildlife Institute, Investment Build-
        ing, Washington, D. C.), Transactions, Fourth, pp. 514-518.

Spencer, David L.
    1940. The value of kettleholes to wildlife in southern Michigan. University
        of Michigan (Ann Arbor). Unpublished thesis.

Sperry, Charles C.
    1941. Food habits of the coyote. U. S. Dept. of the Interior (Washington,
        D. C.), Wildlife Research Bulletin 4, 69 pp., 3 pls., 3 figs., 10 tables.

Tolstead, Wm. L.
    1942. Vegetation of the northern part of Cherry County, Nebraska. Ecologi-
        cal Monographs (Duke University, Durham, N. C.), 12, pp. 255-292.

Townsend, Charles W.
1920. Supplement to the birds of Essex County, Massachusetts. Memoirs of the Nuttall Ornithological Club (Secretary, Cambridge, Mass.), 5, 196 pp., 1 pl., 1 map.

Trippensee, R. E.
1934. The biology and management of the cottontail rabbit, *Sylvilagus floridanus mearnsi*. University of Michigan (Ann Arbor). Unpublished thesis.

Wallace, George
1937. Vermont's pheasant situation. North American Wildlife Conference (American Wildlife Institute, Investment Building, Washington, D. C.), Transactions, Second, pp. 340-345.

Wight, Howard M.
1933. Suggestions for pheasant management in southern Michigan. State Department of Conservation (Lansing, Mich.), 25 pp., 9 figs.

Wilder, Norman G.
1941. A study of the pheasant on typical ranges in Connecticut. University of Connecticut (Storrs). Unpublished thesis.

Wilder, Norman G., and Ernest W. Gould
1940. Hunting pressure on pheasants in the East Concord Research Area. New Hampshire Fish and Game Department (Concord), Technical Circular 8, 6 pp. (mimeographed).

Wright, Thomas, Jr.
1941. A study of the fall food supply of the ring-necked pheasant and the bob-white quail in Washington County, Rhode Island. Journal of Wildlife Management (Secretary, Wildlife Society, State College, Pa.), 5(3), pp. 279-296, 6 tables.

INDEX

317